C. Cawthorne

FLOWERS IN BRITAIN

THE PEA FAMILY
(Leguminosae)

WILD	ORNAMENTAL	ECONOMIC
Gorse, Vetches,	Sweet Pea, Lupin	Garden Pea, Broad Bean
Clover, Trefoils	Laburnum	Scarlet Runner

FLOWERS IN BRITAIN

WILD, ORNAMENTAL AND ECONOMIC

AND SOME RELATIVES IN OTHER LANDS

BY

L. J. F BRIMBLE

B.Sc. (London and Reading), F.L.S.

Joint Editor of *Nature*. Formerly Lecturer in the Universities
of Glasgow and Manchester

MACMILLAN AND CO. LIMITED
ST. MARTIN'S STREET, LONDON
1947

TO MY MOTHER

PREFACE

This book has been written for anyone who is interested in or wants to know something about flowering plants. It is not intended solely for the professional botanist, and therefore no previous knowledge of botany is assumed.

There are thousands of non-botanists in this country who are interested in British flowers and, frequently knowing quite a lot about them, want to know still more or the reasons for what they know. Such people often find themselves handicapped because they do not know the botanical names of the flowers with which they are familiar. This can be a real disadvantage because one cannot retain, much less cultivate, an intelligent interest in the flora of the country without understanding, up to a point, the relationship which flowers bear to one another and to their environment; and such understanding is helped considerably by knowing the botanical names of the plants. The book accordingly uses these names, but if a plant has a common English name (which is usual), this is also given, and any synonyms (frequently restricted to certain areas only, or now altogether out of date) are cited where they are known.

Then there are those who are familiar with, or especially interested in, the native flora of the country, most of which is made up of wild plants. Such people frequently want to know in what way garden flowers are related to the wild species.

Gardeners (especially those living in the country) who are keen on flower cultivation, on the other hand, are sometimes surprised to learn of the interesting relatives of their flowers, which exist in the wild state. So garden-lovers too would do well to correlate the cultivated flowers with their more lowly wild brethren.

At the other end of the scale, one frequently finds that academic botanists, though thoroughly well-versed in the classification, structure, function, and so forth, of the British native flora, are unfamiliar with garden flowers, many of which are really exotics. It is sometimes a matter of wonder to a non-botanist that many academic botanists, even those who have taken a university degree in the subject, know much less about the flowers of our gardens than the ordinary gardener. Finally there are those people, including townspeople visiting the countryside, and visitors from abroad, who are greatly attracted by the British wild and cultivated floras, yet know very little about either.

To all these people this book is addressed. For obvious reasons, technical terms have been kept to a minimum, though I think it is a mistake to avoid them altogether.

Garden flowers, sometimes being subjected to intense cultivation, crossing and so forth, present endless varieties, so here only the more generally well-known ones are mentioned.

Apart, however, from the structure of plants, their classification, habit and habitats, all of which naturally find a place in a book of this sort, there are other aspects of plant life which most books tend to overlook. This is a pity, because the broader aspects of plant life often add considerably to the interest of botany in general. I am referring especially to the part played by plants in folk-lore and, above all, their role in literature. Both these aspects have, therefore, been emphasised in this book. It has not been possible to make more than a limited selection of appropriate passages, because plants figure so largely in lore and literature; but it is hoped that enough has been said to encourage those whose interest is aroused to penetrate still further into folk-lore and prose and poetry for still further examples.

In order to satisfy those readers for whom this book is intended, and still keep the whole work on a sound scientific basis, it was thought best to arrange the plants in their botanical families. Each family is then sub-divided into those plants which are wild and therefore in-digenous to Great Britain, those plants which are cultivated for their ornamental beauty, and those which are grown for economic purposes to supply food, textiles, drugs, etc. In doing this it has, of course, been impossible to avoid considering quite a number of plants which are not cultivated in this country at all. We may take as an extreme case the melon family. Whereas there is only one British wild member of this family, namely, the white bryony, it contains a large number of plants not originally native to this country, which are cultivated for their economic value, for example, vegetable marrow, pumpkin, cucumber, etc. Furthermore, there are still other members of this family not cultivated at all in this country, which are known to us, and have accordingly been mentioned; for example, the cantaloupe melon, squirting cucumber, and the plant which supplies the loofah of the bathroom (Chap. 23).

This principle of treatment is illustrated in the frontispiece, in which a vase of flowers is represented by members of one family only, namely, the pea family.   This collection is somewhat idealised, of course, because it is not likely that all the flowers would bloom at the same time ; but an examination of the frontispiece will show very familiar wild flowers, flowers cultivated for ornamental purposes, and those cultivated for the food products which they yield ;   yet they all belong to one family.

Our common wild and cultivated trees have received only a bare mention (to retain the sequence of plant classification), because it is intended to deal with them more fully in another book.

The coloured plates have been prepared by artists who have specialised in this field.   Apart from the frontispiece, about 160 wild flowers are depicted in colour.   Most of the 130 photographs are of cultivated plants, chiefly ornamental and economic.   Except where otherwise stated, these have been supplied by Messrs. Sutton & Sons, Ltd., Reading, and I am particularly grateful to that firm for the courtesy they have shown in helping to choose the illustrations and supplying the plates from which the illustrations were prepared.   Naturally, since the book is intended for the non-botanist as well as for the botanist, a certain amount of introductory work is necessary, and here some line drawings are essential.   About thirty such line drawings, for which I am responsible, are used.

I have received considerable help in preparation of this book from my friend and colleague, Mr. Thomas Mark, who has also given me the benefit of his profound knowledge of English literature, and thus aided me in making a representative choice of prose and verse.

I am also indebted to Miss M. L. Cox for her assistance in preparing the manuscript for press.

L. J. F. BRIMBLE

LONDON, *August*, 1944

Note to the Second Impression.   During the preparation of the Second Impression I have been able to make several corrections, and to adopt suggestions made by Major T. H. Hawkins, B.Sc., and several other botanist friends, to whom I am indebted.

L. J. F. BRIMBLE

LONDON, *March*, 1945

CONTENTS

PART I

INTRODUCTORY: STRUCTURE OF FLOWERING PLANTS

PAGE

1. The Flowering Plant - - - - - - - - - 1
2. Flowers - - - - - - - - - - - 18
3. Classification of Flowering Plants - - - - - 31

PART II

DICOTYLEDONS: I. FLOWERS WITH FREE PETALS

4. The Buttercup Family - - - - - - - - 37
5. Magnolias - - - - - - - - - - 45
6. Water-lilies - - - - - - - - - - 47
7. Poppies - - - - - - - - - - - 52
8. The Fumitory Family - - - - - - - - 57
9. The Wallflower Family - - - - - - - - 58
10. Violets and Pansies - - - - - - - - 66
11. Mignonette and Milkwort - - - - - - - 70
12. A Water-storing Family - - - - - - - 72
13. The Saxifrage Family - - - - - - - - 74
14. Campions and Carnations - - - - - - - 78
15. Two Minor Families - - - - - - - - 84
16. Docks, Sorrels and Rhubarb - - - - - - 86
17. The Beetroot Family - - - - - - - - 89
18. The Geranium Family - - - - - - - - 92
19. Three Popular Families - - - - - - - 96
20. Some Semi-Aquatic Plants - - - - - - - 100
21. The Willow-herb Family - - - - - - - 102
22. Miscellany - - - - - - - - - - 107
23. The Melon Family - - - - - - - - - 111
24. Some Handsome Exotics - - - - - - - 114
25. The St. John's Worts - - - - - - - - 116
26. The Mallow Family - - - - - - - - 119
27. A very Useful Family - - - - - - - - 123
28. Currants and Gooseberries - - - - - - - 125

viii

CONTENTS

PAGE

29. HYDRANGEA AND 'SYRINGA' - - - - - - - - 127
30. THE ROSE FAMILY - - - - - - - - - 129
31. THE PEA FAMILY - - - - - - - - - 146
32. SOME USEFUL TREES AND SHRUBS - - - - - - 161
33. NETTLES - - - - - - - - - - - 165
34. HOPS AND BEER : HEMP AND HASHISH - - - - - 168
35. HOLLY : THE HOLY TREE - - - - - - - - 172
36. MISTLETOE : THE GOLDEN BOUGH - - - - - - 174
37. GRAPE AND OTHER VINES - - - - - - - - 177
38. ORANGES AND LEMONS - - - - - - - - 180
39. IVY - - - - - - - - - - - - 182
40. THE PARSLEY FAMILY - - - - - - - - 184

PART III

DICOTYLEDONS : II. FLOWERS WITH UNITED PETALS

41. MOUNTAIN AND MOORLAND PLANTS - - - - - - 189
42. A PLANT SAPROPHYTE - - - - - - - - 193
43. PERIWINKLES - - - - - - - - - - 196
44. SOME GARDEN FLOWERING SHRUBS - - - - - - 197
45. THE BEDSTRAW FAMILY - - - - - - - - 200
46. ELDER AND HONEYSUCKLE - - - - - - - - 204
47. THE VALERIAN FAMILY - - - - - - - - 207
48. THE SCABIOUS FAMILY - - - - - - - - 208
49. THE LARGEST FAMILY OF ALL - - - - - - - 211
50. GENTIANS - - - - - - - - - - 234
51. THE PRIMROSE FAMILY - - - - - - - - 237
52. THRIFT AND STATICE - - - - - - - - 245
53. THE PLANTAIN FAMILY - - - - - - - - 247
54. BELL-FLOWERS - - - - - - - - - - 248
55. PHLOX AND PHACELIA - - - - - - - - 253
56. THE FORGET-ME-NOT FAMILY - - - - - - - 254
57. THE POTATO FAMILY - - - - - - - - 259
58. THE CONVOLVULUS FAMILY - - - - - - - 268
59. THE SNAPDRAGON FAMILY - - - - - - - 272
60. MORE PARASITES - - - - - - - - - 283
61. PLANTS WHICH PREY ON INSECTS - - - - - - 284
62. SOME CULTIVATED FAVOURITES - - - - - - - 291
63. THE MINT FAMILY - - - - - - - - - 295

PART IV

MONOCOTYLEDONS

		PAGE
64.	SOME AQUATIC MONOCOTYLEDONS	306
65.	SOME ORNAMENTAL AND EDIBLE MONOCOTYLEDONS	311
66.	LILIES AND THEIR RELATIVES	315
67.	ARUMS	329
68.	BURWEEDS AND REED-MACES	333
69.	DAFFODILS AND SNOWDROPS: GARLIC AND ONIONS	336
70.	THE IRIS FAMILY	343
71.	SOME TUBEROUS CLIMBERS	350
72.	PALMS AND THEIR RELATIVES	351
73.	ORCHIDS	357
74.	RUSHES AND SEDGES	364
75.	GRASSES AND CEREALS	368
	INDEX OF BOTANICAL NAMES	379
	GENERAL INDEX	386

COLOURED PLATES

		FACING PAGE
Frontispiece.	THE PEA FAMILY	
PLATE 1.	THE BUTTERCUP FAMILY	44
PLATE 2.	MISCELLANEOUS FAMILIES	58
PLATE 3.	THE WALLFLOWER AND PRIMROSE FAMILIES	67
PLATE 4.	THE CAMPION AND CRANE'S-BILL FAMILIES	92
PLATE 5.	MISCELLANEOUS FAMILIES	120
PLATE 6.	THE ROSE FAMILY	144
PLATE 7.	THE PEA FAMILY	160
PLATE 8.	MISCELLANEOUS FAMILIES	202
PLATE 9.	THE COMPOSITE FAMILY (1)	211
PLATE 10.	THE COMPOSITE FAMILY (2)	218
PLATE 11.	THE COMPOSITE FAMILY (3)	227
PLATE 12.	MISCELLANEOUS FAMILIES	250
PLATE 13.	THE FORGET-ME-NOT AND PARSLEY FAMILIES	259
PLATE 14.	THE SNAPDRAGON FAMILY	280
PLATE 15.	THE MINT FAMILY	302
PLATE 16.	MISCELLANEOUS FAMILIES	350
PLATE 17.	MISCELLANEOUS FAMILIES	372

PART I

INTRODUCTORY: STRUCTURE OF FLOWERING PLANTS

I

THE FLOWERING PLANT

Nature will bear the closest inspection. She invites us to
lay our eye level with her smallest leaf, and take an insect
view of its plain.   *Journal*: H. D. THOREAU

PLANTS AND MAN

There are several hundreds of families, and hundreds of thousands of
species, of flowering plants distributed throughout the world. Some
are to be found in many different parts of the world, others are much
more restricted in distribution. The majority of them grow in the wild
state and have developed through the ages, in all their diversity of size
and form, by the process of evolution. Many plants are beneficial to
mankind, and certain of these are cultivated for this reason. In most
such cases, every effort is made to produce the best kind of plant attain-
able under the prevailing conditions of site, soil and climate. This is
done by careful cultivation in garden or on farm. But plant improve-
ment is also constantly under investigation, chiefly at various scientific
research institutes. Here plant hybridisation, plant genetics and so
forth are continually adding to our knowledge.

At the other end of the scale are those plants which are a real
nuisance to man. These are the weeds.

Most plants, however, are of no economic value, though from our
point of view they are quite harmless. All the same, many of them have
an intrinsic value by the very fact of their beauty. This can be said of
most of our wayside, woodland and meadow plants, and of those which
we grow in our flower gardens.

ECONOMIC PLANTS

Certain plants are of direct value to us as sources of *food supply*. These are, of course, far too numerous to consider in detail. Perhaps the most important are the cereals such as wheat, maize, rye, oats, rice, barley and millet (Chap. 75). Then there are the fleshy fruits, the root crops, nuts and the many plants which have edible leaves or stems (Fig. 1). Thus do plants form the basis of the agricultural industries of the world, some of which are centuries old, and others more recently established as our knowledge, and consequently demands, increase.

Most *beverages* are extracted or manufactured from plants. Throughout the world, certain plant infusions are used for this purpose. Many are of national interest only, since the taste for them is confined to those peoples who grow them. Others, such as tea, coffee and cocoa, have now attained international importance. Tea, for example, is drunk throughout the world. The tea plant probably originated in China, where tradition has it that it was discovered by the Emperor Shên-nung in 2737 B.C. It is now known that, apart from China, the tea plant is also a true native of Upper Assam. From China, knowledge of the stimulating properties of this plant became widespread—westwards to India and Ceylon in the sixth century, and eastwards to Japan in the ninth. It was not until the middle of the seventeenth century that the English began to drink tea, and then it cost about £8 a pound. Today, tea is such a commonplace, indeed almost necessary, drink that it seems

R. A. Malby & Co.

Fig. 1.—A Group of Edible Plant Products.

almost incredible that any civilised age managed without it. Thus
Sydney Smith (1771–1845) wrote :

> Thank God for tea ! What would the world do without tea ? How
> did it exist ? I am glad I was not born before tea.
>
> Lady Holland. *Memoir*, Vol. I. : s. SMITH

Alcoholic beverages, too, are universally popular, though again there
are many that are confined to those areas of the world where they
are produced. Others, on the other hand, have achieved almost world-
wide distribution. All of them are brewed or distilled from plants. Beer
is perhaps the oldest of alcoholic beverages ; in fact, there is evidence
that prehistoric man was able to brew it. It is, of course, the product of
barley and hops (Chap. 34). Then there are the many wines, products of
grapes ; whisky from barley or rye or other cereals ; brandy, distilled from
fermented grape juice ; rum, from fermented cane-sugar or molasses ;
gin is flavoured by the berries of the juniper ; and so forth.

Vinegar is obtained chiefly from grapes. Certain *condiments*, such as
pepper and mustard, and *spices*, such as cinnamon, spikenard and frankincense, are the products of plants too. And scarcely a *perfume* exists
which is not distilled from flowers and other plant organs.

The *medicinal* properties of plants have been known since time
immemorial. Though primitive man never cultivated plants himself,
he must have known a great deal about the wild ones growing around
him—using many for food and discovering those which were useless
or indeed poisonous and even those which had curative values. Gradually as they learned more about such medicinal herbs, certain members of
primitive tribes began to specialise in the preparation of curative decoctions. These men were known as medicine-men or witch-doctors. But
much of the treatment prescribed by these men was the product of their
imagination or traditional beliefs, with the result that a great deal of
their advice was futile. Yet those ' doctors ' must have been familiar
with a large number of plants which contained genuine curative substances. Profound belief in these witch-doctors is slow in dying out ;
in fact, such witchcraft holds sway in some primitive tribes to this
day.

In this country something similar was extant for centuries, though
the preparation of those decoctions was usually left to certain women.
In *Macbeth,* for example, we read how the witches used :

> Scale of dragon, tooth of wolf,
> Witches' mummy, maw and gulf

Of the ravin'd salt-sea shark,
Root of hemlock digg'd i' the dark,
Liver of blaspheming Jew,
Gall of goat, and slips of yew . . . .
           Macbeth, Act 3, Sc. 4 : SHAKESPEARE

As the study of medicine developed, however, these supposed curative properties of herbs have been brought into question, and the genuine cases sifted from the false. In medieval times, the botanists studied plants from scarcely anything but the medicinal point of view, and herb gardens were cultivated (Fig. 2). Nowadays we know of many plants with medicinal properties. Apart from a large number of medicines prepared from native plants, others used extensively for healing the sick are quinine (obtained from the bark of *Cinchona*), strychnine (wood and bark of *Strychnos*), cocaine (leaves of coca), opium (opium poppy), and so forth.

Farewell, dear flowers, sweetly your time ye spent,
Fit, while ye liv'd, for smell or ornament,
And after death for cures.   *Life* : GEORGE HERBERT

FIG. 2.—A Medieval Herb Garden.
(*From Petrus Crescentius's ' Opus Ruralium Commodarum '*)

Other valuable drugs and chemotherapeutical agents are extracted from plants which are much lower in the scale of evolution than are the flowering plants ; for example, penicillin is obtained from *Penicillium notatum* and patulin from *Penicillium patulum*, both of which are fungal moulds.

Reference to any book on *materia medica* will surprise many readers with the enormous number of plants or plant products which are now used for medical purposes ; and all this in spite of Oliver Wendell Holmes' caustic comment in a lecture at the Harvard Medical School :

> I firmly believe that if the whole *materia medica* could be sunk to the bottom of the sea, it would be all the better for mankind, and all the worse for the fishes.

Rubber, the natural product which will remain of great economic significance until such times as the chemically synthetic substitutes are more fully developed, is also produced from plants. It is manufactured from the latex of several species of tree, the chief ones being of the genus *Hevea*, though other plants, even some herbs, are now being exploited for their rubber content (Chap. 27).

Tobacco and *snuff* are prepared from the leaves of the tobacco plant, a native of Central America, which was first brought to Europe in 1558 by a Spaniard named Francisco Fernandes and later popularised in England by Sir Walter Ralegh (Chap. 57). Since then, smoking has become such a habit that it is indulged throughout the known world, inspiring enthusiasts to acclaim its virtues in song and poem.

> Sublime Tobacco ! which from east to west
> Cheers the tar's labours or the Turkman's rest ;
> Which on the Moslem's ottoman divides
> His hours, and rivals opium and his brides.
> *The Island* : BYRON

> A cigarette is the perfect type of perfect pleasure. It is exquisite, and it leaves one satisfied. What more can you want ?
> *Dorian Gray* : OSCAR WILDE

Cotton, artificial silk, Rayon and *linen*, together with *hemp* and *jute*, are among the important textiles which originate in plants. *Paper*, too, is made from plant products—chiefly wood pulp.

The *timber* or wood of many trees has numerous economic uses today, thus making forestry one of the world's great industries (Fig. 3).

The Times.

FIG. 3.—Foresters at Work.

Though certain *vitamins* essential to our health and well-being can now be produced synthetically in the laboratory, we still depend on plants for most of them, since, with certain exceptions, our own bodies (like those of other animals) are incapable of making them. Most of the vitamins are present in fruits, leaves and roots.

ORNAMENTAL PLANTS

So one could go on discussing the economic uses of plants; but only a few have been mentioned. Many other plants of economic importance enter into our lives almost every day; but no account should leave unmentioned the thousands of different plants which have no economic value apart from their own intrinsic beauty, and for which so many of us work so enthusiastically in our gardens.

> See how the flowers, as at parade,
> Under their colours stand display'd:
> Each regiment in order grows,
> That of the tulip, pink and rose.

But when the vigilant patrol
Of stars walks round about the pole,
Their leaves, that to the stalks are curl'd
Seem to their staves the ensigns furl'd.

A Garden : A. MARVELL

Nearly all peoples throughout the world love flowers, but none more than the British, as may be seen by our parks, our gardens, our window-boxes. Ornamental plants may be trees, shrubs or herbs ; but by far the majority of plants cultivated in our gardens are grown for the beauty of their flowers (Fig. 4).

WEEDS

But not all plants are useful or, at worst, harmless. As in many other aspects of life today, in order to get what we want (in this case useful or beautiful plants) we have to be constantly contending with that which we do not want. Every farmer and gardener knows the

FIG. 4.—A Herbaceous Border.

curse of weeds. A weed may be described as a plant which is growing where it is proving itself a nuisance. 'Nuisance' is perhaps the best word, for many weeds, such as ragwort on agricultural land and bindweed in gardens, are as beautiful as many garden plants. How often must the tired gardener have experienced thoughts parallel with those of Shakespeare!

> O thou weed,
> Who art so lovely fair and smell'st so sweet
> That the sense aches at thee, would thou hadst ne'er been born !
>
> *Othello*, Act 4, Sc. 2 : SHAKESPEARE

Weeds are persistently cropping up among cultivated plants, and so have to be periodically eradicated ; otherwise they will reduce the cultivated plants in size and vitality either by robbing them of their nourishment, or by shading them from the sunlight or by choking them out of existence altogether. Eradication of weeds is still done chiefly by hand or by hoe ; but sometimes chemical weed-killers are used, and in some cases spraying methods are adopted.

Other plants cause even more extensive damage among our garden and farm crops by infecting them with disease, such as the potato blight. However, the plants which are mainly responsible for such diseases are not flowering plants, but usually Fungi, and therefore do not concern us here.

A TYPICAL FLOWERING PLANT

In order to identify a plant, to appreciate its position in plant classification, and above all to be able to cultivate it intelligently and successfully, it is desirable, in fact, essential, to understand the elements of plant structure and the functions of the various parts of plants.

A typical flowering plant, such as a buttercup or wallflower or elm tree, is clearly composed of various organs. These organs may be divided into two main groups, namely those which grow above the soil (collectively called the shoot) and those which grow below the soil (collectively called the root) (Fig. 5).

But flowering plants, while conforming to general rules of structure, diverge specifically from such rules in all sorts of ways. For example, some stems, such as that of the couch grass and the potato tuber, grow underground, whereas some roots, such as those of the climbing ivy plant, appear above ground. Certain of these modifications will be mentioned in the appropriate places.

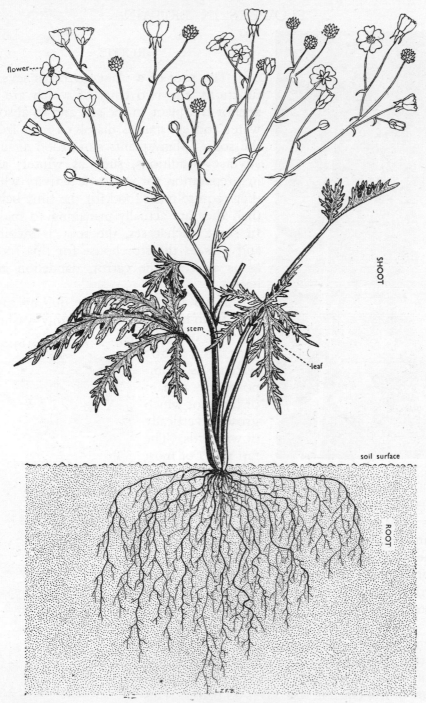

flower

SHOOT

stem

leaf

soil surface

ROOT

FIG. 5.—A Buttercup Plant.

Dr. H. H. Mann.

FIG. 6.—A Sugar-beet in the
Soil.   The tape-measure gives
some idea of its length.

ROOTS

The root of a plant performs several functions, the two chief of which are to anchor the plant in the soil and to absorb water and substances dissolved in it from the soil.   Many plants store food against adverse conditions, such as winter, and in preparation for energetic activity when they require more food for the time being than they are actually managing to make. In some such cases, the root is swollen and acts as the storehouse for this food, as is seen in the carrot, dandelion and beet.

If a wallflower plant be dug up carefully from the soil and thoroughly washed, it will be seen that the root system is composed of a main or tap root which grows vertically downwards. The tap roots of most plants are much longer than we usually imagine, for they are frequently broken off when the plant is roughly pulled from the soil (Fig. 6). The tap root gives off branch roots, and these branch roots are further branched, and so forth, thus giving a very extensive root system (Fig. 7).

Differing from the tap root system is that system, equally common, where the first root, instead of persisting and thus remaining the main root, withers away, and a series of roots, more or less equal in size, takes its place.   This can be seen in the grasses and cereals, and is

FIG. 7.—A Tap Root System.

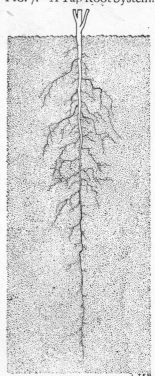

called a fibrous root system (Fig. 8). The majority of the roots in the fibrous root system are given off from the lower parts of the stems, and are therefore not a branch product of the first root. A root which is not part of the original root system is said to be adventitious, and such roots are seen not only in a fibrous root system, but also in such plants as ivy, where they are given off high up on the stems, and in *Begonia* plants, where they are sometimes given off even from the notches of the leaves.

The extent of fibrous root systems is also frequently under-estimated. If all the roots of the fibrous root system were placed end on end, they would often extend several miles. A Canadian botanist once estimated the total length of the roots of a single two-year-old grass (*Agropyron cristatum*) and found it to be 319 miles.

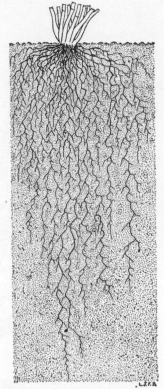

FIG. 8.—A Fibrous Root System.

SHOOTS

So from the root springs lighter the green stalk, from thence the leaves
More aerie, last the brighter consummate flower.   *Paradise Lost* : MILTON

The shoot is normally composed of stems which bear leaves and flowers. In the case of the buttercup or wallflower the shoot is composed of a central axis or main stem which terminates in a bud. Wherever this terminal bud is only a leaf bud, it is capable of opening out and continuing the growth in length of the main stem. If, however, the terminal bud contains a flower, then growth in that direction ceases once it has opened and produced the flower or flowers (Fig. 9).

BUDS

On the side of the stem the leaves are borne (Fig. 9). That part of the stem to which the leaf is attached is called the node. The angle

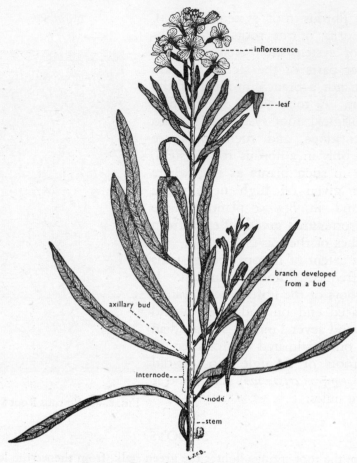

FIG. 9.—Part of a Wallflower Shoot.

which the leaf makes with the stem is called the axil, and borne in the axil almost invariably is a bud, which is called the axillary bud. In contradistinction to the terminal bud, it is lateral in position. These axillary buds often grow out to produce branch stems (Fig. 9). That part of the stem stretching between two nodes is called the internode. Appendages such as leaves are never given off from an internode.

Buds are young, undeveloped shoots. If they are leaf-buds only, they finally grow out to produce branch stems bearing leaves and possibly flowers. On the other hand, if they are flower-buds, they finally produce the flower or flowers and then their growth ceases. The production of a flower anywhere almost invariably results in the cessation of development in that direction. Axillary buds produce branch shoots; but not all axillary buds develop in normal conditions. Such sleeping buds are said to be dormant. In exceptional conditions, however, dormant buds will awaken to activity and develop new branches. This happens frequently when the terminal bud has been accidentally or deliberately severed.

GROWTH IN THICKNESS

Many plants, especially perennials, could not continue indefinitely to grow in length unless there were also some growth in thickness, else the plant would become so long and slender as to be unable to remain upright. Such growth in thickness takes place, of course, in the stems and the roots.

Nearly all stems and roots contain a certain amount of wood, and when such stems and roots begin to thicken, they do so chiefly by the formation of new wood. This growth in thickness is known as secondary thickening. Trunks of trees, which are nothing but secondarily thickened stems, are therefore composed chiefly of wood (Fig. 10).

FIG. 10.—Trunk of an Oak.

TRUNKS

If the trunk or thick branch of a tree be severed, the cut surface will reveal to what extent the deposition of wood has taken place in that stem. The wood forms the chief part of the thickened stem, and it can now be seen to be composed of two sections: that in the centre which is darker in colour (heart-wood), and the lighter part surrounding it (sapwood). The heart-wood is darker because it is dry and contains no sap. The sap, which is water containing dissolved substances

Henry Irving.

passing from the soil, through the roots up to the various aerial organs of the tree, travels through the sap-wood.

Every year, during the growing season, which is spring to early autumn in Great Britain, the tree develops a fresh layer of wood in its trunk and branches. This layer is deposited on the outside of the already existing cylinder of wood. No new wood is formed during the winter. Wood is composed chiefly of a series of minute tubes. Therefore, when we examine the cut surface of a trunk with a hand lens, these tubes will look like thousands of minute circles. The tubes which are produced during the spring period of growth are much larger than those produced during the autumn. Then during winter growth ceases. Eventually during the following season wood deposition begins again. Thus between each season's growth there is a distinct line of demarcation which can be clearly seen even with the naked eye. So the complete cross-section of the trunk presents the appearance of a series of roughly concentric rings. These are called annual rings. Furthermore, some annual rings are wider than others, thus showing that during the year in question growing conditions were favourable. By counting the number of annual rings it is possible to tell the age of the tree (Fig. 11).

Annual rings are useful in forestry and even in meteorology. To be able to tell the age of a tree is often desirable, and in some cases gives surprising results. For example there is a trunk (in section) of a Californian redwood tree in the British Museum (Natural History) which shows 1,335 annual rings.

By examining comparatively the growth of the annual rings of a single trunk, it is possible to tell what kind of weather that tree experienced during its years of existence. This idea has been carried still further by an American, Dr. A. E. Douglas, who examined the trunks of some fossilised trees which must have been alive many millions of years ago. From his results he was able to deduce certain interesting facts of meteorological and geological interest about the times when those trees were growing. Dr. Douglas has also made some interesting discoveries concerning climates of more recent times, by adopting the same method. For example, he has been able to show that in the United States there was a great drought which commenced in 1276 and lasted for twenty-three years.

FIG. 11.—Transverse Section of a Larch Trunk showing Annual Rings.

BARK

Surrounding the woody cylinder of the thickened stem are other important layers. Some are not visible to the naked eye. Immediately surrounding the wood, however, is one which may sometimes be identified. This is very thin and is called the phloem. Down this layer pass to the rest of the plant those foods which have been manufactured in the plant's green leaves. Outside the phloem is another layer which varies considerably in thickness according to the species of tree. This is the cork. Finally, outside this again is the bark. This layer also shows great variation in thickness and in texture. Many trees can be identified by their bark. That of the elm, for example, is thick and broken up, giving a wart-like appearance, whereas that of the beech is thinner and smoother. The bark of the plane tree (so common in the London streets) is so thin that it naturally peels off in patches, leaving the underlying yellowish tissues exposed.

LEAVES

Leaves are diverse in size and shape. Thus, we have the comparatively small leaf of the privet, and in contradistinction to this is that of the banana plant which, though roughly similar in shape, is anything from one to three yards long. Though leaves vary in shape, they do conform roughly to certain types. One should be able to recognise the simple privet leaf or tulip leaf with their smooth margins, the elm leaf with its serrated edge, the oak leaf with its deeply indented margin, the compound leaf of the horse-chestnut and ash, the linear leaf of the bluebell and so forth (Fig. 12).

A typical leaf is composed of a leaf-stalk or petiole which usually widens at its base where it joins the node of the stem. Sometimes this leaf-base is merely a thicker structure as in the horse-chestnut, or it may become elongated to form a sheath as in the buttercup. In grasses, this sheath enfolds the stem for a considerable distance.

The main, flattened portion of the stem is called the leaf-blade or lamina. In some species of plants, the leaf-blade is borne direct on to the stem, that is, it has no leaf-stalk, in which case it is said to be sessile.

Very commonly wing-like outgrowths arise at the base of the petiole. They may clearly be seen in the leaf of the rose, and even more so in the leaf of the garden pea (Fig. 13). These outgrowths, again, vary

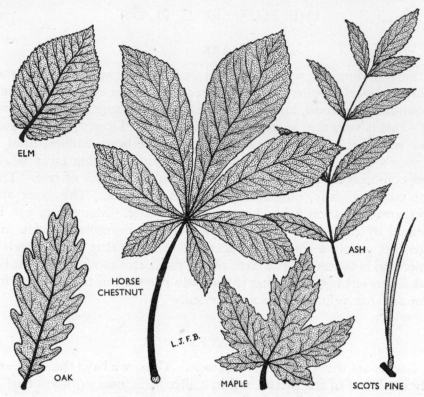

ELM

HORSE
CHESTNUT

L. J. F. B.

OAK

MAPLE

ASH

SCOTS PINE

FIG. 12.—Different Kinds of Leaves.

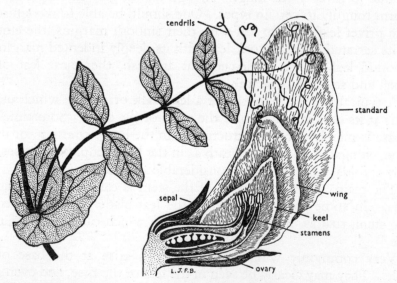

tendrils

standard

sepal

wing

keel

stamens

ovary

L. J. F. B.

FIG. 13.—The Garden Pea. Complete Leaf and section of a Flower.

in size and shape. They are called stipules. In many leaves, however, stipules are absent.

It is in the leaf-blade that leaves demonstrate their great diversity of shape and size. On the leaf-blade, thicker lines are visible. These are the veins, and are the channels for conducting water, with its dissolved substances, into the leaf, and foodstuffs which have been manufactured by the leaf from these substances (together with carbon dioxide from the air) away from the leaf. The main veins give off branch veins, thus presenting a complete net-work of veins. The whole arrangement is called venation. In some leaves, there is one main vein, which branches. These branches give

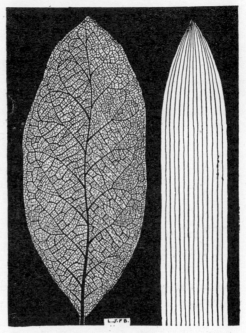

FIG. 14.—Net and Parallel Leaf Venation.

off secondary branches, and so forth, thus producing a reticulate or net venation (Fig. 14). This is seen in such leaves as elm, cabbage, and so forth. In other cases, especially the blade-like leaves of grasses, irises, bluebells, etc., instead of one main vein with branches, there are several veins of equal size running parallel to each other. This is therefore called parallel venation (Fig. 14).

In many leaves, despite diversity of shape, the whole leaf-blade is a single structure, as is the case in the elm, oak, tulip, dandelion, daisy, etc. Such leaves are simple. In other cases, each leaf is composed of several leaflets, for example, horse-chestnut, rose and ash. Such leaves are compound.

2

FLOWERS

Were I, O God, in churchless lands remaining,
Far from all voice of teachers or divines,
My soul would find, in flowers of thy ordaining,
Priests, sermons, shrines !
Hymn to the Flowers : HORACE SMITH

There is no other part of a plant which presents such diversity of form, size, colour and beauty than the flower itself.

The flower is really the normal mechanism whereby a plant reproduces itself, for it is so constituted as to produce seeds, and inside each seed is a young, embryonic plant.

SEXUAL REPRODUCTION

Seeds are produced by a process of sex, and therefore plant reproduction by means of seeds is called sexual reproduction.

Sexual reproduction involves two important cells, both microscopic in size. These special cells are called gametes, and there are two kinds, namely, male and female. The female gamete is not as a general rule capable of developing to produce a new plant like the parent in which it was formed until it has received some form of impetus. This is given by the male gamete. The female gamete is usually called the egg or ovum : the male gamete is the sperm.

Fusion between a male and female gamete is the basis of sexual reproduction, and such fusion is called fertilisation. In flowering plants, the organ which produces both eggs and sperms is the flower ; hence its fundamental importance to the plant.

HERMAPHRODITE AND UNISEXUAL FLOWERS

Many species of flower are capable of producing both eggs and sperms : this is so with such common flowers as the buttercup, wallflower, tulip, pea and violet. These flowers are said to be hermaphrodite.

In some plants, however, the sperms are produced in one kind of flower and the eggs in another. Such flowers which can produce only one form of gamete are said to be unisexual. In other words, there are separate male and female flowers in such species. Here again there are two further possibilities, and Nature supplies both, namely those species which bear both female and male flowers on one and the same plant, and those which bear female flowers but not male on one plant, and vice-versa. Examples of those plants which bear both sexes of unisexual flowers are oak, hazel, sycamore, coltsfoot and cuckoo-pint; those which bear the two types of flowers on different plants are willow, poplar and hop.

THE INFLORESCENCE

In some plants, the flowers are solitary, for example, buttercup and tulip. On the other hand, many plants bear their flowers in definite clusters which are called inflorescences, such as pea, daisy, wallflower and foxglove. The inflorescence takes on a definite form such as a raceme or spike and so forth.

THE FLOWER

A comparatively simple type of flower is that of the buttercup. In it there are four sets of organs, all borne upon a swollen part of the stem called the receptacle (Fig. 15). Passing from the outside inwards, the four sets of organs may be clearly distinguished. All the organs are arranged around the receptacle in definite groups called whorls.

The outermost whorl is composed of five green, boat-shaped structures called the sepals. The complete whorl of sepals is called the calyx. The function of the sepals is not very important so far as the flower is concerned; in fact, some species of flowers have no sepals at all. The main function of the sepals is that of protecting the more delicate and much more important organs nearer the centre of the flower. In the buttercup, the sepals surround all the other floral organs while it is in bud. Thus the sepals form a protective covering from cold, rain and so forth. When the flower eventually opens, the sepals continue, at any rate for a time, to support the inner floral organs.

Next to the whorl of sepals comes the whorl of petals, collectively called the corolla. In the buttercup there are usually five petals, though this number varies somewhat. The buttercup petal is roughly heart-

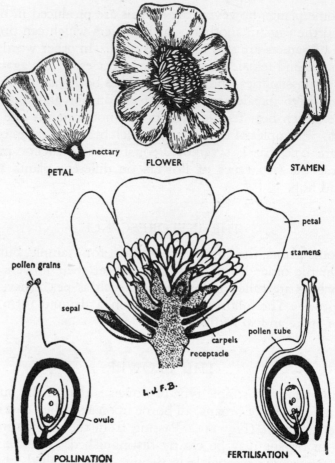

FIG. 15.—Diagrams illustrating the structure of a Buttercup Flower.

shaped, and at its base it bears a small sac containing nectar. The sac is therefore called the nectary. Insects visit this flower to collect the nectar from which they make honey. The petals alternate in position with the sepals.

Next to the corolla, passing inwards, are several whorls of organs, yellow in colour and shaped like Indian clubs: these are the stamens. The number of stamens in the buttercup flower varies, but it is always large. This is quite different from many other flowers where the number of stamens is small and definite, as six in the tulip, five in the primrose, ten in the pea, etc.

The innermost whorls of the buttercup flower are composed of an indefinite number of organs called carpels, each of which is more or less kidney-shaped and hooked at the tip. Again, in many the number of carpels is small and definite.

Thus, in the buttercup flower we have four sets of organs—sepals, petals, stamens and carpels. Neither the sepals nor the petals are directly connected with the production of eggs and sperms, therefore they are considered to be of secondary importance. The sepals are used for protection and support ; the petals for attracting insects to the flower for reasons which will be appreciated later.

It is the stamens and the carpels which are the main organs of reproduction, for it is they which produce the male and female gametes. The stamens are responsible for the production of sperms, and the carpels for the eggs. Therefore, in hermaphrodite flowers, such as the buttercup, stamens and carpels are present in each flower ; whereas in unisexual flowers either stamens or carpels are present, but not both.

If a single stamen be examined under a hand lens it will be seen to be composed of a stalk or filament which supports a swollen head called the anther. The anther is not a solid mass of tissue (at any rate when ripe), but contains four cavities running along its length. In each cavity there are hundreds of very small spherical bodies called pollen grains. These pollen grains are not the male gametes or sperms, but they are responsible for producing the latter. Consideration of this will be left until we deal with the process of fertilisation.

The main bulk of the carpel of the buttercup is called the ovary. The hooked projection of the carpel is the style, and at its tip is a sticky area called the stigma. The ovary encloses a cavity, and from the base of the cavity a structure projects into the ovary space. The projection is more or less ovoid in shape and is borne on a short stalk. It is called the ovule.

DIVERSITY OF FLORAL STRUCTURE

The next stage in the process of seed production is the fusion of the sperms from the pollen grains with the eggs in the ovules. But this cannot take place before the two gametes come into direct contact with each other. At the present stage they certainly are not in contact, for the pollen is in the anther, and the ovule in the ovary ; and both organs are some distance away from each other. Therefore, the next stage is to bring the pollen into contact with the carpel. This process is known as pollination. The methods of pollination in flowers are manifold, and this is where the secondary floral organs, especially the petals, are helpful. So before considering pollination (which is followed by the main process of fertilisation), let us examine some different examples of floral arrangement and see how such differences affect pollination.

CALYX

The calyx of flowering plants shows little diversity. There is considerable variation in number, however : the poppy has two sepals, the lesser celandine three, the buttercup five, while in a few flowers, such as the water-lily, the sepals are numerous.

Sometimes the sepals of the calyx are joined along most of their length, thus forming a tube. This is well seen in the primrose (Fig. 16).

Frequently the calyx, instead of being green, becomes brightly coloured and enlarged and carries on the function of the petals of the corolla. The calyx is then said to be petalloid. This is the case in the marsh marigold, where the five large sepals look exactly like five petals. The same is true of the wild clematis or traveller's joy, though here the sepals are not so conspicuous. In both these cases, since the petals are not required, they are entirely absent. In the Christmas rose, on the other hand, though the sepals are white and petalloid, the petals are not absent but are reduced to small tubular nectaries.

COROLLA

It is usually in the corolla that we see the greatest diversity of shape, colour and arrangement. Herein lie most of the reasons for a flower's characteristic beauty. Yet in some flowers the petals are entirely absent, for example, the willow.

In many cases, the petals join for varying degrees of their length to form a tube, as in the primrose (Fig. 16).

The number of petals, too, shows considerable variation. For example, the wallflower has four, the pink and the buttercup five, and many flowers have an indefinite number of petals.

The arrangement of the petals of a flower may be regular or irregular. For example, in the case of the buttercup or the wallflower, the petals, and, indeed, all the floral organs, are symmetrical around any vertical plane passing through its centre. That is, it does not matter in what vertical plane we cut the flower in half, the two halves will be the mirror image of each other. Such flowers are said to be regular.

On the other hand, the pea flower, like many others, is irregular (Fig. 13). This flower has five petals. Looking straight towards the inside of the flower, we see one large petal standing up as a background to the rest. It is large and spreading, and is called the standard. Then, in front of the standard and to each side, are two wing-like petals, which are therefore called the wings. At the bottom are two smaller petals, facing each other, and together looking somewhat like a ship's keel. They are therefore collectively called the keel. Thus, in the pea flower it is clear that there is only one vertical plane through which it could be cut in order to get two halves of the flower symmetrical. The plane

FIG. 16.—A Primrose Flower. Note that the sepals and the petals are united and are regular.

would pass vertically downwards through the standard and between the two wings and the keel. So the flower is irregular.

In some flowers, it is impossible to tell the difference between the sepals and the petals. This is because the sepals have become petalloid and similar to the petals of the same flower. This is seen in such familiar flowers as the tulip, crocus, bluebell, and so forth. In such cases, the collection of whorls is called a perianth, and no attempt is made to differentiate between petals and sepals.

STAMENS

The stamens of flowering plants are also diverse. The diversity comes out chiefly in number in each flower. There is, for example, an indefinite number in the buttercup and poppy, four in the deadnettle, six in the wallflower, six in the bluebell and tulip, and ten in the pea. Sometimes the filaments of the stamens differ markedly in length in the same flower ; in the wallflower, for example, there are four long and two short ones (Fig. 33), whereas in the deadnettle there are two long and two short (Fig. 136).

In the buttercup, the stamens are joined directly on to the receptacle, whereas in other cases they are attached to other floral organs. In the bluebell, for example, they are inserted on the perianth members (one to each). In certain flowers the stamens are joined together. Thus, the five stamens of the dandelion flower are joined to form a tube (Fig. 17), and in the bird's-foot trefoil nine of the stamens are

c

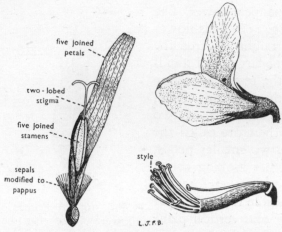

joined together, while the tenth is free (Fig. 17).

CARPELS

In the buttercup, all the carpels, indefinite in number, are free (Fig. 15). In many other flowers, on the other hand, the number of carpels is small and definite, and frequently they are fused together in a variety of ways. The pea has one carpel only (Fig. 13). The gooseberry has two, the tulip, three, also similarly

FIG. 17.—Left, a single Flower of the Dandelion ; right (top), Flower of the Bird's-foot Trefoil ; right (bottom), Stamens and Style of the Bird's-foot Trefoil.

fused along their longitudinal margins, the joined, and so forth.

RECEPTACLE

The receptacle varies considerably in shape, so that the floral organs seem to be inserted in different positions. In the buttercup, for example, the receptacle is cone-shaped, and the outer floral whorls are inserted around its lower margin. This places the carpels above the rest of the floral whorls. In the pear flower, the opposite is the case, because the receptacle is shaped like a basin.

POLLINATION

Having made a brief survey of the diversity of floral structure, we are now in a better position to cast our minds back and follow up the methods of pollination, and then go on to the process of fertilisation which leads to seed production. Pollination is the process whereby the pollen (which produces the male sperms) can be brought into such a position that the sperms can approach the eggs present in the ovules of the carpels and thus make fusion possible. The position which the pollen takes up in order to do this is on the stigma of the ovary. The stigma is by nature sticky, so that the pollen easily adheres to it once it touches it.

Pollination can take place in two general ways. Either the pollen from the stamen of a flower can pass to the stigma of the same flower, or it can be transported to the stigma of a different flower. The former is self-pollination and the latter cross-pollination.

When the pollen within the anther head of the stamen is ripe it becomes dry and loose within the anther. Then the anther becomes ruptured ; though some anthers have pores and others valves.

SELF-POLLINATION

In most cases of self-pollinated flowers, the pollen falls by virtue of its own weight on to the stigma. The flower of the common chick-weed is a good example of this simple type. Although self-pollination, for various reasons, is not so desirable as cross-pollination, certain plants resort to it if cross-pollination has failed to take place. Sometimes most elaborate methods are adopted. *Nigella,* or love-in-a-mist, for example, is a flower which is usually cross-pollinated. In it, the styles of the carpels are much longer than the stamens, so that it is impossible for the ripe pollen to fall on the stigmas and induce self-pollination (Fig. 26). If, however, for some reason or other, cross-pollination has not taken place when the pollen is ripe, the styles gradually bend backwards until they come into contact with the exposed pollen on the anthers, just as an elephant bends its trunk backwards to take a bun from the rider.

Certain plants, such as the violet, bear special flowers which do not open but, though they remain in bud, their stamens and carpels ripen. Thus, when the pollen is shed it immediately comes into contact with the stigma within the confines of the bud. Thus self-pollination is assured.

CROSS-POLLINATION

Many plants devise the most wonderful methods to ensure cross-pollination of their flowers ; and some go still further and, by varying means, ensure that self-pollination is virtually impossible. In some the stamens and the carpels of the same flower do not ripen at the same time. The plantain is a good example of this. The purple loosestrife (Chap. 20) has evolved a most elaborate method of ensuring cross-pollination. Many others will be seen when considering the families.

Wind-pollination.—The simplest method of cross-pollination is by means of the wind. This is very common among unisexual flowers

H. Dustin.

FIG. 18.—Insect Pollination of a Dog-rose.

such as those of sycamore and hazel. Wind-pollination is common among most British trees and grasses. For this reason, the flowers are frequently inconspicuous, for in wind pollination it is not necessary to attract insects by means of conspicuous flowers. Naturally the chances of a pollen grain reaching a stigma (probably some distance away) through the agency of the wind are very remote, so many thousands of times more pollen is produced than can actually be used for fertilisation. The method is therefore very wasteful, and explains why clouds of pollen can sometimes be seen being blown away from catkin-bearing hazel trees.

Insect-pollination.—A more efficient method of cross-pollination involves insects—chiefly bees, wasps, butterflies, moths, flies and beetles—as the agents of distribution of the pollen. These animals can easily collect pollen on their hairy backs and legs, when visiting the flower for nectar. So, as the insect passes from flower to flower, the pollen picked up from the stamens of the first is passed on to the stigma of the next. In its simplest form this is just what happens in the buttercup.

But some flowers are prepared for the insect's visit, with the result that various devices in such flowers make pollination by insects certain.

First of all, of course, the flowers must attract the insects. They do this in several ways. One is by the bright, attractive colours of their petals. This is one of the functions of the petals. Another is by the production of the delicate perfume so familiar to us in certain flowers. Insects are attracted by this perfume: in fact, perfume attracts insects more surely than brightly coloured flowers do.

Flies and beetles, sometimes agents of cross-pollination, have only short tongues, and such insects are useful only to such widely open flowers as the buttercup and dog-rose (Fig. 18). Bees and butterflies, on the other hand, have long tongues. The flowers that attract these, therefore, usually have their nectar deeply seated, so that the insect has to push its way right into the flower.

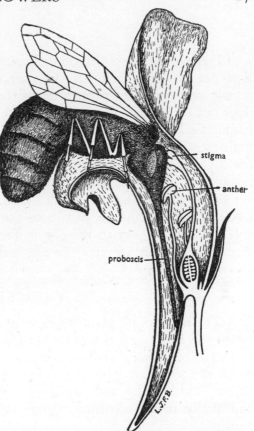

FIG. 19.—Insect Pollination of the Toadflax.

Thus the flower makes sure that the insect touches both anther and stigma (Fig. 19). And so one could go on. The various methods adopted by flowers of ensuring pollination make fascinating study. Further examples will be examined as occasion arises.

The attractiveness of the flower is all that matters to the visiting insect, and to it, in its quest for nectar, colour and scent are all important.

> The honey-bee that wanders all day long . . .
> Seeks not alone the rose's glowing breast,
> The lily's dainty cup, the violet's lips,
> But from all rank and noxious weeds he sips
> The single drop of sweetness closely pressed
> Within the poison chalice.
>
> *Lesson of the Bee* : ANNE BOTTA

FERTILISATION

Having got the pollen on the stigma of the ovary, the next problem is to see how the male gametes (sperms) from the pollen get to the female gametes (eggs) present inside the ovary. The egg is passive and does not move : it is the male gamete that does the moving. This is made possible by the pollen grain. Once on the stigma, the pollen grain sends out a tube, called the pollen tube, which grows down the style (Fig. 15). Growth of this pollen tube continues until it reaches the cavity of the ovary containing the egg. Then it passes across the cavity, and the end of the pollen tube forces its way into the ovule. The pollen tube, of course, contains the sperm and this is now able to make its way to the egg in the ovule. This it does and fuses with and thus fertilises it. The egg is then able to develop and produce an embryonic plant.

THE SEED

The new young plant developing in the ovule within the carpel is called the seed. All the time that this young seed is developing, the carpellary or ovary wall, is getting stronger and stronger, so that when the seeds are ripe, the ovary wall is strong enough to contain them. This ovary wall develops into a thick and hard or thick and fleshy tissue according to the species of plant.

Fig. 20.—Ovary of pea cut in section (left) and the fruit (right) which develops from it.

The whole ovary, with its developed wall, containing the seeds inside, now forms what is called the fruit.

Within the fruit, therefore, we have the most important part of the plant, namely, the seed, for it is the seed which is responsible for carrying the plant into the next generation. The fruit is really only a means of protection or distribution, etc. for the seed or seeds which it contains. As Nietzsche expresses it :

> Everyone who enjoys thinks that the principal thing to the tree is the fruit, but in point of fact the principal thing to it is the seed.— Herein lies the difference between them that create and them that enjoy.
> *Maxims* : NIETZSCHE

The number of seeds in any one fruit depends upon the number of ovules which have been fertilised. In the carpel of the buttercup there is one ovule, so there is one seed in its fruit. In the ovary of the pea, there are about eight ovules, so in the fruit, called a pod, there are about eight seeds (Fig. 20).

The production of seeds, as we have seen, is a complicated process. Nothing is created spontaneously : everything has to go through a complex series of processes known as reproduction.

> No great thing is created suddenly, any more than a bunch of grapes or a fig. If you tell me that you desire a fig, I answer you that there must be time. Let it first blossom, then bear fruit, then ripen.
>
> *Discourses* : EPICTETUS

VEGETATIVE REPRODUCTION

Many plants can reproduce themselves without the help of seeds. New plants are produced direct from the tissues of the parent plant. This is called vegetative reproduction. In certain cases, special tissues develop for the purpose of vegetative reproduction ; but in many cases, almost any part of the plant will produce a new one. Here there is no question of sex.

The Canadian water weed develops chiefly by the growth of any part severed from the parent plant. This makes it such a nuisance in our ponds and streams. The plant is a native of North America, hence its name. It was mysteriously introduced into Ireland in 1836 and into England in 1841. Today it is very common owing to its prolific vegetative reproduction (Chap. 64).

The potato tuber is another example of vegetative reproduction. The tuber is really the swollen part of an underground stem. This is able to lie dormant in the soil and produce a new plant in the following season. No sex is involved, in fact, the seeds of the potato plant, produced by its flowers, are very rarely seen.

The corm of the crocus is another example of vegetative reproduction. Each shoot of the crocus which grows above the soil gradually develops a new corm at its base during its growing season. The corm is actually a swollen stem surrounded by a few membranous leaves, in the axils of some of which are axillary buds. The corm can rest in the soil during the summer and winter and then develop into a new plant in early spring.

The creeping stems of grasses and the runners of strawberries are further examples of vegetative reproduction.

Most organs of certain plants are capable of reproducing vegetatively in some form or other. This method of reproduction is extensively utilised by the gardener, especially in the case of potato tubers, corms of gladiolus and crocus, bulbs of many plants such as onions, tulips, and so forth. Frequently the gardener uses unspecialised parts of plants. In the case of the geranium, pelargonium, chrysanthemum, and so forth, for example, he just uses cuttings of parts of the parent plants. In the case of roses, he uses the more artificial method of budding, and in fruit culture he often adopts the method of grafting (Fig. 65).

3

CLASSIFICATION OF FLOWERING PLANTS

I love these beautiful and peaceful tribes [flowers]—and wish I was better acquainted with them.

W. S. LANDOR in a letter to Southey

Although there are many thousands of different plants in the world, some varying considerably from others, so many of them are either closely or distantly related to each other, that it is possible to grade them into various divisions, classes, families and so forth. This is known as plant classification, and no student of the British flora, or indeed anyone with only a passing interest in flowers, will get very far with his interest unless he makes himself familiar with the elements of this classification.

The basis upon which plants are classified rests, so far as possible, on their evolutionary sequence, that is starting with the simplest and graduating, usually upwards, in direct accordance with complexity. It must be realised, however, that increasing complexity or efficiency are not the only natural results of evolution. For evolution is both upwards and downwards, and the latter involves degradation and degeneration of any or all of the plant organs. Some become modified, others vestigial, and sometimes they disappear altogether. In this way we discover which plant is related to which and to what extent. For example, there are some plants closely related to each other, such as primroses and cowslips. Others, on the other hand, are vastly different from each other, such as daisies and roses.

In classifying flowering plants, we must take into consideration all their characteristics ; but it is obvious that the most useful characters are those which vary the most. The root, for example, is scarcely a suitable basis for classification, because it is the least changeable organ. That of the primrose is not very different from that of the dandelion, yet the two flowers are vastly different. The root is, in fact, the most conservative organ of the plant. The most changeable organ of the

By *courtesy of the Linnean Society of London.*

FIG. 21.—Linnaeus (1707–1778).

plant is the flower, and therefore the classification of flowering plants
is based chiefly, though not wholly, on the characters of the flowers.

Plant nomenclature of today follows closely along the lines set forth
by the great Swedish botanist, Carl von Linné, usually called Linnaeus
(Fig. 21). He announced his system first in 1735, but published it in
complete detail in 1753. Though many thousands of plants have been
discovered and added to the flora of the world since the days of Linnaeus,
we still use his methods in principle though they have been modified in
the light of modern knowledge.

There are several systems of plant classification in use today, but
they differ only in detail. Here we are adopting (with certain modifications) that originally proposed by Dr. J. Hutchinson of the Royal
Botanic Gardens, Kew, in his *Families of Flowering Plants*. So far as the
flowers and fruit are concerned, Dr. Hutchinson points out several trends
during the history of flowering plants on this earth. A few examples
may prove of interest. (1) Hermaphrodite flowers preceded unisexual
flowers, and of the latter those produced on two different plants (male
on one and female on another) are probably more recent than those
produced on the same plant. (2) The solitary flower is more primitive
than that produced in inflorescences. The higher form of inflorescence
is that of composite flowers, for example, daisy and dandelion (Fig. 97).

(3) Many-parted flowers preceded those with few parts. (4) Those flowers having no petals followed the petalled flowers, the petals being the result of reduction. (5) The regular flower is an earlier type than the irregular. (6) Free carpels are more primitive than fused. (7) Evolutionary reduction in number of parts makes the few-carpelled flower more recent than the many-carpelled. (8) Aggregate fruits followed single fruit. There are other general principles, and *all* of them have to be considered before assigning a plant its place in the general classification.

Apart from the division to which all conifers and a few others belong (which do not concern us here), all other flowering plants may first be divided into two great groups. They are the monocotyledons and the dicotyledons.

The first leaf present in the young embryonic plant embedded in the seed is called a seed-leaf or cotyledon. In monocotyledons there is only one cotyledon, and in dicotyledons there are usually two. Besides this difference there are others. Few monocotyledons show secondary thickening of their stems, so that there are not many trees in that group. Most dicotyledons, on the other hand, do show secondary thickening. The leaves of monocotyledons are usually parallel-veined, whereas those of dicotyledons are net-veined. The flowers of the two groups are also characteristic within very wide limits. The parts of the flowers of dicotyledons are either indefinite or in fours or fives or their multiples. The parts of the monocotyledonous flower are usually in threes or multiples of three. The tulip and grass are examples of monocotyledons, and the rose and dandelion examples of dicotyledons.

Every plant belongs to a species. For example, among the buttercups there are several common types, such as creeping buttercup, bulbous buttercup, water buttercup (or crowfoot) and so forth. Each is a separate species, because each varies slightly from the other. But all these species are sufficiently similar to warrant being grouped together, so they are all placed in a single group called a genus. Therefore we can say that all kinds of buttercup belong to the same genus but to different species.

In order to assign the necessary distinction yet to emphasise the close relation, Linnaeus suggested each plant having two names, one to designate the genus, the other the species. This is now done for all plants. Every buttercup, for example, belongs to the same genus, which is called *Ranunculus*. This name is the first of the two applied to any plant, and is called the generic name. Then each species of *Ranun-*

culus has a second name called the specific name. Thus the botanical names of the buttercups mentioned above are : creeping buttercup, *Ranunculus repens* ; bulbous buttercup, *Ranunculus bulbosus* ; water butter-cup, *Ranunculus aquatilis*. Then there is the celery-leaved buttercup, *Ranunculus scleratus*. The lesser celandine is also sufficiently closely related to the buttercup to be placed in the same genus, and its botanical name is therefore *Ranunculus ficaria*.

Further details of classification involve subdivision of the species. They will not concern us very much, but they do exist, and these sub-divisions of species are known as subspecies and varieties. This applies especially to cultivated plants, and such subspecies and varieties have been created chiefly by cross-breeding and hybridisation. For example, the potato is a single species called *Solanum tuberosum*, but the species is subdivided into the many varieties so well known to the gardener. The same may be said of such cultivated plants as the apple (*Malus pumila*) and the garden rose (*Rosa centifolia*) and a host of herbaceous garden flowers.

Plant genera frequently resemble each other rather closely, though they differ sufficiently clearly to be kept as separate genera. For example, closely related to the genus *Ranunculus* is the garden paeony. A detailed consideration of this plant shows it to be very akin to an ordinary buttercup. Though larger, the shoot and leaves are very similar in form ; so also are the flowers except that they are larger, the petals are more numerous and the colour is usually white, pink or red instead of yellow. Thus the paeony, though very similar botanically to the butter-cup (*Ranunculus*), is sufficiently different to be placed in a separate genus (*Paeonia*).

Other genera very closely related to the genera *Ranunculus* and *Paeonia* are : *Caltha* (for example, marsh marigold), *Nigella* (love-in-a-mist), *Aquilegia* (columbine), *Delphinium* (larkspur and other well-known garden species and varieties), *Aconitum* (monkshood), *Clematis* (clematis or traveller's joy), *Anemone* (wood anemone and several garden species), *Helleborus* (the hellebores, Christmas rose, etc.), *Trollius* (globe flower), *Thalictrum* (meadow rue), *Adonis* (pheasant's eye), *Myosurus* (mouse-tail), and several other genera. All these genera are so closely related to each other that they are placed together in a still larger group called a family. In this case, the family is called RANUNCULACEAE.

The accompanying table illustrates the classification into genera and species of most common members of the buttercup family (RANUN-CULACEAE). (See also Plate i.)

THE BUTTERCUP FAMILY		
RANUNCULACEAE		
GENUS	SPECIES	COMMON NAME
Caltha	*palustris*	marsh marigold
Helleborus	*viridis*	green hellebore
	foetidus	stinking hellebore
	niger	Christmas rose
Trollius	*europaeus*	globe flower
Aquilegia	*vulgaris*	columbine
Delphinium	*ajacis*	larkspur
Aconitum	*napellus*	monkshood
Paeonia	*sinensis*	Chinese paeony
Ranunculus	*aquatilis*	water crowfoot
	ficaria	lesser celandine
	acris	common buttercup
	bulbosus	bulbous buttercup
	repens	creeping buttercup
	scleratus	celery-leaved buttercup
Anemone	*nemorosa*	wood anemone
Thalictrum	*minus*	lesser meadow rue
	flavum	common meadow rue
Clematis	*vitalba*	traveller's joy or old man's beard
Adonis	*autumnalis*	pheasant's eye
Myosurus	*minimus*	mouse-tail

N.B.—There are a few more genera and several more species belonging to this family, but they are not very common.

Families are then arranged in evolutionary sequence, so that those naturally closely related to each other come near each other in the scheme of classification. For example, other families closely related to RANUNCULACEAE are CERATOPHYLLACEAE (for example, *Ceratophyllum submersum*, hornwort, an aquatic submerged plant); NYMPHAEACEAE (for example, *Nymphaea alba*, white water-lily and *Nuphar luteum*, yellow water-lily); and BERBERIDACEAE (for example, *Berberis vulgaris*, barberry).

Finally, all families of flowering plants (excluding the conifers and a few others) are segregated into monocotyledons or dicotyledons.

It will be noted that whereas most wild plants have a common name, many garden plants have not, and are usually referred to by their generic name, for example, *Delphinium, Dahlia, Clarkia,* and *Wistaria*.

HOW TO STUDY FLOWERS

A study of flowers cannot be made either with pleasure or with profit from a book alone. The only way to understand them and their relationships with each other is to go into the country and examine the plants, first growing in their natural surroundings, and then more closely at home. Then compare and contrast them with the related species available in the garden. When doing this, it must be borne in mind that garden plants have been subjected to artificial cultivation, to cross-breeding, and so forth. Thus superficially they may appear quite different from their natural or wild counterparts.

But when examining flowers in this way, though great satisfaction can come from being able to name and identify and even to classify them, this is not enough. We must be able to understand them, to appreciate them, else we shall find ourselves becoming aloof from the real value and love of flowers and be as one of those who, as Emerson wrote :

> Love not the flower they pluck and know it not,
> And all their botany is Latin names.

On the other hand, the more one studies plants, the more one recognises the necessity for correct nomenclature, in spite of what Tennyson wrote :

> What is it ? a learned man
> Could give it a clumsy name.
> Let him name it who can,
> The beauty would be the same.
> *Maud* : TENNYSON

A final word to those who gather wild flowers. Never gather more than are actually needed, either for home decoration or for study. Do not pull up a complete plant unless it is essential. In the case of trees and shrubs, never cut more than the minimum of twigs, otherwise the future form and beauty of that tree may be permanently impaired. Furthermore, in gathering wild flowers, tread carefully and do not destroy a hundred in an effort to get one.

> When you defile the pleasant streams
> And the wild bird's nesting–place,
> You massacre a million dreams
> And cast your spittle in God's face
> *Olton Pools : To the Defilers* : DRINKWATER

PART II

DICOTYLEDONS

I. FLOWERS WITH FREE PETALS

The dicotyledons can be subdivided into two groups according to whether their petals are free or are joined to each other. Those with free petals are considered to be the more primitive, especially since their mechanisms for pollination are not so specialised as those of the flowers with united petals. The dicotyledons with free petals, up to, and including, the family UMBELLIFERAE, will be considered in this Part.

4

THE BUTTERCUP FAMILY
(Ranunculaceae)

The buttercups, bright-eyed and bold,
Held up their chalices of gold
To catch the sunshine and the dew.
Centennial Poem : JULIA DORE

The buttercup family (RANUNCULACEAE) is considered to be one of the simplest and most primitive of the dicotyledons.

WILD PLANTS

Buttercups are frequently the most conspicuous plants flowering in our meadows and fields during the months of May and June; they still persist, but are not so much in evidence, into August.

There are three common species of buttercup, namely **common buttercup** (*Ranunculus acris*), **bulbous buttercup** (R. *bulbosus*) (Plate 1), and **creeping buttercup** (R. *repens*). All are perennials, that is, each plant lasts for several years.

It is interesting to note that in earlier days, the yellow buttercups

37

were called 'butter-flowers'; the change occurred some time during the middle of the eighteenth century.

The flowers of the three species are similar. They have already been described on p. 19. The leaves are divided into three lobes, and each lobe is deeply segmented to a varying degree. The stems and leaf-stalks are usually covered with fine silky hairs.

The bases of the leaves of the bulbous buttercup are swollen and act as a food store to tide the plant over the winter months. These swollen leaf-bases collectively form a loosely constructed bulb (Plate 1). The leaves of all buttercups have a bitter taste, and that explains why animals feeding in the pastures leave them severely alone. It is said that a few centuries ago beggars used buttercup plants to induce large sores on their skin and thus inspire sympathy.

The fruit is a collection of dry, one-seeded structures called achenes. Each achene is formed from one carpel and each contains one seed.

A less common species of buttercup, which flowers until September, is the **celery-leaved buttercup** (or **crowfoot**) (R. *scleratus*). This may be found growing in wet ditches. The leaves are smooth, and the flowers are smaller and paler in colour than those of the other species of buttercup.

Another species belonging to the same genus is the **lesser celandine** (R. *ficaria*), a beautiful plant which flowers rather early in the year, that is, between March and May (Plate 1). The leaves are heart-shaped with rounded divisions at their margins.

The lesser celandine produces two rather unusual but interesting organs. Between the axils of some of the leaves borne on the flower stalks, tiny swellings are to be found. These swellings are called bulbils, and they are a means of vegetative reproduction. Towards the approach of winter they break away from the plant and become buried in the soil where they lie dormant during the winter. In the following spring they produce new plants (Plate 1).

The other unusual organs are the **root tubers** found among the normal fibrous roots. They are swollen, and, like the bulbils, they are a means of food storage and are capable of developing into new plants during the following season. The cultivated dahlia also has root tubers which are very large and fleshy. The lesser celandine has, therefore, two methods of vegetative reproduction; which is just as well, for the fruit seldom ripen owing to the usually inclement weather prevailing at the time.

The flower of the lesser celandine is a glistening golden yellow. There are usually three sepals and five to eight narrow petals ; otherwise the flower is similar to that of the buttercup. The petals are able to move under the stimulus of changing light intensity ; thus they close up at night or during dull weather, and open again during clear or sunny weather.

> There is a Flower, the lesser Celandine,
> That shrinks, like many more, from cloud and rain ;
> And, the first moment that the sun may shine,
> Bright as the sun himself, 'tis out again !
> *The Small Celandine* : WORDSWORTH

On rare occasions, lesser celandine flowers may be found which are ' double ', having several whorls of petals.

The lesser celandine is in no way related to the greater celandine, which belongs to a different family (the poppy family, p. 54).

There are several other species belonging to the genus *Ranunculus*, most of which grow in meadows, woods or waste places. Few are to be found growing in water, with the exception of the **water crowfoot** (R. *aquatilis*) (Plate 1). The white and yellow starry flowers of this lovely plant appearing on the surface of ponds or slow-moving streams during the months of May to August make a very pretty sight.

> And all along the stream
>   My care hath not forgot
> Crowfoot's white galaxy,
>   And Love's Forget-me-not.
> *The Idle Flowers* : R. BRIDGES

To each flower there are five sepals and five petals ; in fact, apart from unimportant details such as colour, it is very similar to that of the true buttercup.

The water crowfoot is especially interesting in that, unlike most plants, it has two kinds of foliage leaves. Those which are floating on the surface of the water are kidney-shaped, and lobed at the base of the blades ; those which are submerged are finely divided, in fact, almost hair-like. The fine hair-like leaves allow the water to pass freely between them.

There are other species of water crowfoot.

A genus closely related to *Ranunculus* is *Clematis*, a very common wild member of which is the **wild clematis** or **traveller's joy** (*Clematis*

D

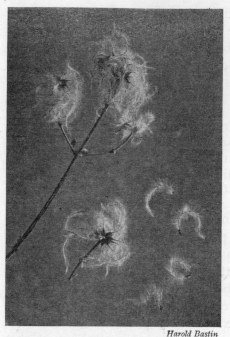

Harold Bastin

FIG. 23.—Fruit of Wild Clematis.

vitalba) (Plate 1). This is a climbing plant of woody texture and is perhaps most attractive when it is in fruit, for then the hedgerows over which it climbs are white with its fleecy, plumed fruit (Fig. 23). During the summer, the plant grows over the supporting plants in the hedge-rows. The leaves are borne in pairs. Each is divided into five leaflets—two lateral pairs and one terminal. The leaf-stalks bend around any support with which they come into contact so that it is difficult to dislodge the plant.

The flowers of traveller's joy appear during July to September. They are whitish-green with four to six sepals—usually four. There are no petals. The rest of the flower is rather like that of the true buttercup. So also is the fruit, namely, a collection of achenes, except that from the tip of each achene grows a plume (Fig. 23). This gives the fruit the familiar feathery, beard-like appearance, hence the alternative common name, **old man's beard.** The plume on the fruit has a real function ; by its means the fruit can be carried by the wind and thus be disseminated far and wide.

> Over the hills and far away
> The road is long on a summer day ;
> Dust glares white in the noontide heat,
> But the Traveller's Joy grows strong and sweet,
> Down the hollow and up the slope
> It binds the hedge with a silken rope.
>
>   *Vespertilia* : R. MARRIOTT-WATSON

Anemone is another genus representative of the family RANUNCULACEAE, and the most common example of this genus is the **wood anemone** (*Anemone nemorosa*), whose white flowers carpet our woodlands in the early spring. Though the flowers are generally white, some of pinkish hue may be seen. The plant is at its best during March to June.

The buttercup family comprises a large percentage of plants which have petaloid sepals and either no petals at all or very much reduced. The wood anemone is a further example of this. The petals are absent and the six sepals are petaloid and white on their inner surface, with a purplish tinge on the outside. Invariably the flower hangs facing away from the wind, hence its alternative common name, **windflower.**

> Anemone, so well
> Named of the wind, to which thou art all free.
> *Wild Flowers*: G. MACDONALD

The wood anemone (like its cultivated garden varieties) has two types of green leaves. There are the true foliage leaves which grow on their own stalks from ground-level. Then there are others, similar in appearance, which are borne in threes on the flower stalks. They are actually bracts which protect the flower when in bud. After the flower has begun to open, it grows out still further on its own stalk, leaving the bracts further behind on the stalk, and these eventually develop into leaves very similar in size and form to the true foliage leaves (Plate 1).

The wood anemone spreads vegetatively by means of a short, underground stem.

In the cold, inhospitable surroundings of marshlands and other water-logged places, it is scarcely likely that plants will begin to blossom early ; but almost the first to do so is the **kingcup** or **marsh marigold,** also known in some localities as **soldier's button** (Plate 1). This plant is perhaps the most striking and most beautiful of all our marsh plants, both in foliage and flowers. It begins to bloom in March and continues to do so until the end of May.

The marsh marigold is also a member of the buttercup family ; but it is sufficiently distinct to be placed in a genus of its own (*Caltha palustris*).

The stem is thick and juicy and contains a large number of air-spaces. These are essential to a plant growing in a soil where air is not easily available below ground (and all living parts of plants must have access to air). The leaves are large, smooth and shiny : they are heart-shaped.

In many parts of the United States, though not often in this country, the leaves and young stems of the marsh marigold are boiled and served like spinach. The young flower-buds are also sometimes used as substitutes for capers.

Again, as in the case of the wood anemone and traveller's joy, the sepals of the marsh marigold are petaloid. They are large and golden-yellow in colour and there are five of them. The petals have not disappeared altogether, but are reduced to small tubular nectaries. The fruit is a collection of follicles which differ from achenes in that they are able to split and thus release the seeds inside.

The **pheasant's eye** is worth looking for when on country rambles, though it is not easily found, for it is rather rare. It also is a member of the buttercup family, and is placed in a genus of its own (*Adonis autumnalis*). It grows chiefly in cornfields and blooms during July, producing very attractive red flowers (Plate 1). The leaves are very finely divided. The number of petals varies from five to ten and they are bright red in colour.

The **columbine** (or **granny's bonnet** as it is called in some localities) is another generic member of the buttercup family. The wild columbine (*Aquilegia vulgaris*) (Plate 1) is not common, though it may sometimes be found in the woods and thickets of certain districts. The flowers are purple, though the garden varieties (see p. 44) show a wide range of colours.

The columbine is yet another member of the buttercup family having petaloid sepals. There are five of them. In this case, however, the petals are also very much in evidence, and each extends backwards

FIG. 24.—The Monkshood Flower and Fruit.

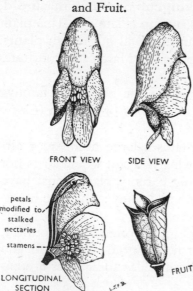

FRONT VIEW   SIDE VIEW

petals modified to stalked nectaries

stamens

LONGITUDINAL SECTION

FRUIT

into a long spur containing nectar. As in the buttercup, there is an indefinite number of stamens ; but the carpels are limited to five. The fruit is a collection of follicles which, like those of the marsh marigold, split when ripe to expose the many seeds they contain.

Perhaps the tallest-growing genus of the buttercup family in the wild state is that of *Aconitum* to which belongs the **monkshood** (*A. napellus*) (Plate 1). This handsome plant is not very common in the wild state, though it can be found in some woods and thickets. It is, of course, frequently cultivated in gardens. Care must be taken in handling this plant, for it produces a deadly poison. The flowers appear during July and August, and are very conspicuously borne in long inflorescences with the younger flowers at the top.

Monkshood also has petaloid sepals, five in number, which are responsible for the deep blue colour, whereas the petals, reduced to two in number, are modified to long claw-like tubes containing nectar (Fig. 24).

Unlike most members of the buttercup family (though like the cultivated genus *Delphinium*), monkshood flowers are irregular. The two lower sepals form a kind of platform on which insect visitors may alight. Two more sepals form wing-like side pieces, and the fifth sepal takes the form of a protective hood at the back. The nectar in the tube-like petals is deeply seated so that only long-tongued insects, such as bees, can get at it. The stamens are indefinite in number and there are three carpels which, after fertilisation, form follicles (Fig. 24).

FIG. 25.—Delphiniums.

ORNAMENTAL PLANTS

Perhaps the two most familiar and indeed most beautiful genera represented among the cultivated members of the buttercup family are those of *Delphinium* and *Paeonia*.

Belonging to the genus *Delphinium* are the true **delphiniums** and the **larkspurs**. Delphiniums are of stately beauty, and are the ideal plants for herbaceous borders since they are so striking and, being hardy perennials, are easy to cultivate (Fig. 25). The flowers are irregular and have pronounced spurs on the sepals. The shades of colour are most delightful, varying from a lovely soft azure blue to an intense purple and with various combinations.

The larkspur (*D. ajacis*) may be looked upon as being an annual delphinium. Larkspurs are more graceful than the stately delphiniums and present a striking variety of colours—scarlet, pink of varying depths, deep blue, mauve and white.

The **paeony** is another member of the buttercup family cultivated in herbaceous borders and elsewhere for its sturdy habit and showy flowers. Perhaps the most popular varieties of this plant grown in Great Britain are those derived from the **Chinese paeony** (*Paeonia sinensis*). The foliage is large and handsome, and the delicately scented flowers which appear in May and June vary in shade from white through pink to deep crimson. Most of the varieties are ' double ', that is, there is an indefinite number of petals. Unlike delphinium, the flowers are regular.

The **globe flower** (*Trollius europaeus*) is actually wild, and may be found in moist woods ; but most people will more easily find it cultivated in gardens. This handsome plant has large yellow flowers which appear during May and June. They are globular in outline, hence the common name. The petals are five to fifteen in number and are small and narrow. There is about the same number of sepals, but these are large and petaloid. Apart from this, the flowers resemble the true buttercups.

Monkshood (already described on p. 42) is frequently cultivated.

Many garden varieties of the **columbine** (*Aquilegia*) (see p. 42) are cultivated, especially in herbaceous borders. The flowers present all shades of blue, purple, pink, yellow, white and variegated.

Love-in-a-mist (*Nigella* species) is another member of the buttercup family which finds considerable favour among gardeners. It is a hardy annual and continues flowering until the end of the summer. The shades of colour vary between purple, blue and white ; but the sky-blue varieties are the most popular. Unlike most members of the buttercup family, love-in-a-mist presents five carpels which are joined to form a five-chambered ovary, though the five long styles are separate (see p. 25). The fruit is large and conspicuous, and since the carpels are joined, the fruit is a five-chambered capsule. It is the sepals which are responsible for the flower's striking beauty, for they are petalloid (Fig. 26), and the petals are reduced to short-stalked pitcher-like nectaries.

Other garden varieties of wild genera of RANUNCULACEAE include those of *Anemone* and *Clematis*. The description of the wild anemone (p. 40) covers that of the garden varieties with the exception of size and colour. The garden varieties are larger and present an exceptionally

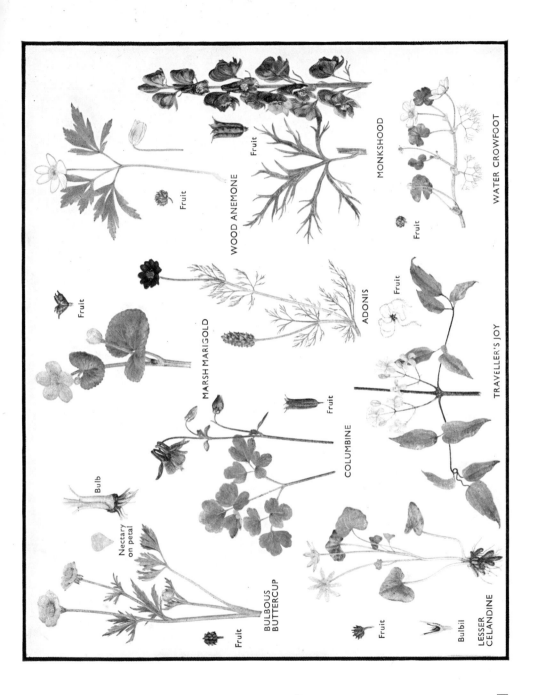

WOOD ANEMONE

Fruit

MONKSHOOD

Fruit

WATER CROWFOOT

MARSH MARIGOLD

Fruit

ADONIS

Fruit

TRAVELLER'S JOY

COLUMBINE

Fruit

Fruit

Bulb

Nectary
on petal

BULBOUS
BUTTERCUP

Fruit

Fruit

Bulbil

LESSER
CELANDINE

PLATE I

wide range of colours. In some cases, the flowers are double. They are useful hardy perennials.

There are several species of *Clematis* cultivated in gardens for their large, showy flowers. The plants are well adapted for covering trellis-work and walls. The very large sepals are deep purple, varying shades of blue, or white. A scarlet species does exist, though it is not often seen in this country.

ECONOMIC PLANTS

No member of the buttercup family is cultivated for food, and few members are of any other economic value to man.

The root of the monkshood (*Aconitum napellus*) contains a poisonous substance, aconitine, which is used as a liniment or tincture. The preparation, which is usually an ointment, must not be applied to any part of the skin where there is a crack or cut.

FIG. 26.—*Nigella.*

Certain other members of the family are used in *materia medica*.

5
MAGNOLIAS
(*Magnoliaceae*)

Perhaps the most primitive of all flowering plant families is the MAG-NOLIACEAE—indeed more simple and primitive than the RANUN-CULACEAE. It was not dealt with first because the family contains no flowers native to this country, though there are some familiar flowering trees and shrubs belonging to it which are frequently seen cultivated in our parks and gardens and are therefore worthy of mention. Furthermore, the RANUNCULACEAE has so many common flowers from which

an advantageous study can be made, that it was considered better to
open up with that family.

Perhaps the most popular genus in the family MAGNOLIACEAE is
that of *Magnolia* itself. This genus is often cultivated in gardens and
parks for its showy flowers. It thrives especially in the warm south.
Most members of the genus are deciduous, that is, they shed all their
leaves in the autumn; and the flowers open out before the new leaves
do. The species *M. grandiflora*, however, is evergreen. Most members
of the genus have white or cream flowers, though a few have white
flowers flushed with purple.

Each flower is borne singly, and, in spite of its large size, it is very
simple in structure. When in bud it is protected by sheathing stipules
of the unopened leaves. These are shed later. There are several whorls
of sepals and petals, all of which are alike—usually white. The outer
whorls are, however, sometimes sepaloid. Inside the innermost whorl
of petals are several whorls of stamens making up a large indefinite
number altogether. Inside the stamens is a large number of simple,
free carpels arranged spirally on an elongated axis which is really an
extension of the receptacle. The fruit is a collection of follicles, which
in due course split. As each follicle splits, the seeds are exposed hanging
each on a single thread. The outer layer of each original ovule becomes
fleshy after fertilization, and this fleshy layer which now surrounds the
seed enables the latter to be distributed by birds.

The curious **tulip tree** (*Liriodendron tulipifera*) is also a member of
the MAGNOLIACEAE. It is a native of eastern North America, but attains
its maximum size in Ohio and Florida. It is often cultivated in parks
and on estates, and derives its common name from the fact that when
in flower the tree looks as if it is covered with masses of white or cream
tulips. Each flower is, however, very similar in construction to a
Magnolia flower. The leaf of the tulip tree, too, is characteristic since it
is four-lobed, so that at its physical tip there is a large re-entrant notch.
The wood of the tree is the well-known canary white wood or white
'poplar'.

———————

Two other families more advanced than the RANUNCULACEAE (and
there are several others) are LAURACEAE and MYRISTICACEAE, which
have some familiar component members.

The LAURACEAE is composed chiefly of tropical and sub-tropical
trees and shrubs. None is native to this country; but several genera
are cultivated here for their beautiful evergreen habit. The **sweet bay**

or **true laurel** (*Laurus nobilis*) is a very useful evergreen for garden ornament, and *Laurus benzoin* is an odorous shrub displaying beautiful crimson tints. Several plants of economic importance belong to this family also. The **cinnamon** (*Cinnamomum zeylanicum*), a native of Ceylon, gives cinnamon. The bark is peeled off, then rolled and dried. Then it is powdered. **Cassia** (*Cinnamomum cassia*), of China and Japan, gives a bark which is used for adulterating cinnamon, and the flower buds are used as spices. **Camphora** (*Cinnamomum camphora*), also of China and Japan, yields camphor, which is produced by distilling the shoots. The **avocado pear** (*Persea gratissima*), a native of tropical America, produces a luscious fruit.

The LAURACEAE is allied to the MAGNOLIACEAE, but the former shows signs of reduction rather than progression during evolutionary sequence.

In the other allied family (MYRISTICACEAE) the genus *Myristica* contains the **nutmeg** plant (*M. fragrans*), a native of the Indian Archipelago, though now cultivated elsewhere in the tropics. The fruit is a berry which produces one large seed—the nutmeg. This is surrounded by a curious red network called an aril.

6

WATER-LILIES

(*Nymphaeaceae*)

If we accept the word 'lily' as applying especially to the numerous kinds of lilies (tiger-lily, Madonna lily, lily-of-the-valley), all of which belong to the family LILIACEAE, then it is a misnomer in the case of the water-lily and the arum-lily, for both these plants are totally different from the true lilies and belong to different families altogether. In fact, the true lilies are monocotyledons, whereas the water-lilies (though not the arum-lily, see Chap. 67) are dicotyledons.

WILD PLANTS

There are two kinds of water-lilies which may be found growing wild in this country—the white and the yellow; but both are sufficiently different from each other to warrant the establishment of two genera for them—*Nymphaea* and *Nuphar*. Both are members of the family NYMPHAEACEAE.

Both plants grow in stagnant water with their leaves floating on the surface (Fig. 27). The leaves are large and leathery; they are almost circular in shape, and the leaf-stalks are long to enable the leaf-blade to rise and fall with the surface of the water. Also both plants spread by means of thick horizontal stems at the bottom of the water or even buried in the mud.

> That winding streamlet, limpid, lingering, slow,
> Where the reeds whisper when the zephyrs blow;
> Where in the midst, upon her throne of green,
> Sits the large lily as the water's queen.
>
> *The Borough* : G. CRABBE

The **white water-lily** (*Nymphaea alba*) has larger and more beautiful flowers than the yellow. Furthermore, that of the former, when open, floats on the surface of the water, whereas that of the latter is borne

Eric Hosking

FIG. 27.—White Water-lilies.

vertically on a stalk some inches above it. When the flower of the white water-lily is closed (at night and during inclement weather) it sinks beneath the surface of the water.

The flower of the white water-lily has several interesting features. It is regular and comparatively simple—in fact, not very far removed from that of the buttercup. There is an outside whorl of four green sepals. Inside this there is a large number of petals unusually arranged. The first whorl of petals consists of four which alternate with the sepals. Inside this and alternating with it is a further whorl of four petals. Each of these eight petals forms a starting-point of petals inserted on the receptacle in a spiral fashion. Starting from each of the first eight there are about four. As we pass inwards, the petals become narrower and show a gradual transition into stamens. (This transitional form, partly petal and partly stamen, can sometimes be seen in other flowers, such as the paeony and the rose. Similar transitional forms between sepal and petal are also quite common.) The stamens of the white water-lily are numerous, ranging from fifty to a hundred. The carpels are also numerous, and are usually embedded in the receptacle and fused with each other to form an ovary divided into ten to twenty chambers each containing numerous seeds. The stigmas of the fused carpels have no styles, but form a number of rays on the upper surface of the ovary as in the case of the poppy (p. 53).

The fruit of the white water-lily is interesting since it shows a remarkable adaptation for wide dispersal by means of the water in which the plant is growing. The fruit is a large berry which ripens under the water. After ripening, it splits, and the seeds rise in a mass to the surface. Each seed is covered with a spongy mass of tissue called an aril, and this contains many air-bubbles. Later the seeds separate, then their buoyancy due to the air-bubbles helps them to float away from the parent plant. Finally the air in the bubbles escapes and then the seed sinks to the bottom where it eventually germinates.

The **yellow water-lily** (*Nuphar luteum*) is sometimes called 'brandy-bottle' because its flowers smell like brandy. The flowers of this genus (Plate 2) are not so conspicuous or so attractive as those of the white water-lily. There are five coloured sepals, and inside these are about thirteen small petals arranged on the receptacle in a spiral fashion. Then follow numerous stamens alternating spirally with the petals. The carpels vary between ten and sixteen, forming an ovary similar to that of its white relative. The fruit is a large berry which eventually breaks away from its stalk and then splits into separate parts. The seed has no aril like that of the white water-lily, but its outer wall is slimy and contains air-bubbles. Thus is it able to float away until the outer wall decays.

ORNAMENTAL PLANTS

Some species of *Nymphaea* are hardy, and are therefore frequently used in this country for water gardening, making a very pleasing sight. The cultivated species vary in size and colour; some are white like their wild counterpart, but others are cream, pink, vermilion, crimson, lilac and shaded.

There are two genera of the water-lily family which, while not native to this country and not often cultivated since they are tropical, are so interesting as to be worth mentioning.

Species of the **lotus** plant (*Nelumbium*) grow in the United States and Central and South America and in Asia, Japan and Australia. The species *N. speciosum* is the sacred lotus. Although examples of it have become conventionalised in ancient Egyptian sculptures and are mentioned in Egyptian writings, it no longer grows in the Nile. It does, however, still grow in India, Tibet and China, where it is also looked upon as sacred. In Cashmere the inhabitants eat the seeds.

The **Victoria water-lily** (*Victoria regia*) is the giant water-lily of the Amazon. It is cultivated in a few greenhouses in this country, especially botanic gardens, chiefly for its botanical interest. A good example can usually be seen at the Royal Botanic Gardens, Kew (Figs. 28 and 29). The plant resembles the white water-lily in form but not in size, for it is enormous. It was discovered so recently as 1801, though it was not brought to general notice until 1837. The inhabitants of Brazil roast and eat the seeds.

FIG. 28.—*Victoria regia* in Bloom.

Harold Bastin

The leaves of the *Victoria* are so large that even when floating on water they are able to support the weight of a baby. They are frequently a yard and a half across. Flooding on the top of the leaf is prevented by a vertically growing margin which is two to three inches high, making the leaf look like a floating tray. (This is necessary, for such leaves must not be permanently submerged since they absorb gases from the atmosphere, and, incidentally, give off gases—processes essential to the life of the plant. Most land-living plants interchange such gases through the lower surfaces of their leaves, but for obvious reasons floating leaves do so through their upper surfaces. In the cases of naturally submerged leaves, special adaptation is necessary, and such exists.) On the lower side of these gigantic leaves of *Victoria* the main veins project as ribs and are armed with large spines.

About a dozen families come between the NYMPHAEACEAE and the next family to be considered in some detail, namely, PAPAVERACEAE; but few members of these dozen families are native to this country or display flowers of any particular interest. Several are, however, worth mentioning.

The BERBERIDACEAE is composed of herbs and shrubs, some of which are cultivated for ornamental purposes. The most familiar are the various forms of **barberry** (*Berberis*). The **common barberry** (*B.*

Harold Bastin

FIG. 29.—*Victoria regia* showing immense Floating Leaves.

vulgaris) has oval, serrated and prickly leaves. The yellow flowers hang in pendulous inflorescences. Each flower has six yellow petaloid sepals, six stamens and one carpel. The fruit is a conspicuous red berry. This species is sometimes seen growing wild ; but it is probably a garden escape. Among the large number of species and varieties of *Berberis* are some highly ornamental plants, displaying attractive spiny foliage which often gives lovely tints during autumn, bright yellow or orange blossoms, and rich red berries.

The family ARISTOLOCHIACEAE is composed chiefly of shrubby climbers, a number of which are cultivated in greenhouses here. *Aristolochia sipho* is the popular **Dutchman's pipe,** having delicately scented tubular flowers curved in a curious pipe-like fashion. The leaves are heart-shaped. *A. gigas* is the **pelican flower**—another greenhouse favourite.

The family PIPERACEAE is almost entirely tropical, but is worth noting because it contains the climbing **pepper plant** (*Piper nigrum*). The fruit of this climber is a berry. The pepper plant owes its pungency to a resin it contains, and its flavour to an oil. It is one of the oldest condiments known to mankind. The dried berries are ground to produce the condiment. If the whole berries are used, black pepper results. If the outer skins of the fruit are first removed, then we get white pepper. Red or Cayenne pepper is not produced from this plant or any other related to it. It is actually made by powdering the spice chilli, the fruit of the plant *Capsicum annuum*, a relative of the potato (Chap. 57), and thus much higher in the evolutionary scale.

7

POPPIES

(*Papaveraceae*)

This is not a very large family, but the flowers of most of its members are very conspicuous owing to their large and strikingly coloured petals.

Most members of the poppy family (PAPAVERACEAE) contain a coloured juice, chiefly in the stem and veins of the leaves, which is either poisonous or narcotic. There are several genera, but only a few are common in this country.

WILD PLANTS

Perhaps the most common wild genus of this family is the poppy itself (*Papaver*). The **common red poppy** is *P. rhoeus*. This plant flowers during June to August, and its brilliant scarlet flowers may frequently be seen in cornfields, sometimes converting the whole field or large patches of it into a sea of red. In fact, the poppy is an agricultural weed.

> On one side is a field of drooping oats,
> Through which the poppies show their scarlet coats,
> So pert and useless, that they bring to mind
> The scarlet coats that pester human-kind.
>
> *Epistle to my Brother George* : KEATS

The poppy flower nods, especially when in bud; but this is not due to its own weight but to unequal growth in the higher parts of the flower stalk. The upper surface grows more than the lower (Plate 2).

The leaf is deeply segmented and has no stalk. The plant is very hairy, growing hairs on its stems, leaves and even sepals.

The beautiful flower is comparatively simple and is borne singly, not in inflorescences. There are two boat-shaped sepals, green in colour. These are shed as soon as the flower opens. The four red petals are soft in texture, and the two outer ones are larger than the two inner. The stamens are numerous and black (Plate 2). The carpels are indefinite in number, but they are joined together to form a single-chambered ovary. On the upper surface of this ovary there is a collection of stigmas without styles arranged like the spokes of a wheel.

The poppy contains no nectar, but insects visit it to collect the pollen with which to make ' bee-bread '. The flowers may be self- or cross-pollinated. Immediately after pollination, the petals fall.

The fruit of the poppy is of particular interest. It becomes rather large and globose, and since the ovary is single-chambered so is the fruit. It is called a capsule. Unlike the follicle of the marsh marigold, it is not capable of splitting open, but it has a different arrangement for the dissemination of its seeds. The many seeds inside the ovary soon become dry and loose. The rays of the stigmas on the upper surface of the capsule project like the eaves of a roof, and these projections protect the dry seeds from the rain, for just beneath them there is a circle of

FIG. 30.—Fruit of Poppy.

perforations. Through these holes the seeds are scattered by the swaying of the fruit on its long stalk in the wind—a pepper-box mechanism (Fig. 30). During damp weather the seeds cannot escape, for the pores are closed by means of flaps.

There are several other species of red poppy, including *P. argemone*, which is smaller and paler.

The poppy plant contains a milky juice which stains the hands a dark red.

The **yellow horned poppy** is a seashore plant. It is never found inland. It is sufficiently different from the common poppy, especially in its fruit, to warrant a separate genus (*Glaucium flavum*).

The leaves of this plant are thick and leathery. They present a bluish-grey colour because they are covered with a layer of wax. (This waxy layer is a feature of many seashore plants for it prevents a too-ready loss of water—an essential need where soil water is not easily available.) The leaves of the yellow horned poppy have a wavy margin, and their lower parts embrace the stem on which they are borne (Plate 2).

The flowers appear during June to September. So far as the sepals, petals and stamens are concerned, the flower of the yellow horned poppy is similar to the common poppy except that the petals are yellow and there are no hairs on the sepals. The fruit, however, is vastly different. Here it takes the form of a pod or 'horn', six to twelve inches in length (Plate 2). Inside the pod are two chambers, each containing a large number of seeds.

> A poppy grows upon the shore,
>   Bursts her twin cups in summer late :
> Her leaves are glaucus-green and hoar,
>   Her petals yellow, delicate.
>
>   *   *   *
>
> She has no lovers like the red,
>   That dances with the noble corn :
> Her blossoms on the waves are shed,
>   Where she stands shivering and forlorn.
>   *Shorter Poems* : R. BRIDGES

As pointed out on p. 39, the **greater celandine** must not be classified with the lesser celandine, for the two plants are different in many

respects. The latter belongs to the buttercup family, and the former to
the poppy family. It forms a genus of its own (*Chelidonium majus*). This
plant grows in waste places and sometimes on walls, but it is not very
common. The leaves are compound. The flowers, which appear during
May to August, are pale yellow and are borne in inflorescences. The
ovary is single-chambered, and the stigma two-lobed.

The plant contains a yellow juice, chiefly in the stems and veins of
the leaves, which in olden days was used for dyeing fabrics, but it was
not very successful since it is not a fast dye.

ORNAMENTAL PLANTS

Poppies are a familiar sight in the flower garden during the
summer. When grown in masses they produce a gorgeous effect.
Garden annual poppies are usually varieties of the common poppy
(*Papaver rhoeas*). The garden perennial poppies are usually varieties
and hybrids of the **Oriental poppy** (*P. orientale*) (Fig. 31). These
present a variety of shades—scarlet, pink, crimson. Other species
of garden *Papaver* are white or yellow, for example, the popular
yellow Iceland poppy (*P. nudicaule*), also a perennial.

Californian poppies belong to another genus (*Eschscholtzia*). These are wild
natives of the United States,
but are frequently cultivated
in the flower gardens of this
country (Fig. 32). They are
splendid flowers for summer
bedding and produce many
shades of red, orange and
yellow. Some are double.
They are actually perennial,
but are usually cultivated as
hardy annuals.

Meconopsis is another genus
of poppies cultivated for their
showy flowers. *M. baileyi* is
the **Tibetan blue poppy**; and
M. cambrica is the **Welsh yellow
poppy.** There are others.

FIG. 31.—Oriental Poppy.

E

FIG. 32.—Hybrids of *Eschscholtzia*.

Romneya is the **Californian tree poppy** which is a perennial. It produces white flowers during July to October.

ECONOMIC PLANTS

Few poppies are of economic importance. In fact, were it not for their very beautiful flowers, we should look upon them as garden and agricultural pests.

Only one poppy is worthy of mention as being useful to man, and that is the **opium poppy** (*Papaver somniferum*), with a white satin-like flower having a purple blotch at the base of the petal. The opium is present in the juice of the plant, but it is extracted chiefly from the fruit. The opium poppy grows wild on the northern shores of the Mediterranean, but it is cultivated in many parts of the world. The chief drug extracted from opium is morphine, a valuable asset in medical practice.

8

THE FUMITORY FAMILY

(*Fumariaceae*)

The fumitory family (Fumariaceae) is so closely related to the poppy family that some botanists group the two families together under Papaveraceae. There are two wild genera of Fumariaceae and several which are cultivated.

WILD PLANTS

The most common genus of this family found in the wild state is *Fumaria*, to which belongs the **common fumitory** (*F. officinalis*) (Plate 2). This plant is frequently seen growing by the road-side, in dry fields, and, like its relative the poppy, in cornfields. It is of an erect habit, with leaves very finely divided and flowers borne in very graceful purple inflorescences, which appear during May to September.

The flower has two sepals which, again like the poppy, are soon shed. But here the petals are irregular, the two outer ones being larger and dissimilar. One of these large outer petals is spurred, and the spur contains nectar. The petals together form a tube which is mauve in colour with a purple spot at the mouth to attract visiting insects. There are six stamens grouped in two bundles of three each.

In the past, the fumitory enjoyed a considerable reputation for healing, and especially for treating the skin.

The **rampant fumitory** (*F. capreolata*), like the clematis, climbs by means of twisted leaf-stalks. There is a variety of this species which shows an unusual colour change : before pollination, the flowers are white, but after pollination they turn pink or carmine.

The other wild genus belonging to this family (*Corydalis*) is not very common. The **white climbing corydalis** (*C. claviculata*) can sometimes be discovered growing in copses and on banks. The flowers are small and white, but they resemble that of the fumitory in general character. The fruit, however, is a narrow, two-valved pod containing many seeds. The leaves terminate in tendrils, by which the plant climbs.

The **yellow corydalis** (*C. lutea*) and the species *C. solida*, the former with large yellow flowers and the latter with large purple flowers, are probably garden escapes.

ORNAMENTAL PLANTS

Corydalis cheilanthifolia is a hardy perennial, sometimes grown in rock gardens and dwarf borders. The large flowers are produced in spike-like inflorescences and are yellow in colour. The foliage is of an attractive pale green and is fern-like.

Dicentra (or *Dielytra*) *spectabilis* is a handsome old-fashioned perennial which originally hailed from China. The pink and white flowers are comparatively large, and are heart- or lyre-shaped, hence the common name, **lyre flower**. The general habit of this plant is very similar to that of the wild fumitory though much more expansive, so it should be easily identified.

9

THE WALLFLOWER FAMILY
(*Cruciferae*)

No-one can be unacquainted with this family (CRUCIFERAE), for so many well-known plants belong to it. It is also what one might call a very natural family, for, though all its members differ markedly from other flowers, yet they are so obviously similar to each other that one does not need to go too deeply into the botany of these plants to appreciate their close relationship.

It is significant, too, that many members of the CRUCIFERAE are edible, and a large number of them are cultivated for food, in most parts of the world.

In spite of this, the wallflower family does show certain resemblances to the poppy family, and that is why we place it so near in the scheme of classification.

Most members of the family are herbs. In nearly every case, the petals spread themselves in the form of a cross, hence the family name. They are said to be cruciform.

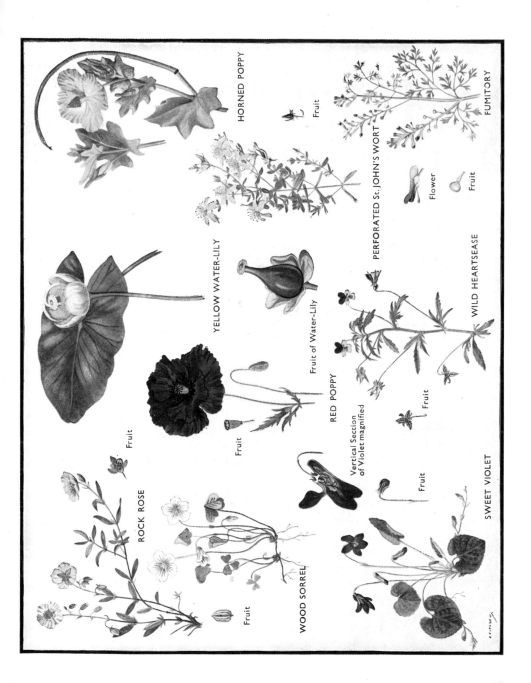

HORNED POPPY

Fruit

FUMITORY

YELLOW WATER-LILY

Fruit of Water-Lily

PERFORATED St. JOHN'S WORT

Flower

Fruit

WILD HEARTSEASE

RED POPPY

Fruit

Fruit

Vertical Section
of Violet magnified

Fruit

Fruit

ROCK ROSE

Fruit

WOOD SORREL

Fruit

SWEET VIOLET

PLATE 2

WILD FLOWERS

The **wallflower** is very typical of the whole family. Though for centuries it has sometimes been called the 'gilliflower', this name is also applied to other flowers (p. 63). It belongs to the genus *Cheiranthus* (*C. cheiri*). As its common name implies, this flower is found growing on walls. Although it is now sometimes found growing in the wild state, it is probably really a garden escape.

> As I stood by yon roofless tower,
> Where the wa'flower scents the dewy air.
> *A Vision*: BURNS

The leaves are lance-shaped and they crowd up the stem. The flowers are borne in inflorescences (Plate 3), and appear during May and June. When found wild they are orange in colour.

The four sepals are long and narrow, purplish in colour and erect in habit. The four petals alternate with them. Each petal is heart-shaped, but its narrow end is extended, and these four extensions form an unjoined tube within the erect sepals (Fig. 33). There are two whorls of stamens, an outer whorl of two short ones and an inner whorl of four long ones—six altogether. At the base of the stamens, nectaries can be found. The two long carpels are joined along their margins forming an ovary down the centre of which is a partition. The two stigmas are borne on one style common to both carpels. There are many ovules.

FIG. 33.—Wallflower; complete Flower, section of Flower showing four long and two short Stamens, and Fruit.

After fertilisation, the fruit grows larger, while the petals and the sepals shrivel and fall off. When the fruit is ripe, it forms what is called a siliqua. When the seeds are ready for dispersal, the two carpellary walls begin to break away from the central partition from the bottom upwards,

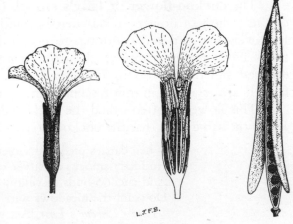

L.J.F.B.

leaving the seeds attached to the partition (Fig. 33). The seeds are very light and are therefore very easily blown off and disseminated by the wind.

A very common wild crucifer (much more common than the wild wallflower), especially in waste places, is the **shepherd's purse** (*Capsella bursa-pastoris*) (Plate 3). This plant is also a common weed in gardens and on agricultural land. The leaves of the shepherd's purse are deeply segmented, especially those growing from ground-level. These form a rosette flattened to the ground.

The flowers of the shepherd's purse are borne in inflorescences, but only a few of them are open at any one time. After the flowers are fertilised, the fruit stalks continue growing for a time, so also does the main axis of the inflorescence, so that the fruits are separated from each other (Plate 3). The flower is small and white. It is self-pollinated.

The fruit of the shepherd's purse differs from that of the wallflower in that it is heart-shaped, and the two halves separate from the central partition downwards. It is called a silicula. The common name of this plant is explained by the fact that its fruit is shaped like the purse which peasants of the olden days used to carry tied to their waists.

At one time the shepherd's purse was used as a pot-herb : it is still eaten in China.

Certain species of the genus *Lepidium* grow wild. They are the **pepperworts** ; but a more familiar species is the garden cress (p. 65).

The small plant known as **whitlow grass** (*Draba verna*) can be found almost anywhere growing on old walls. It also is a member of this family. The flowers are white and insignificant with deeply notched petals. There are many varieties of this plant, all of which breed true.

The **cuckoo-flower** or **lady's smock** (*Cardamine pratensis*) is one of the earliest of flowers in our marshes and damp meadows (Plate 3). It flowers in April and continues to do so until June. The leaflets of the leaves of this plant which grow from ground-level are deeply toothed, but those growing on the stem are lance-shaped. The lovely flowers are arranged in inflorescences and vary from white to mauve.

This flower is often called the cuckoo-flower because it blooms at about the same time that the cuckoo arrives.

> When daisies pied and violets blue,
> And lady-smocks all silver-white,
> And cuckoo-buds of yellow hue
> Do paint the meadows with delight.
>
> *Love's Labour's Lost*, Act v, Sc. 2 : SHAKESPEARE

In some parts of the country, the leaves of this plant are used as a substitute for watercress.

Related to the lady's smock, and therefore in the same genus are various species of the bitter-cress. The **large-flowered bitter-cress** (*C. amara*) blooms along river-sides during April and May : the **hairy bitter-cress** (*C. hirsuta*) grows almost everywhere, displaying its small white flowers over a long season (March to August).

Certain species of *Arabis*, another crucifer, are also found growing wild, for example, the **hairy rock-cress** (*A. hirsuta*) with its small white, cruciform flowers borne in crowded inflorescences. Most species of this genus, however, are cultivated for ornamental purposes (p. 64).

Water-cress is well known to most people, but town-dwellers come across chiefly that which is cultivated for food. Nevertheless, water-cress (*Nasturtium officinale*) is a common wild plant, and is found growing in ditches, streams and ponds. An outstanding feature of this plant is the adventitious roots given off at the nodes, which make vegetative reproduction possible. By this means the plant spreads.

The inflorescence of the water-cress bears many small, white cruciform flowers. This grows above the surface of the water.

Country people still gather wild water-cress for salads ; in fact, they often prefer the wild plant to the cultivated. It has a stronger flavour. It is not easy to find a more picturesque description of the old water-cress gatherer than this :

> All the bloomy flush of life is fled.
> All but yon widow'd, solitary thing
> That feebly bends beside the plashy spring ;
> She, wretched matron, forced in age, for bread,
> To strip the brook with mantling cresses spread.
> *Deserted Village* : GOLDSMITH

Closely related to the water-cress are the **creeping yellow-cress** (*N. sylvestre*) and the **marsh yellow-cress** (*N. palustre*), both of which have yellow flowers.

(It should be noted in connexion with the water-cress that its generic name is *Nasturtium*. This has no connexion with the so-called garden nasturtium (cultivated for its beautiful yellow and orange flowers) which actually is wrongly named. The garden nasturtium is not *Nasturtium* at all but *Tropaeolum*, and it belongs to a different family altogether (Chap. 19).)

The **hedge mustard** (*Sisymbrium officinale*) is a tall plant having small yellow flowers appearing during June and July. Most of the leaves are borne near the base of the shoot and are shaped like those of the dandelion. They are very hairy. The fruit is similar to that of the wallflower. Certain Indians of the southern United States mix the seeds of a closely related species with their corn-meal in order to flavour it.

Jack-by-the-hedge, or **garlic mustard** (*Erysimum alliaria*) is another tall plant common in hedgerows and along the banks of ditches. The whole plant smells of garlic, especially when bruised. The leaves of this plant are comparatively large and heart-shaped with toothed margins (Plate 3). The small, pure-white flowers are, like those of shepherd's purse, borne in a flat-topped head, but the axis of the inflorescence and the fruit-stalks continue to grow for some time after fertilisation. The flowers appear during May and June.

Certain species of the highly important genus *Brassica* are sometimes found growing wild; but most of them, especially cabbages and turnips, are cultivated for food (p. 65).

Rather similar to the genus *Brassica* is the genus *Sinapis* to which the **charlock** (*S. arvensis*) belongs (Plate 3). This plant is tall and the leaves are, like those of the hedge mustard, similar to that of the dandelion. The stems and leaves are very hairy. The flowers appear during June to August and are bright yellow. Charlock is a persistent weed, especially on agricultural land, sometimes covering cornfields and other arable land with a sea of yellow. This is probably because the seeds can retain their viability, that is, keep their potentiality for germination, a long time. They have been proved to remain viable for so long as twenty-five years, and thus remain dormant in the soil until such time as the soil is turned, making conditions for germination more favourable.

> The charlock on the fallow
> Will take the traveller's eyes,
> And gild the ploughland sallow
> With flowers before it dies.
> *More Poems*: A. E. HOUSMAN

> What dazzled all, and shone far-off as shines
> A field of charlock in the sudden sun
> Between two showers, a cloth of palest gold.
> *Gareth and Lynette*: TENNYSON

Closely related to the charlock are the **white mustard** (*S. alba*) and the **black mustard** (*S. nigra*), both of which may be found growing wild, especially in cornfields, though both are cultivated (p. 65).

The cultivated **radish** (p. 66) has its wild counterpart (*Raphanus raphanistrum*) found growing in cornfields. The flowers, which appear during June to September, are yellow veined with purple.

The **woad** (*Isatis tinctoria*) is another member of this large family. It has small yellow flowers. It is not very common, but before the introduction of indigo and synthetic dyes it was frequently used as a dye. This was prepared by grinding the leaves to a paste and leaving them to ferment. The Ancient Britons used it for painting their bodies.

ORNAMENTAL PLANTS

Many beautiful plants used in beds, borders and rockeries are represented in the family CRUCIFERAE.

Perhaps the most familiar is the wallflower itself. Most wallflowers are perennials, though they are frequently treated as biennials. The flowers vary in shade from deep purple, brown, through red to yellow.

The **Siberian wallflower** (*Cheiranthus allionii*, etc.) is a showy plant with yellow or orange flowers. A curious half-hardy hybrid wallflower, easily cultivated in greenhouses, is *C. kewensis*, whose flowers open pale yellow then change to mauve.

Certain species of *Erysimum* (p. 62) are sometimes cultivated. They are called **alpine wallflowers** and are mauve, yellow or orange.

Honesty (*Lunaria biennis*) is a hardy perennial, and is grown chiefly for its shiny, silvery fruit which are large and oval in shape, the central partition persisting as a tissue-like plate to which the seeds adhere.

Stocks are so popular that they scarcely need mentioning. They all belong to the genus *Matthiola*. The parent species of all garden stocks is *M. incana*. There are a host of varieties, some of which are single and obviously cruciform, but most of which are double presenting many different shades (Fig. 34). They are very delicately perfumed. The stock was also at one time called 'gilliflower', possibly from its French name *giroflée* (p. 59).

The **candytuft** (*Iberis amara*) is a very popular annual in our flower gardens, and it is of unusual interest, for though the flowers are borne in the usual flat-topped inflorescences, the outer petals are

FIG. 34.—Double and Single Stocks.

decidedly larger than the inner ones. These flowers vary in shade from white to pink, carmine and purple.

Arabis, Aubretia and Alyssum are all great favourites for cultivation on walls and in rock gardens. The most familiar Arabis is white, both single and double; but there are pink and deep rose varieties. These are all relations of the rather rare wild rock-cress   Some varieties are double. Aubretia is another rock-cress and presents a number of varieties varying in colour from pink to deep purple. Alyssum is sometimes called the **madwort**. Its varieties are either single or double; many are yellow, and others white or lilac in colour. These three genera are frequently grown together, and there is considerable confusion over their names in different parts of the country.

Giant forms of the **lady's smock** (Cardamine) (p. 60) are sometimes cultivated. There are a single species and a very beautiful double species.

ECONOMIC PLANTS

Brassica is a genus of the family CRUCIFERAE. To it belong all varieties of cabbage and certain other well-known vegetables. All cabbages are varieties of the species Brassica oleracea, and the variety is usually indicated by means of a third or even a fourth name. For example, the **Savoy cabbage** is *Brassica oleracea bullata*. Members of the species *Brassica oleracea* include **broccoli, cauliflower, Brussels sprout, garden cabbage, Savoy cabbage, kale** or **borecole** (Fig. 35) and **kohl-rabi**.

The **turnip** belongs to the same genus as the cabbage but to a different species (*B. campestris*). The **swede** is a variety of this. A closely related species is *B. napus*, the **rape**, frequently used in salads, and from the seeds of which rape- or colza-oil is extracted.

FIG. 35.—Kale.

Relatives of the wild charlock (*Sinapis arvensis*, p. 62), namely the **white** and **black mustards** (*S. alba* and *nigra*, p. 63), are commonly cultivated. The white mustard is cultivated in the kitchen garden as a salad and on the farm as a forage crop, whereas the black mustard is cultivated for its seeds from which the condiment is made. Sometimes the seeds of black and white mustard are mixed to make the condiment. The name is connected with *must*—new unfermented wine, which was at one time mixed with it. Several centuries ago, Dijon was noted for its mustard, and in 1382, the Duke of Burgundy granted the town armorial bearings with the motto *Moult me tarde* (I ardently desire). This was eventually adopted by the mustard merchants and later became abbreviated to *moult-tarde* (to burn much). It was not until 1720 that the condiment appeared in Great Britain, when a Mrs. Clements of Durham prepared it. For years she kept the recipe a secret.

Of the cresses, **water-cress** is frequently cultivated (p. 61). Species of *Lepidium* are also cultivated, chiefly *L. sativum* (the **garden cress**), for salads. The very young plants are familiar in salads and as a garnishing. They are usually brought on in frames or greenhouses, the seeds usually being sown on the surface of soil or on wet flannel.

R. A. Malby & Co.

FIG. 36.—Radishes.

The **radish**, another familiar salad vegetable (Fig. 36), is also a member of the wallflower family, but it belongs to another genus (*Raphanus sativus*) (see also p. 63).

The **horse-radish** (*Cochlearia armoracia*) is also a member of this family. The condiment is prepared from the thick root.

It will thus be noted that an exceptionally high percentage of the members of the wallflower family are cultivated for food. In this connexion, varying parts of the plants are used, namely : *as vegetables*, broccoli and cauliflower (leaves and flower buds), Savoy cabbage, garden cabbage, kale and kohl-rabi (leaves), Brussels sprout (young leaf buds), water-cress (leaves and stems), white mustard and cress (complete young seedlings), turnip and radish (swollen roots) ; *as condiments*, mustard (seeds), horse-radish (swollen roots).

The flowers of these food plants are not very often seen, but they are all typically cruciform and may be white, yellow, mauve or purple.

10

VIOLETS AND PANSIES
(*Violaceae*)

The violet family (VIOLACEAE) is a small one; nevertheless, it is very important because it counts among its members some of our most popular wild and cultivated flowers. There is only one well-known genus to be found in this country, and that is *Viola*, to which all violets and pansies belong. A genus very common in tropical regions is *Alsodeia*.

WILD PLANTS

Among the familiar wild species of violet are the **sweet violet** (*V. odorata*) and the **dog violet** (*V. canina*). There are two varieties of the sweet violet, the blue (Plate 2) and the white. The chief difference

PLATE 3

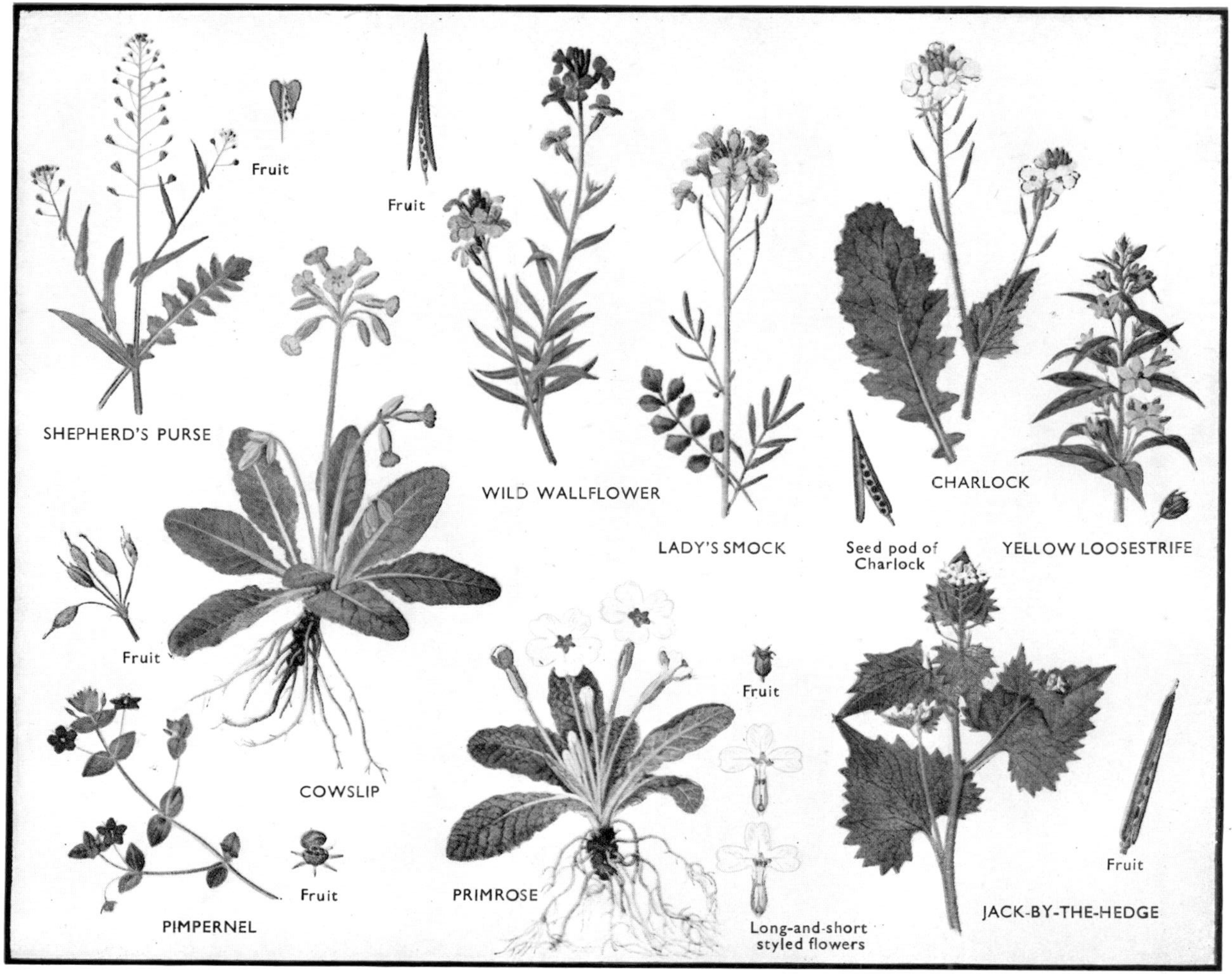

CHARLOCK

YELLOW LOOSESTRIFE

Seed pod of
Charlock

JACK-BY-THE-HEDGE

Fruit

Long-and-short
styled flowers

WILD WALLFLOWER

LADY'S SMOCK

Fruit

PRIMROSE

Fruit

SHEPHERD'S PURSE

Fruit

COWSLIP

Fruit

Fruit

PIMPERNEL

between these sweet violets and the dog violet is the charming scent of the former. All the organs of the dog violet, also, are somewhat larger than those of the sweet violet. Furthermore, the dog violet blooms rather later—during May to August, whereas the sweet violet flowers in March and has been known to show its first blooms so soon as January.

We have been told by Herrick how the violet became blue :

> Love on a day, wise poets tell,
>   Some time in wrangling spent,
> Whether the violets should excel,
>   Or she in sweetest scent.
> But Venus having lost the day,
>   Poor girls, she fell on you ;
> And beat ye so, as some dare say,
>   Her blows did make ye blue.
>
> *Hesperides* : HERRICK

Both species of violet are perennial. The leaves are heart-shaped and tend to get larger and more pointed at their tips after the flowers have died down. Yet, despite the enlargement of the leaves, the whole plant is comparatively small and never grows more than a few inches in height.

> Those veiled nuns, meek violets.
> *Plea of the Midsummer Fairies* : HOOD

The violet reproduces itself freely by vegetative means. In this case, runners are produced—branch stems which, like those of the strawberry, take root at the nodes and thus form new plants.

There are two other species of wild violet, the **marsh violet** (*V. palustris*) and the **hairy violet** (*V. hirta*) ; but neither of them is very common.

The common **wild pansy,** or **heartsease,** grows in pastures and cornfields and on waste land. It is very like the familiar garden pansy, though smaller in general habit (Plate 2). The most common species is *V. tricolor*; but there is a rarer species, *V. lutea*, which grows in hilly districts. In the common heartsease, the two upper petals are purple and the other three yellow, and in the rarer species of the hills, the whole flower is yellow with just a small patch, if any, of purple.

The leaves of heartsease are quite different from the comparatively simple ones of the violet ; they have deeply segmented stipules which are quite large, and leaf-blades which are also large with deep divisions on their margins.

Heartsease is a very lovely plant, especially when growing in its natural surroundings.

Heart's ease or pansy, pleasure or thought,
Which would the picture give us of these?
Surely the heart that conceived it sought
Heart's ease.
The Flower Piece of Fantin : SWINBURNE

The flowers of both the violet and the pansy are irregular. There are five sepals which project backwards. There are also five free petals, arranged irregularly, two at the top, one each at the side and one at the bottom. This last has a spur containing honey. There are five stamens and three carpels joined to form a single-chambered ovary.

The flowers are sometimes fertilised by bees and are so constructed to aid this purpose. The lower petal forms a landing-stage, and since the nectar is in its long spur only long-tongued insects such as bees can get at it. Guides to this are seen in the heartsease : they take the form of dark lines on the yellow side and lower petals but not on the two upper purple petals.

In the heartsease there is a method for preventing self-pollination. For various reasons, cross-pollination is better than self-pollination, and in this case the plant is quite safe, for it does not flower until May to September, when there are plenty of bees about. But it is not so with the violet. Most violets flower very early in the year. During this time, cross-pollination by means of insects is not certain, for the bees are not usually available. The violet, therefore, resorts to a very unusual method for ensuring the production of seeds. The first flowers to open scarcely ever set seed. Later in the year, however, other flowers are produced, but these never open. In spite of this, their carpels and stamens ripen, so that the pollen, when it is released from the stamens finds itself in a tightly packed flower bud. It is therefore forced into contact with the stigmas, and thus self-pollination, with the eventual production of seeds, is ensured.

The fruit of the pansy and violet is a three-valved capsule (Plate 2, unripe in violet, ripe in heartsease). When it is open, it looks like three tiny boats joining each other at their bows. Each boat-shaped cup contains a large number of very hard but slippery seeds. The cups gradually become dried by the sun and thus shrink, pressing the seeds more closely together. Eventually the sides of the cups meet and the seeds are shot out. This ensures that the seeds are well distributed.

CULTIVATED PLANTS

Varieties of most species of *Viola* are cultivated. Among garden varieties of the **sweet violet**, *V. odorata*, are singles and doubles in shades of white, lilac, blue and deep violet. All these have a very seductive perfume.

Then there are the **violas**, sometimes known as **tufted pansies**. These very lovely flowers are frequently seen in

FIG. 37.—Pansy ('Sutton's Perfection').

borders and beds. They begin flowering in spring and, provided the dead flowers are periodically removed, will continue to do so until the late autumn. The flowers are very large, with enormous petals (compared with their wild counterpart, the wild pansy). The shades of colour are very charming—white, yellow, apricot, red, crimson, pale blue, mauve, to almost black, together with certain mixed colours.

Pansies are perhaps most familiar in our gardens. They also are varieties of the wild pansy, or heartsease. The beautiful and rich colours of this flower are scarcely surpassed (Fig. 37). Although, like the rest of the family, these flowers are really perennial, they are best treated as biennials, that is, brought on as seedlings in the first year and bedded out in the second.

The varieties of colour and form in the pansy are almost legion. Some of them have frilled petals—a charming sight.

Most pansies are probably derived from the wild heartsease (*Viola tricolor*); they are some of the oldest flowers in cultivation. This raises the question: What is the difference between a violet and a pansy? Well, such differences as there are are more striking to the eye than botanically fundamental. In fact, a botanically technical description of a violet flower could just as well be applied to that of a pansy. The main differences are the superficial ones of colour distribution and intensity, proportion and size. The petals of the pansy have become more circular, whereas those of the violet are long and oval. Furthermore, the petals of the pansy have become flattened out into a 'face'.

II

MIGNONETTE AND MILKWORT

(*Resedaceae* and *Polygalaceae*)

Each of the families RESEDACEAE and POLYGALACEAE is small; in fact, there is only one representative genus of each family in this country. Both families are closely related to each other and take their position in the scheme of classification between the VIOLACEAE and the CRASSULACEAE.

MIGNONETTE

The mignonette belongs to the first of the families—RESEDACEAE. It is placed in the genus *Reseda*, to which belong two wild species, the **wild mignonette** (R. *lutea*) and the **dyer's weed** or **weld** (R. *luteola*).

The wild mignonette can be found growing in waste places and flowering during June to August. Its leaves are so deeply notched as to be almost compound. The small pale yellow flowers are borne

FIG. 38.—Mignonette.

in dense inflorescences. Each flower has six small narrow sepals, six petals each cut into irregular segments, many stamens and several carpels united to form a single-chambered ovary with a stigma but no style.

The dyer's weed blooms at the same time and can also be found in similar surroundings. This is so-named because in olden days a valuable yellow dye was extracted from it. In this case, the leaves are lance-shaped with smooth margins. The small, yellowish-green flowers are also borne in dense inflorescences, but the flower has only four sepals.

Neither of these wild plants is perfumed, but the garden species (R. *odorata*) has the most charming scent; in fact, it is obviously this which inspired the name of the plant, which in French means ' little darling '. Cowper refers to the mignonette in *The Task* as the ' Frenchman's darling '. He is considered to be the one who gave the plant its now common name.

Apart from its scent the cultivated mignonette with its varieties of white, yellow and red, can make a charming display in the garden and in vases (Fig. 38).

MILKWORT

The **milkwort** is the only plant commonly found in this country which belongs to the family POLYGALACEAE. It is placed in the genus *Polygala* (P. *vulgaris*). It is a small plant found growing on cliff-tops, downs and railway sidings (Plate 5). The generic name, *Polygala*, is derived from the Greek, πολύς (much) and γάλα (milk), because at one time it was considered that cows were stimulated in producing more milk when they ate it.

The leaves are lance-shaped and are arranged on the stem either alternately or in opposite pairs.

The flowers of the milkwort, which appear during a long season (May to September), show an unusual range of colours for a wild flower, because not only are there varying shades of white, deep blue, purple or mauve, but also two differently coloured flowers may be seen growing on the same plant. The floral organs, too, show considerable irregularity. There are five sepals, three of which are green and insignificant, but the other two are comparatively large and coloured (petalloid)—in fact, the colour of the flowers is due to them. The petals themselves are very much reduced, the lowest one forming a crest-like organ. There are eight stamens and the ovary is two-chambered.

Milkwort is sometimes cultivated, though not often, for ornamental purposes.

In other countries, certain genera which also belong to the POLY-GALACEAE are used in medicine, for example, the **senega snake-root** (*Polygala senega*) of North America.

F

12

A WATER-STORING FAMILY

(*Crassulaceae*)

Nearly every member of this family (CRASSULACEAE) grows in hot, dry places, such as dry walls, where its water economy is a serious question. Therefore water has to be stored whenever it becomes available. This is done in most cases by the production of thick, fleshy leaves which act as water-pots.

Three genera of the CRASSULACEAE can be seen growing in this country, though the family is very widespread in South Africa, and all the wild species are also cultivated either for their peculiar habit or for their beautiful flowers and leaves.

WILD PLANTS

Dry, bare walls, and other sites exposed to the hot sun, are usually the haunts of the very attractive stonecrop (*Sedum*). The most common species is *S. acre*, the **biting stonecrop**, so called because its leaves have a biting taste. For this same reason it has been called **wall pepper** or **poor man's pepper**. This small plant sometimes covers old walls, and their masses of star-like flowers make a lovely sight (Plate 5). So the plant is well named, for *Sedum* is from the Latin *sedeo* 'I sit'. The leaves are swollen and fleshy since they contain much water-storing tissue. Some leaves grow from the base of the plant and others crowd up the flowerless stems. Some also grow on the flower-stalks.

The flowers appear during June and July, and are borne in cymes. Each flower has five sepals and five, bright yellow, pointed petals which are held wide open to the hot sun. There are ten stamens and five carpels ; the latter form follicular fruit which therefore split along one side.

The **orpine live-long** (*S. telephium*) is not a very common species ; it is related to the stonecrop. It is of a taller habit, growing from six inches to two feet in height. During July and August it produces deep purple flowers. The leaves are round and fleshy, and, since they contain a good storage of water, the plant will live a long time even if uprooted—hence the common name.

There are four or five other species of stonecrop, none of them very common, though it should not be very difficult to find the white species (*S. album*).

The **wall pennywort** (*Cotyledon umbilicus*) is another member of the CRASSULACEAE, and, like all the others, has thick, fleshy, water-storing leaves, in this case, round and flat (somewhat smaller than the size of a penny) sinking towards the centre. In fundamentals, the flower of the pennywort is similar to that of the stonecrop. The plant blossoms during June and July and the flowers are borne in greenish yellow, pendulous inflorescences.

In general habit, the **house-leek** (which is the third genus

Harold Bastin

FIG. 39.—Houseleek (*Sempervivum arachnoides*), showing Flowers and Off-sets.

representative of this family in Great Britain) is larger than the stonecrop. It belongs to the genus *Sempervivum* (*S. tectorum, S. arachnoides*, etc.) (Fig. 39).

All the leaves are fleshy since the plant is another inhabitant of old walls. It also grows on the roofs of old houses, and at one time was deliberately placed there in order to keep the tiles together. The leaves are large and grow in tight rosettes, which themselves are very attractive. They frequently have purple edges. Fleshy, but much smaller leaves, are also to be seen scattered up the flower stem.

The houseleek reproduces itself vegetatively by means of very short, thick runners (branch stems) each of which produces a new plant at its apex. These runners are called off-sets.

The flowers of the houseleek appear in inflorescences. They are a reddish purple in colour, and each flower is much larger than that of the stonecrop, being anything from a half to one inch in diameter.

There are twelve sepals and twelve petals. The stamens are arranged in two whorls of twelve each, though the inner whorl is usually sterile. The twelve carpels are joined.

ORNAMENTAL PLANTS

All three wild genera of the family CRASSULACEAE so far described, namely, *Sedum*, *Cotyledon* and *Sempervivum*, are sometimes cultivated.

The **yellow stonecrop** (*Sedum acre*) is frequently grown on dry walls, rockeries and paved walks. Then there are other cultivated species and varieties, having white, pale blue, purple or red flowers, whereas others have variegated foliage.

The cultivated species of **pennywort** (*Cotyledon*) is very like the wild except that the flowers are more golden yellow.

In the case of the **houseleek** (*Sempervivum tectorum*), all the cultivated varieties, usually to be seen in rockeries, old walls and small crevices, are chosen for the variety of the colour of their rosettes of leaves. These may be almost completely pale green, deep green, bright green, red or maroon, or they may be variegated—usually red with sea-green tips.

13

THE SAXIFRAGE FAMILY
(*Saxifragaceae*)

The saxifrage (SAXIFRAGACEAE) and stonecrop (CRASSULACEAE) families are very closely related. There are some succulent, water-storing saxifrages, though they are not common. In fact, most wild succulent species of this country are not common. On the other hand, there are many succulent species which are to be found growing in alpine and arctic regions where the water supply is often very poor, either because the soil is rocky and barren or because what water there is is frozen. Some succulent saxifrages are cultivated.

Few species of saxifrage are of economic importance. In some Floras the currants and gooseberry are placed in the same family; but many botanists nowadays prefer to keep them in a family apart (GROS-SULARIACEAE, Chap. 28) since they are considered to be more advanced in the scale of evolution. The same can be said of the popular garden favourites, 'orange blossom' and *Hydrangea* (HYDRANGEACEAE, Chap. 29).

WILD PLANTS

Three genera of the SAXIFRAGA-CEAE are represented in this country, and the largest, of which there are about a dozen (mostly rare) species, is *Saxifraga*. Although these are not so succulent as the stonecrops and the houseleeks, some of them do grow where water is not plentiful and therefore like the stonecrops are adapted accordingly. For example, the leaves show tufted growth and close packing into rosettes, hairiness and so forth. Many of the saxifrages reproduce themselves vegetatively by means of off-sets or bulbils.

FIG. 40.—Meadow Saxifrage.

The **meadow saxifrage** (*S. granulata*) reproduces itself vegetatively by means of bulbils (p. 38). The leaves of this plant are kidney-shaped and lobed. The lower ones have long stalks, whereas those on the flower-stalks have scarcely any leaf-stalks (Fig. 40).

The flower, which appears in May and June, is regular, large and star-like. It has five sepals, five large petals which are white, ten stamens and two carpels joined together but diverging at the top (Fig. 40).

A related species, the **rue-leaved saxifrage** (*S. tridactylites*) may be found growing on walls. It is not a large plant, the flower-stem being about two to four inches high. The leaves are wedge-shaped and divided into three, though the upper ones have entire margins.

One genus of this family is found growing in quite different surroundings, that is, marshy and other wet places. This genus is *Chrysosplenium*. In this genus are the **golden saxifrage** (*C. oppositi-folium*) and the **alternate-leaved golden saxifrage** (*C. alternifolium*). Both of these handsome plants are common. The leaves are heart-shaped and the leaf-stalks join the leaf-blades towards the centre of the latter ; the margins have rounded divisions. The chief distinction lies,

as their specific names imply, in their leaf arrangement; the leaves of
C. oppositifolium are arranged in pairs opposite each other, and those
of *C. alternifolium* alternate. The flowers of this genus are borne in
inflorescences. The flower has no petals, and since the sepals are not
petalloid the whole flower is insignificant and greenish.

The third genus of this family found growing wild in Britain is a
native of the north and of wet moors and bogs. The sole representative
is the **grass of Parnassus** (*Parnassia palustris*) (Plate 5). It blooms late
in the year (August and September).

> Pale star that by the lochs of Galloway,
>   In wet places 'twixt the depth and height
> Dost keep thine hour while Autumn ebbs away,
>   When now the moors have doffed the heather bright.
>   *Grass of Parnassus* : ANDREW LANG

The deep green leaves of this plant are heart-shaped, and, like
those of the saxifrage, have long stalks if growing from ground-level
but almost sessile if growing on the flower-stalks.

Again, the flowers are star-like. They are large and solitary.
There are five sepals and five petals. The latter are large and white
with outstanding green veins. There are five real stamens and five
others which have become very much modified. These are reduced to
scales with fan-shaped fringes of white gland-tipped filaments. These
modified stamens contain nectar and are therefore useful in attracting
insects to ensure cross-pollination. There are two carpels joined to
form a single-chambered ovary.

The fruit of all members of
the SAXIFRAGACEAE is a capsule.

FIG. 41.—Saxifrage (' Rosy Queen ').

ORNAMENTAL PLANTS

A large number of species
and varieties of the **saxifrage**
(*Saxifraga*) is cultivated, especially in rock gardens. The tufted
habit of the leaves and the conspicuous nature of the flowers
make the plants exceptionally
ornamental in rockeries and

paved paths (Fig. 41). Some species form such dense tufts of small leaves that they are called the mossy-leaved saxifrages.

London pride (*Saxifraga umbrosa*) makes an attractive border, and its small pink flowers borne in graceful inflorescences are useful for household decoration.

The cultivated genus *Astilbe* is also a member of the SAXIFRAGACEAE; it is frequently, though wrongly, called *Spiraea* (actually a member of the rose family). It is a handsome plant, a favourite for potting, but also suitable for borders, damp situations and the margins of ornamental pools. The plant grows two or three feet high, and the

FIG. 42.—*Astilbe*.

small flowers are arranged in massive inflorescences. The leaves are large and compound. The flowers may be white, pink or deep red. Some varieties of *Astilbe* are hardy perennials, but a large number of them are greenhouse plants used for household decoration (Fig. 42).

Another genus suitable for planting in damp situations is *Rogersia*. *Heucheria*, on the other hand, is suitable for rock gardens. The flowers are large and arranged in graceful inflorescences. They present all shades of red—chiefly pink, crimson and scarlet.

Following the family SAXIFRAGACEAE are two families of plants, namely DROSERACEAE and SARRACENIACEAE, which entrap and absorb insects. Only DROSERACEAE is native to this country. These families will be considered with the rest of the insectivorous plants in Chap. 61.

14

CAMPIONS AND CARNATIONS

(*Caryophyllaceae*)

All members of the pink family (CARYOPHYLLACEAE) are graceful herbs. Their delicate habit is due chiefly to the long, very slender, though usually strong, stems, which have swollen nodes from which the simple leaves are given off in pairs. The branching of the stems, too, contributes to the general beauty of the plant. Each main stem usually terminates in a flower ; but just below this terminal flower are two more buds, opposite each other, which eventually grow out and then themselves terminate in a flower bud with two more buds below. Thus the branching continues, giving an inflorescence very characteristic of this very natural family. The branching is well brought out in the illustration of the greater stitchwort on Plate 4.

The leaves of most species of this family are simple, long and lance-shaped, usually borne in opposite pairs and bending in most graceful curves. This is well seen in carnations and pinks.

The CARYOPHYLLACEAE is a very big family and comprises a large number of well-known wild and cultivated flowers. There is none of economic value. The family is confined to north temperate and cold regions.

WILD PLANTS

During the summer months, it is not easy to come across a more pleasing natural sight than a group of **red** or **rose campions** growing in damp banks or at the edges of woods. The beautiful red flowers are at their best during June and July (Plate 4), though often they are seen much later on in the year. In certain localities they are called **cock robins.**

The red campion belongs to the important genus, *Lychnis*, to which other familiar species of the pink family also belong. The full name of the red campion is *L. diurna*. The general habit of the plant is very similar to that already described for the family in general, except that the leaves are unusually broad, and the stems, leaves and even sepals are very hairy—not a common feature of the family,

The flower of the red campion is very characteristic of the CARYO-PHYLLACEAE. There are five sepals, joined to form a tube with five projecting teeth. The sepals are usually greenish-red in colour, as is also the stem. The five petals are free. Each is heart-shaped but very deeply divided down the middle and having a scale near the throat. The main blades of all the petals flatten out collectively to form a salver.

Again, unlike most members of the pink family, the flowers of the red campion are unisexual and only one sex is found on any one plant. The male has ten stamens; the female, five carpels joined to form a single-chambered ovary, but with all five styles and stigmas free (Plate 4).

The fruit is a rounded capsule with ten teeth on the upper surface.

The **white campion** (*L. vespertina*) is similar to the red campion except that the flowers are white and are very fragrant towards the evening. The whole plant is sturdier, and there is no red shading of the stems and leaves. The flowers, too, continue right into September.

The **ragged robin** (*L. flos-cuculi*), which appears at the same time as the red campion and in similar vicinities, resembles the latter very closely except that each petal is divided deeply into four linear segments, which gives the whole flower a ragged appearance (Plate 4). Also, in this case, the flowers are hermaphrodite, having in the one flower ten stamens and five carpels joined to form a single-chambered ovary with five free styles.

The handsome **corn cockle** (*L. githago*) is another closely related species whose purple flowers can be seen in cornfields during June to August. The flower is somewhat larger, with sepals which project beyond the petals (Plate 4). The petals are neither divided nor segmented. The plant is very hairy.

The **bladder campion,** a very familiar country flower, is sufficiently different from the other campions to warrant another genus (*Silene*). There are several species belonging to this genus, but only two are at all common. The most common of the lot is the bladder campion itself (*S. inflata*), so called because its five sepals are joined and swollen up like a bladder (Plate 4). The plant is to be found in many places, especially pastures, flowering during June to August. Apart from this, it is similar to the white campion, though not hairy. There are only three styles, however. The **sea campion** (*S. maritima*) is common on sea-shores and closely resembles the bladder campion.

The **wild carnation** or **maiden pink** (Plate 4) is the only common wild species of the genus *Dianthus* to which so many garden favourites belong. The wild carnation is *D. caryophyllus*. Even this species is not very common, but may sometimes be seen growing on old walls or in hilly districts. The lovely pink flowers appear during June to August. The leaves are comparatively very small.

The flowers of the pink or carnation is somewhat like that of the campion. Near the throat of the five petals is a red ring which acts as a honey-guide for visiting insects. The nectar is secreted at the base of the ten stamens, as it is in all members of the CARYOPHYLLACEAE. There are only two styles in the pink.

The name ' pink ' does not refer to the colour, but is connected with the verb ' to pink ' or ' to pierce ', indicating that the petals are usually indented.

Several other wild genera are members of this family, for example, *Sagina*, the **pearlworts** and *Arenaria*, the **sandworts**. The **sea purslane** (*Arenaria peploides*) is common on seashores. So also is the **seaside sandwort spurrey** (*Spergularia marina*). There are others not so common.

We now come to another series of genera of the pink family which are somewhat different from those so far considered. The most important genus in this series is *Stellaria* to which belong the stitchworts.

One of our prettiest white roadside flowers of early summer is the **greater stitchwort** (*S. holostea*) (Plate 4). The plants frequently grow in large clumps (Fig. 43), and their slender stems and small leaves assist the starry white flowers to stand out boldly when they appear during April to June. The stem in this case is so long and slender that it often depends on the surrounding plants, especially grass, for support.

FIG. 43.—Greater Stitchwort.

In the flower of the greater stitchwort the five sepals are not joined. The five white petals are deeply cloven and are netted with pronounced green veins. There are ten stamens and three styles. The fruit again is a capsule with six teeth on the upper margin (Plate 4).

The **lesser stitchwort** (*S. graminea*) is not so common as its greater relative; furthermore it is usually found in drier situations and flowers later (May to August). Though in general habit smaller than the great stitchwort, the lesser is frequently taller. There are several other stitchworts, namely, **water** (*S. aquatica*), **marsh** (*S. glauca*), **wood** (*S. nemorum*) and **bog** (*S. uliginosa*).

Another member of the stitchwort genus is the **chickweed** (*S. media*), and this is indeed a weed. It grows everywhere, and especially in gardens and on agricultural land. The leaves of this species are more oval. The flowers are similar to those of the stitchworts, but very much smaller. They appear for a very long season, namely, March to October, and this explains the intense nuisance of the weed.

It may surprise many to learn that the chickweed makes good eating. In some parts of Europe it is used as a pot-herb ; but Charles Pierpoint Johnson in his *Useful Plants of Britain* writes : " It forms when boiled an excellent green vegetable much resembling spinach in flavour and is very wholesome ".

All other chickweeds belong to another genus, *Cerastium*. In all cases there are five sepals, five petals, ten stamens, five styles and a single-chambered ovary which, after fertilisation, forms a capsule with ten teeth. In general, the leaves are oval or lance-shaped, and the flowers are small. The two most common species are the **mouse-ear chick-weed** (*C. glomeratum*) and the **narrow-leaved mouse-ear chickweed** (*C. triviale*).

ORNAMENTAL PLANTS

Although no members of the pink family are of any economic value, there is scarcely any gardener who is not acquainted with at any rate some of the garden species and varieties grown for their floral beauty.

But here again, the very natural characters of the family stand out so clearly that there can be no mistaking any of its members.

> You take a pink,
> You dig about its roots and water it,
> And so improve it to a garden-pink,
> But will not change it to a heliotrope.
> *Aurora Leigh* : E. B. BROWNING

Among the species of *Dianthus* are to be found most of our popular garden plants which belong to the CARYOPHYLLACEAE.

D. barbatus is the lovely, old-fashioned **sweet William** with its flowers massed in heads of white, pink, scarlet or deep red. Some are

FIG. 44.—Carnation.

'eyed' with a different colour. Most varieties of this plant are hardy perennials, though there are some annuals. The leaves in this case are unusually large and broad.

Carnations are the garden varieties of the wild carnation or maiden pink (*D. caryophyllus*). Some of these are perennials, others annual ; some flourish in the open, others only in the greenhouse. All are double (Fig. 44). It would be superfluous to attempt to describe here all the different kinds of carnation in their various shades of colour, stripes, frilled petals and perfumes (especially the clove), and so forth, for they are familiar in most gardens of the rural dweller and in the florists' shops for the town dweller.

Few flowering plant families can excel the CARYOPHYLLACEAE in the wondrous profusion of different flowers it has given the gardening enthusiast, for here again we have the **pinks** of our borders and rockeries. These also are members of the genus *Dianthus*. Some are single, others are double. The colours vary from violet, through mauve and pink, to white. Some are 'eyed' and some are picotee. (The term 'picotee' was at one time confined solely to those varieties of carnations whose petals have a ground of a light colour with edges of a darker colour; but now the term is applied to varieties of all flowers showing a similar colour distribution.) The rock varieties of pinks grow in great masses, but the flowers of these are usually

FIG. 45.—Hybrids of Pink.

smaller and single; but collectively they make a lovely sight (Fig. 45).

Several species of the **campion** (*Lychnis*) are cultivated for their showy flowers which may be pink, rose, scarlet or rosy-purple. The plants are usually more sturdy than the wild species, and frequently more velvety. There are also some cultivated varieties of the **bladder campion** (*Silene*), giving single or double, white or purple flowers. These make a brilliant show in early summer. Some species of **sand-wort** (*Arenaria*) also are cultivated.

Species of *Cerastium* can sometimes be found cultivated, chiefly for their ornamental foliage. But the most important close garden relative of the stitchworts is *Gypsophila* or **chalk plant**. Most, but not all, of the species and varieties of this lovely plant are hardy annuals. Their typically caryophyllaceous habit of growth makes them very useful as backgrounds and 'clouds' for other flowers in vases. The flowers may be white, pink or rose in colour. Some varieties are double.

Other genera of the pink family, infrequently, if at all, found growing wild, but sometimes cultivated, are *Tunica* and *Saponaria*. The rare **soapwort** (*S. officinalis*) which is sometimes found growing wild derives its name from the fact that the leaves produce a lather on being rubbed with water. The cultivated varieties of *Tunica saxifraga* (pink or white) resemble dwarf species of *Gypsophila* and make useful carpet plants.

15

TWO MINOR FAMILIES

(*Ficoidaceae* and *Portulacaceae*)

At this point in our scheme of plant classification come two smaller families, but we must pause over them for a while because, though they have few, if any, wild representatives indigenous to this country, some of their members are well-known in the flower garden.

FICOIDACEAE

The first of these small families is FICOIDACEAE, which contains the genus *Mesembryanthemum*, a plant becoming increasingly popular in cool greenhouses and on rockeries in the warmer parts of the south.

The plants of this family are low shrubs or more frequently herbs. Often they are fleshy, with succulent leaves packed closely together. Most native species are to be found in South Africa, California and in various parts of tropical America, Asia, Australia, frequently growing on seashores and in desert places.

FIG. 46.—*Mesembryanthemum criniflorum.*

There are four or five sepals, usually joined to form a tube: the petals may be present in large numbers or absent altogether: the stamens may be definitely three or five or indefinitely large in number. In the last case, those on the outside often become sterile and petalloid. The carpels are either three or indefinite in number, joined, and after fertilisation form a capsular fruit with pronounced ridges on the top.

Many varieties of this beautiful genus are cultivated, since they become literally covered with flowers, varying in tints of primrose, apricot, crimson, rose, purple or white edged with pink, rose or buff. On casual glance from a distance, *Mesembryanthemum* flowers look like those of the daisy ; but they are not—in fact, these two plants are very remote from each other (Fig. 46).

The **ice plant** or **sea fig** of California (*M. crystallinum*) is used in green salads. It derives its common name from the fact that the leaves are covered with glistening, globular hairs. The **Hottentot fig** (*M. edule*), of South Africa, now introduced into California, contains an edible pulp.

PORTULACACEAE

The next small family, PORTULACACEAE, also contains some ornamental plants—*Portulaca*, for example.

This family is native mainly to America, but the plants are often fleshy so that they thrive in desert regions. In the flower, there are two sepals ; about five petals, large and coloured ; five, ten or many stamens ; two to eight carpels, usually fused to form a one-chambered ovary with the styles variously divided.

FIG. 47.—*Portulaca.*

Portulaca, the main genus of the family, is a half-hardy annual, producing beautiful large flowers in various shades of white, yellow or scarlet. Some varieties are double. They form a lovely floral carpet (Fig. 47). *P. oleracea*, the **purslane**, is a native of India, but it is sometimes grown in this country. It is interesting in that its stamens are sensitive to touch, and bend towards the side touched. For centuries this plant has been used for food. For two thousand years it has been eaten in India. Since its introduction into Europe several centuries ago it has been used as a pot-herb in certain areas. In various parts of Armenia it is cooked and served like spinach, and in Great Britain the young stems and leaves are sometimes served in green salads.

Another genus, *Calandrinia*, is represented in some gardens enjoying a hot sunny position by the **rock purslane** (*C. umbellata*) which has brilliant crimson flowers. There are other species. These flowers quickly close in the absence of sunlight.

Another Californian visitor to some of our gardens (chiefly those having gritty soil) is *Lewisia*, which presents handsome rosettes of fleshy leaves with salmon-coloured flowers growing out from them in spikes. The Californian species, *L. rediviva* is of particular interest, for with its thick fleshy roots and leaves it is so well adapted to arid conditions that it can survive for two years in the dry state.

16

DOCKS, SORRELS AND RHUBARB

(*Polygonaceae*)

All members of this family have very inconspicuous flowers (owing chiefly to the absence of petals) ; but the flowers are borne in pronounced, very attractive, inflorescences. In many cases, however, the plants stand out conspicuously among their neighbours because of their enormous leaves. The vegetative parts of most of them are edible.

WILD PLANTS

There are about a dozen genera belonging to this very cosmopolitan family, but only a few have representatives in this country.

The docks and the sorrels belong to the genus *Rumex*. In this genus, as in nearly all the genera of this family, the leaves possess peculiar stipules which act as sheaths surrounding the stem for some distance up from the node. This is one of the main characters of the family.

There are about eight different docks growing wild in this country, but not all are common. One of the most common in every part of the country is the **broad-leaved dock** (*Rumex obtusifolius*), commonly seen growing along the roadsides, on waste land and as weeds. The leaves are very large and oval, though broader near the stalk.

The flowers are borne in long inflorescences, brownish when ripe. They appear late in summer—July to September.

The flower is regular, but it has no petals. There are six sepals in two whorls of three each, the three inner ones being larger than the outer ones. The inner three, too, are deeply toothed. There are six stamens and three carpels, the latter joined but with three large styles (because the flower is wind-pollinated). The fruit does not split, but forms a triangular nut.

In other species of *Rumex*, the flowers are unisexual; but, apart from this, most members of the genus are similar in floral structure, though varying in general vegetative habit.

Among other docks to be found growing wild are: the **curled dock** (R. *crispus*) with very wavy-edged leaves, found growing in waste places (Fig. 48); the **sharp dock** (R. *conglomeratus*) without sheathing stipules, growing in wet meadows and waste places; the **red-veined dock** (R. *sanguineus*) whose common name explains itself, growing in hedges; and the **water dock** (R. *hydrolapathum*).

Among the sorrels are two common species, both belonging to the same genus as the docks, namely **common sorrel** (R. *acetosa*) and **sheep's sorrel** (R. *acetosella*). The flowers of the common sorrel are unisexual, and the plants may be all

FIG. 48.—Curled Dock in Bloom.

Harold Bastin.

G

FIG. 49.—Pink Persicaria.

male, all female, or hermaphrodite: on the other hand, the sexes of the unisexual flowers of sheep's sorrel are always segregated on different plants. Both plants are to be found growing in meadows, though the sheep's sorrel prefers drier sites than does the common sorrel. The general habit of the sorrels is smaller than that of the docks.

Both docks and sorrels are edible, but are either bitter or acid. Children often call the leaves of sorrel ' sour leaves ', or ' sour docks ' and eat them. The curled dock and the broad-leaved dock are sometimes used as pot-herbs or cooked as greens, though in the latter case, meat or other material is usually added to the pottage, for the dock leaves are so bitter.

Another genus of the wild members of the family POLYGONACEAE is *Polygonum*. This genus contains the bistorts and the persicarias. Some are common and others are rare. Perhaps the most familiar of the lot is the **pink persicaria** (*Polygonum lapathifolium*) which produces its flowers in small but dense pink inflorescences during July and August. It grows in most waste places and sometimes on agricultural land and in gardens (Fig. 49). The leaves are oval, ending in a long point. In the flower, as in all flowers of the genus, there are five equal sepals, whereas in *Rumex* we saw six—three large and three small: therein lies the chief distinction between the two families.

Among other persicarias are the **spotted persicaria** (*P. persicaria*) and the **biting persicaria** (*P. hydropiper*). The former grows in waste places, and the latter near water.

Of the bistorts, the two most common are the **bistort snake-root** (*P. bistorta*) of moist meadows, and the **amphibious bistort** (*P. amphibium*) of marshes and ponds.

The flowers of all the members of *Polygonum* are usually pink.

ORNAMENTAL PLANTS

Members of this family are not very often cultivated for ornamental purposes. Some species of *Polygonum*, however, are sometimes grown for their pink, rose or crimson flowers. Some species of *Rumex*, too, are grown, especially the water dock, in water gardening, for its impressively enormous leaves.

CULTIVATED PLANTS

The genus *Rheum* supplies the only outstanding example of a plant of this family cultivated for its economic value, namely, the **rhubarb** (R. *rhaponticum*). This is cultivated solely for its red leaf stalks which are edible. In general, the plant is typical of the family, though the leaves are more heart-shaped than usual. The inflorescence is very characteristic, but the flowers are usually an attractive shade of yellow or pink.

Another species, R. *officinale*, supplies medicinal rhubarb.

This family also contains the genus *Fagopyrum*, to which belongs the **buckwheat** (F. *esculentum*), largely cultivated in North America for its floury seeds. The complete plant is also used as fodder.

17

THE BEETROOT FAMILY
(*Chenopodiaceae*)

The beetroot family is not a very important one from the point of view of the pure botanist. It is very small, but it does contain some plants of considerable economic value, especially the sugar beet.

WILD PLANTS

The four main genera of this family are *Atriplex*, *Salicornia*, *Chenopodium* and *Beta*.

In many ways, the family is similar to POLYGONACEAE. The leaves are somewhat similar and, in general, so is the inflorescence. The flower is inconspicuous and has no petals. There are three to five sepals, two to five stamens, and a single-chambered ovary with two pronounced styles. The fruit is a small round nut.

Only one species of *Atriplex*, the **orache** (A. *patula*), is common, being another inhabitant of waste places. The flowers are unisexual, and usually both sexes are found on the same plant. It blooms during July to September.

Of the genus *Salicornia*, the **glasswort** (*S. herbacea*) is interesting, because it grows in salt-marshes and has to arrange its water economy accordingly. This plant must conserve its pure water supply, so the stems have become thick and succulent and the leaves are altogether suppressed. Superficially, the whole plant resembles a small cactus ; there is no mistaking it. The flowers are insignificant and green, borne in groups of three, one on each side of the node, and sunk in the tissue of the stem. The four perianth segments are fleshy, and there are two stamens and two styles.

Chenopodium is represented by **white goose-foot** (*C. album*), **red goose-foot** (*C. rubrum*) and **Good King Henry** (*C. bonus henricus*). All these plants grow in waste places. They are not particularly common, however. Even less common are other related species.

The **wild beet** (*Beta maritima*) is the only representative of the genus growing wild in this country, and even it is not very common. It grows on or near seashores. It is the forerunner of the cultivated beet. Being a seashore plant, it has a fleshy root and fleshy leaves. Those growing from ground-level are broad ; those growing from the stems are smaller and lance-shaped. The flowers are borne in long terminal spikes.

ORNAMENTAL PLANTS

A few members of this family are cultivated in flower gardens, chiefly for their beautiful foliage. For example, species and varieties of *Atriplex* present striking red foliage. The **summer cypress** (*Kochia*) is a familiar, rapidly growing annual, useful for bedding and borders, because its lovely, finely cut, pale green foliage (arranged in the complete shoot like a midget cypress tree) turns a rich crimson in the autumn.

ECONOMIC PLANTS

The plants of this family which are grown on account of their economic value are important, and their importance is becoming more and more recognized, especially in the case of the sugar beet.

The **beetroot** is a garden variety of the wild beet (*Beta maritima*), and is a valuable food plant. It is a biennial, and therefore stores food, taking the form of sugar, to cover the winter, in its well-known red swollen roots. The sugar content of the beet is constantly being increased by scientific breeding and so forth. This can be said especially of the **sugar beet,** which is a variety (*Beta maritima* var. *rapa*). The sugar beet has achieved a much higher economic status during the past two decades. Its roots are not red like the ordinary beetroot.

The leaves of beetroot are sometimes eaten like those of spinach.

The **mangel-wurzel** or **mangold,** another agricultural root crop grown chiefly for cattle, is a further variety of the wild beet. Its name is German, meaning 'root of scarcity', probably because its large yield comes in useful at times when other crops fail.

Spinach is another member of the family CHENOPODIACEAE, but it is placed in a different genus (*Spinacia oleracea*). This annual herb produces a profusion of leaves which are eaten either raw in green salads or cooked. These leaves have a high vitamin content.

A family closely related to the CHENOPODIACEAE is the AMARAN-TACEAE. It is not represented in the wild state in this country; nevertheless it is worth mentioning because several very striking cultivated plants belong to it. In this country these plants are to be found only in flower gardens, but in other countries certain species are grown for food.

The flowers are small like those of the beetroot family, but frequently they are of vivid colours, and since they are borne in large, dense inflorescences, they produce collectively a striking effect.

The genus *Amaranthus* contains **love-lies-bleeding** and **prince's feather.** Love-lies-bleeding (*A. caudatus*) has beautiful, pendulous, deep crimson inflorescences. In tropical Asia this plant and other species are cultivated for their edible grain. Prince's feather (*A. hypochondriacus*) has tall spikes of red flowers. Other species of the same genus are sometimes grown for their strikingly coloured foliage, giving shades of red, scarlet and yellow, and some speckled. The **cock's-comb** (*Celosia cristata* or *plumosa*) is a favourite green-

FIG. 50.—*Celosia.*

house plant, with conspicuous yellow, crimson or scarlet inflorescences (Fig. 50). This plant is a ' monstrosity ', for the flowers have become fasciated (that is, stems and stalks have become laterally fused) ; but the character is now hereditary.

18

THE GERANIUM FAMILY
(Geraniaceae)

The geranium family (GERANIACEAE) is not a very large one, but it contains some common and exceptionally beautiful plants with handsome, brightly coloured flowers. This can be said of certain wild species as well as the very familiar showy cultivated species and varieties. All the same, this family contains little of economic importance.

WILD PLANTS

The most common wild members of the geranium family are the crane's-bills. Most of them belong to the genus *Geranium*, and, apart from the fact that their sepals and petals do not form tubes and that the sepals are free, the flowers are closely similar to those of the pink family. The leaves are usually deeply divided.

In all species of *Geranium* there are five free sepals, five free petals, ten stamens and five carpels joined to form a single ovary. The five styles of the carpels are united, but the five stigmas are usually distinct. In the other British genus of this family, *Erodium*, five of the stamens are sterile.

One of the commonest, yet most beautiful, species of wild *Geranium* is the **meadow crane's-bill** (*G. pratense*), to be discovered blooming in meadows during June and July and displaying very beautiful blue flowers. These are quite large, being about one and a half inches in diameter and usually borne in pairs (Plate 4). The leaves of this plant are also very handsome, being shield-shaped in general outline yet divided into several parts, each part being sub-divided irregularly into fringe-like segments. The whole plant is covered with soft, silky hairs.

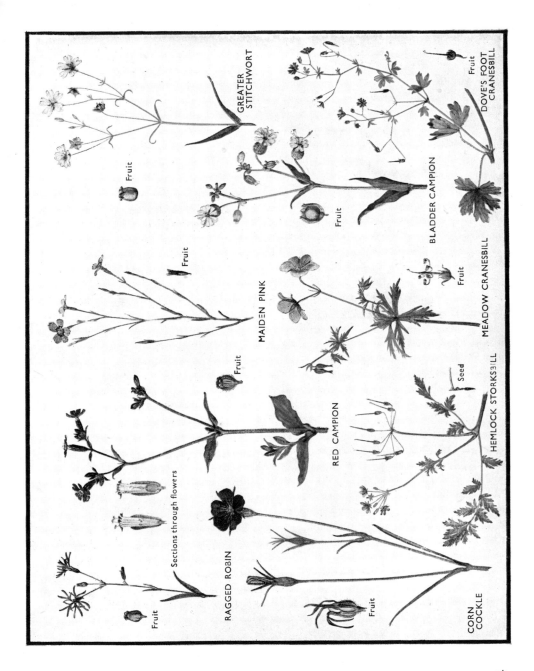

GREATER STITCHWORT

Fruit

DOVE'S FOOT CRANESBILL

Fruit

BLADDER CAMPION

Fruit

MAIDEN PINK

Fruit

MEADOW CRANESBILL

Fruit

RED CAMPION

Fruit

Sections through flowers

HEMLOCK STORKSBILL

Seed

RAGGED ROBIN

Fruit

CORN COCKLE

Fruit

PLATE 4

Fair queen of the meadows, oh where are you hiding?
I miss you at Hampton, I miss you at Kew :
There are ladies a plenty in Mayfair residing,
But none to compare with your beauty so blue.

The Poor Man's Garden : MADELEY

Very characteristic of the whole geranium family is the fruit. When not fully ripe, it is shaped like a bird's beak, hence the common name. (The generic name *Geranium* is derived from the Greek *geranos*, 'crane'.) Such a fruit is called a schizocarp. When ripe, the beak-like styles form a mechanism for dispersing the seeds. On ripening, the whole fruit gradually becomes dry, and during the drying process each of the five lower parts of the ovary bearing a seed tears away from the base of the beak. Each one is attached to a long, narrow strip of the beak-like style, and each strip gradually begins to tear away from the central axis (Plate 4). Eventually this process quickens its pace and the seed-containing portions of the fruit are suddenly swung upwards and eventually shot away for a considerable distance.

There are several other wild crane's-bills, some of them comparatively common. One of these is the **dove's-foot crane's-bill** (*G. molle*) (Plate 4), a smaller plant than the meadow crane's-bill, which is found in flower during April to September in waste places and in cornfields. Its leaves are less fringed, and they turn a deep red during the autumn.

One of our prettiest wayside flowers is **herb-Robert** (*G. robertianum*), with very small, pink flowers. It may also be found in waste places and sometimes even in open woods. The flowers appear during May to September. Its leaves are very deeply cut, and the stem is a pronounced red in colour and is covered with hairs. The whole plant has a very disagreeable odour ; in fact, the plant is sometimes called the **stinking crane's-bill**.

The **bloody crane's-bill** (*G. sanguineum*) is common in dry, rocky places and has large, crimson flowers, which appear during July and August.

There are several other kinds of crane's-bill, all species of the genus *Geranium*, and all closely alike in fundamental structure.

To the genus *Erodium* (having five sterile stamens and five fertile ones) belong the stork's-bills.

The **hemlock stork's-bill** (*E. cicutarium*) is the only common example, and this can be found in dry waste places and sandy

R. A. Malby & Co.

FIG. 51.—*Pelargonium*.

areas (especially near the sea) flowering during June to September. The leaves of this plant are compound, and each leaflet is deeply notched (Plate 4). The pinkish-blue flowers are borne in clusters and all members of one cluster are given off from a single terminal point of the flower stalk, thus forming an umbel (see Chap. 40) (Plate 4). The beak of the fruit is longer than that of the crane's-bill, which explains the distinguishing common name.

This plant not only disperses its own seeds, but also sows them. The strip of the beak which is ejected with the seed is hygroscopic and is therefore affected by humidity. When dry it is twisted, but when damp it straightens out and thus forces the seed into the soil.

There is a rarer species of stork's-bill, the **musky stork's-bill** (*E. moschatum*) with leaflets less deeply cut and not so many flowers in each umbel than in those of the more common species, and the plant has a musky smell.

ORNAMENTAL PLANTS

The very popular bedding, greenhouse and pot plant frequently called 'geranium' is really a member of another genus of the GERANIACEAE—*Pelargonium*. Its leaves, though somewhat lobed, are not usually indented or fringed, though the margin is somewhat wavy. There are many species and varieties of varying habits from sturdy herbs to graceful climbers (Figs. 51 and 52). The flowers also vary from pure white, through pink to red, and they may be single or double. The genus is native to South Africa chiefly, and also to the Mediterranean and Australia. From the South African species, *P. odoratissimum*, an oil is extracted which is used as a substitute for attar of roses.

Many species of true *Geranium* (crane's-bills) are also cultivated for their floral beauty. The flowers may be purple, pink, deep blue or bright blue in colour. Some species of *Erodium*, too, are cultivated.

R. A. Malby & Co.

FIG. 52.—Another Hybrid of *Pelargonium*.

The flowers may be yellow (rare), pink or white. They make attractive rockery plants.

A very small family, closely related to the geranium family, is that of LINACEAE—worth considering, for it contains the lovely flax plant, which is also of such great economic importance.

The LINACEAE is a cosmopolitan family of herbs and shrubs comprising three or four genera, of which only two are represented in this country, namely, *Linum* and *Radiola*. The latter is represented by one plant only, the **allseed** (R. *millegrana*), a plant found, not commonly, growing in sandy, damp places and presenting its minute flowers during the months of July and August. There are four variously toothed sepals, four petals, four stamens and a four-chambered ovary with four styles.

Linum is represented by several species, but the chief one is the **common flax** (L. *usitatissimum*). This lovely plant, with its fragile stem, its tender, small leaves and its outstanding blue flowers may be found growing in cornfields and flowering during the month of July : but when seen cultivated in fields in masses (especially in Northern Ireland and Eastern England) it makes a never-to-be-forgotten sight.

The closely related wild species, the **purging flax** (L. *catharticum*) may sometimes be seen growing in pastures. It has white flowers which appear during June to September. This plant is a true native, whereas the common flax was introduced from the cultivated fields of Ireland.

The leaves of the common flax are small and narrow and are borne alternately on the stem (Plate 5) whereas those of the purging flax (at any rate the lower ones) are borne opposite each other.

There are five sepals, each one being oval and ending in a long point. They form a cup. Then there are five large blue petals with narrow black honey-guides. The stamens and carpels are five each in number, and the latter are joined to form a five-chambered ovary with five separate styles. The fruit is a capsule which splits when ripe to release its seeds.

The flax plant is of considerable economic importance, since it provides more than one commodity. The flax fibre is obtained from the stem by rotting off the softer tissues. This produces the textile, linen. Linen has been made since the earliest periods of history. The development of cotton-spinning in the eighteenth century dealt the linen industry a severe blow. It has, however, partially recovered and is now flourishing in Northern Ireland, in Scotland and in Yorkshire. The shorter fibres are used for making a cloth which is then scraped on one side to form medical lint.

The flax seeds, known as linseed, yield linseed oil (the oil commonly used in paints). This oil is extracted under pressure, and the hard, dry residue, known as ' oil-cake ', is used for feeding cattle. Some American Indians use flax seed for flavouring their food. The specific name *usitatissimum* of the plant, being the Latin for ' much used ' is therefore well applied.

Several species of *Linum* are cultivated for their lovely flowers. Perhaps the greatest favourite is *L. grandiflorum*, with its large scarlet flowers ; but other popular species have bright blue, pale blue, deep blue, bright yellow, pale yellow or pure white blooms. The habits of these ornamental plants also vary. The scarlet species has long- and short-styled flowers.

19

THREE POPULAR FAMILIES

(Oxalidaceae, Tropaeolaceae and Balsaminaceae)

These three families, all of which are closely related to the geranium family, are very small, but each contains a favourite plant. OXALI-DACEAE is represented in the wild state by the shamrock (or wood sorrel) only ; TROPAEOLACEAE has no wild representative in this country, though the so-called ' nasturtium ' of our gardens is very much in evidence ; of the family BALSAMINACEAE, the genus *Impatiens* is also a garden favourite.

THE SHAMROCK FAMILY

The family OXALIDACEAE comprises several genera, but most of them are tropical; the genus *Oxalis* is represented in this country by the **wood sorrel**, or **shamrock** (*O. acetosella*) (Plate 2). An older name for this plant is **alleluia**. This is a delicate plant, very frequently found growing in damp woods and sometimes along hedgerows and river banks. It spreads vegetatively by means of underground stems, and, like the violet (p. 68) sometimes ensures the setting of seeds by means of flowers which never open.

The shamrock is, of course, the national emblem of Ireland.

> O, the shamrock, the green, immortal Shamrock!
> Chosen leaf of Baird and Chief,
> Old Erin's native Shamrock.
> > *Oh, the Shamrock*: THOMAS MOORE

The leaf of the shamrock is characteristic. It is divided into three heart-shaped leaflets borne on long stalks which are sensitive to light and temperature. Thus they close against the stem during the night and also during cold and rainy weather. The leaf is acid to the taste, but it is edible and is sometimes eaten in salads, especially in the United States.

The flowers are borne simply, one on each flower stalk. There are five, toothed sepals forming a cup, five large white petals with pinkish veins, ten stamens, and five carpels joined to form a five-chambered ovary with five separate styles. The fruit is a capsule. Each seed has an elastic covering which, when ripe, turns inside out like a glove and thus shoots the seeds out. The flowers appear early in the year (March to June).

Thus the family OXALIDACEAE is seen to be very similar to the GERANIACEAE, the chief difference being in the fruit. This family contains some plants of minor economic importance. The shamrock itself is sometimes used as a source of oxalic acid. Some foreign genera are a source of food supply through their fruits, such as bilimbi and carambola of India and China, and their stem tubers.

Several species of *Oxalis* have beautiful ornamental flowers and are therefore cultivated for this purpose. The flowers vary in colour, the commonest being pink; but there are also some which are white or yellow. Some yellow species are particularly suited for rockeries since they are low-growing and bloom profusely.

'NASTURTIUMS'

The family Tropaeolaceae comprises one genus only, *Tropaeolum*, and this is represented in Britain by the very lovely garden 'nasturtium', which must not be confused with the true *Nasturtium* or water-cress (p. 61). The family is actually native to Central and South America.

Most species of this family are herbs, and some climb by means of twisting leaf stalks like *Clematis* (p. 40). The leaf-blades are usually round, though those of the **canary creeper** (*T. perigrinum*) are deeply lobed. In some species, the roots are tuberous. The leaves of *Tropaeolum* are frequently eaten in green salads, and the fruits are used as substitutes for capers in sauces.

The flowers of *Tropaeolum* are usually large and showy, though in the case of the canary creeper they are small and pale yellow. Those

Fig. 53.—Single 'Nasturtium' (*Tropaeolum*).

of the common garden ' nasturtium ' vary in shades of pale yellow, buff, golden yellow, orange, scarlet, purplish and bronze. They may be single (Fig. 53) or double and often have a delicate scent.

The *Tropaeolum* flower is very irregular in shape, and is borne solitary. The five sepals are coloured (petalloid), and the upper one is produced backwards in the form of a long spur. The five large petals are very showy and unequal in size. There are eight stamens in two whorls of four, and three carpels joined to form a three-chambered ovary with a single common style. The fruit is a schizocarp like that of the geranium, but it has no beak.

Though the green fruits of *Tropaeolum* are used as substitutes for capers, the true capers are unexpanded flower-buds. They are produced by the plant *Capparis spinosa* of Mediterranean regions. This plant belongs to the tropical family CAPPARIDACEAE, which, in this scheme of classification, comes just before the CRUCIFERAE (p. 58.) In this connexion, *Capparis* may be compared with *Eugenia caryophyllata*, the tropical shrub whose dried flower-buds supply the cloves of commerce. *Eugenia* belongs to the family MYRTACEAE which also includes the eucalyptus and gum trees of Australia. This family comes just before the HYPERICACEAE (p. 116).

SOME BALSAMS

The family BALSAMINACEAE comprises succulent herbs, most of which are native to tropical Asia and Africa ; but certain species of the genus *Impatiens* are cultivated in this country for their ornamental flowers.

The flowers of *Impatiens* are usually brightly coloured and some-what similar to those of *Tropoeolum*. One of the five sepals is hooded and spurred, but very often two are aborted so that only three are present. These are petalloid like those of *Tropoeolum*. Of the five irregular petals, the lateral ones are united. In some species there are only three petals. There are five stamens and five stigmas with no styles. The fruit is an explosive capsule.

These tender perennials are very useful for greenhouse cultivation. The shades vary from lilac, through orange, to scarlet and ruby.

The **balsam** or **touch-me-not** (*Impatiens noli-tangere*) is sometimes found growing wild, though it is rare. It has large showy yellow flowers spotted with orange. It is called ' touch-me-not ' because the outer layers of the fruit capsule are fleshy and turgid. If touched when ripe, the valves roll up violently and the seeds scatter far and wide.

20

SOME SEMI-AQUATIC PLANTS
(*Lythraceae*)

WILD FLOWERS

Although this family (LYTHRACEAE) is cosmopolitan in distribution, and comprises some useful trees, shrubs and herbs, there are only two wild representatives in this country : they are the purple loosestrife (which is no relative of the yellow loosestrife, Chap. 51) and the water purslane. Both these plants are herbs, and, like so many of their relatives, they are to be found in semi-aquatic situations.

Both plants represent different genera of this family.

The **purple loosestrife** (*Lythrum salicaria*) grows in distinctive groups along river banks, on the edges of ponds and in other kinds of water-logged soil. The plant reproduces itself vegetatively by means of short underground stems from which the flower-stalks are given off. On these latter the lance-shaped leaves are borne in pairs.

The purple flowers are borne in conspicuous, spike-like inflorescences (Plate 5). These appear during July to September, and are so striking that a group of purple loosestrife stands out in any landscape.

> Purple are the spires of the velvet loosestrife ;
> On the gliding water lies a purple stain,
> Hour by hour it blushes where the brimming river rushes,
> Rushes gaily, rushes proudly, but cometh not again.
> *The Loosestrife* : A. C. BENSON

The sepals of the flower are united into a tube with eight to twelve teeth, the alternate ones being large and more spreading. There are six conspicuous, free petals ; twelve stamens ; and two carpels joined to form a two-chambered ovary, with a common style and stigma. The fruit is a capsule.

The purple loosestrife flower has evolved a very elaborate method of ensuring cross-pollination. There are three forms of flowers, and each form grows on a different plant. Both stamens and styles project so far that an insect alights directly on them. Each flower has twelve stamens in two whorls of six, each whorl differing in length. Then again, the styles differ in length from either whorl of stamens, in three distinct ways. In one kind of flower, the styles project beyond the stamens (long-styled); in the second one they come half-way between the short and the long stamens (mid-styled); in the third case, the styles are very short (short-styled) (Plate 5). Since the visiting insect enters all flowers in the same way and to about the same depth, it follows that long-styled flowers will be pollinated by mid-

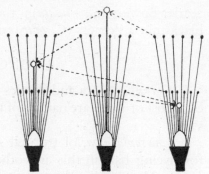

FIG. 54.—Diagram to illustrate Cross-Pollination in the three Types of Purple Loosestrife Flower.

styled and short-styled flowers; mid-styled flowers by long-styled and short-styled flowers; and short-styled flowers by long-styled and mid-styled flowers. This can be understood better by reference to Fig. 54. This is a remarkable adaptation for ensuring cross-pollination.

The **water purslane** (*Peplis portula*) is found growing in wet places and flowering in July and August. It is usually an annual, but if it remains below the surface of the water it becomes etiolated and a perennial. The leaves are borne in opposite pairs and are ovoid with the narrower end near the stem.

The sepals of this flower are joined into a bell-shaped form with twelve teeth, the alternate ones being smaller. There are sometimes six petals, though these may be absent altogether, especially if the plant is completely submerged. There are six stamens and a very short style. Altogether the flower is very inconspicuous, for it is obvious that it could scarcely depend on insects visiting it. The petals, if present, are small and purplish. Pollination, as might be expected, takes place within the same flower by the simple expedient of the stamen filaments bending so that the ripe anthers touch the stigma on the short style.

ORNAMENTAL PLANTS

Some species of *Lythrum* are cultivated for their attractive flower spikes, which may be pink, rose or scarlet in colour. As would be expected, certain species are utilised in water-gardening.

Some gardeners cultivate another genus of this family—*Cuphea*. There are two popular species, one an annual with a profusion of scarlet flowers (*C. miniata*); the other, perennial with small scarlet and black-tubed flowers (*C. platycentra*).

ECONOMIC PLANTS

Certain genera and species of LYTHRACEAE are of economic value, but most of these are natives of tropical regions. A few are of medicinal value.

Lawsonia alba, of tropical Asia, supplies the cosmetic henna, used for dyeing hair in this and other countries, and the finger-nails in the East. The dye is prepared from the dried, powdered leaves.

Physocalymma is a Brazilian tree which supplies the valuable timber called tulip wood.

A useful red dye is extracted from the flowers of *Woodfordia floribunda*, of India, China and Timor.

Lagerstroemia species are East Indian trees cultivated for their lovely ornamental flowers and, in some cases, for their valuable timber.

21

THE WILLOW-HERB FAMILY
(*Onagraceae*)

To this family (ONAGRACEAE) belong some of our most beautiful flowers, familiar to everybody, whether he lives in town or country. Among the wild specimens we have the very conspicuous willow-herbs, to be found growing almost everywhere (one species has proved to be almost the first visitor to the bombed sites of our cities), and among the flower-garden examples are the charming *Clarkia*, the handsome *Fuchsia*, and the popular evening primroses and *Godetia*.

WILD PLANTS

There are two genera of this family frequently found growing wild in this country, namely, *Epilobium* (the willow-herbs) and *Circaea* (the enchanter's nightshades). Some Floras include the genus *Oenothera* (evening primrose) as being a wild one, but it is most probably a garden escape.

All species of the lovely willow-herbs which bedeck our countryside and even open sites of our towns belong to the genus *Epilobium*. Perhaps the most common is the **rose-bay willow-herb** (*E. augustifolium*) whose spikes of pinkish-purple flowers stand out boldly in any environment (Plate 5).

This plant is very tall, varying so much as from four to even six feet in height. Once it becomes established it is difficult to eliminate it, for it reproduces itself vegetatively by means of widespread and very persistent underground stems.

The leaves are long and narrow, lance-shaped, with crinkled margins. They grow densely from ground-level and are also packed on the flower-stalks, diminishing in size passing upwards.

The flowers appear in July and August and are borne in large spikes, the oldest and largest being at the bottom. The main axis of the spike is orange in colour.

This species of willow-herb differs from all the other species of the genus in that the flower is slightly irregular.

Each flower is borne on the axis of the floral spike by a stalk which is purple in colour. There are four long and narrow purple sepals, and four pinkish-purple large petals. The slight irregularity displays itself here, for they are not cruciform, but between two of them there is a gap through which the long stamens and the style protrude (Plate 5). The four carpels are joined and have a common style.

The flower of the rose-bay willow-herb is beautifully adapted for cross-pollination by insects. The honey is secreted in the upper surface of the ovary. The long stamens project horizontally when ripe, and the styles hang downwards. After the insect has removed the exposed pollen, the stamens curve downwards and the style curves upwards ready to receive the pollen from the body of the next insect visitor.

The fruit and seeds of the willow-herbs are of particular interest, and when ripe they are an attractive sight. After fertilisation, the fruit grows into a large capsule (about three inches in length) which is four-cornered and contains many seeds. When ripe, this fruit splits downwards into four equal parts and thus exposes the seeds, each one of which is provided with a parachute taking the form of a tuft of long silky hairs (Plate 5). In this way are the new plants distributed far and wide away from the parent plant, and this, coupled with the easy way in which the plant adapts itself to poor soil conditions, explains why the rose-bay willow-herb soon asserts itself on derelict sites, including bombed and even burnt-out areas. The plumed seeds may

H

frequently be seen parachuting into a room on any summer day when the windows are open. The willow herb is frequently one of the first flowering plants to colonise freshly burnt areas, and for that reason it is sometimes called **fireweed,** though, for the same reason, the name is applied to several different plants, especially in the United States.

Closely related to the rose-bay willow-herb is the **great hairy willow-herb** (*E. hirsutum*), but this plant is even taller and sturdier with larger leaves. Its habitat, also, is rather different, for it lives in watery places such as river and pond banks, marshes and so forth. It flowers during the same season as its relative, and the flowers are of a similar colour but larger and regular, without the gap in the petals. The stigma, too, is cleft into four.

> With many a curve my banks I fret
> By many a field and fallow,
> And many a fairy foreland set
> With willow-weed and mallow.
>
> *The Brook* : TENNYSON

The **small-flowered willow-herb** (*E. parviflorum*) is probably even more like the great hairy willow-herb than the rose-bay. It also is an inhabitant of watery places, chiefly ditches and ponds. Its flowers are regular and the stigmas are four-cleft. The **square-stalked willow-herb** (*E. tetragonum*) is also semi-aquatic, but it is only about a foot and a half in height. Its stigmas are undivided. The **narrow-leaved willow-herb** (*E. palustre*) is about the same height as the square-stalked and is also a water-lover, but the stem is round. The **broad smooth-leaved willow-herb** (*E. montanum*) is an inhabitant of banks and walls and is comparatively short (about twelve inches high). It has smooth leaves.

The other genus of this family commonly found growing wild in this country is *Circaea*, to which belongs the **enchanter's nightshade** (*C. lutetiana*) (Plate 16). This is an inhabitant of damp woods, and flowers during June to August. This tall and slender plant presents its small pink flowers on leafless spikes, many of which are borne laterally on the stem in the axils of leaves which grow in opposite pairs. The leaf is shaped like an elongated heart ending in a long point. Its margins are slightly indented.

The flowers of the enchanter's nightshade show considerable reduction. There are four small sepals, only two heart-shaped petals, two stamens, and four carpels joined to form an ovary with a two-lobed stigma. The fruit is a nut covered with hooked bristles for distribution by animals.

A rarer species, *C. alpina*, may be found in hilly districts. It grows to a height of only six inches and has deeply toothed leaves.

The enchanter's nightshade is in no way related to the other night-shades which belong to a totally different family (Chap. 57). There seems to be no valid reason why the plant should be ascribed to an enchanter, neither is there an explanation for its generic name, which refers to the goddess Circe who transformed men into beasts.

ORNAMENTAL PLANTS

In this family (ONAGRACEAE) are several genera and species very popular among flower gardeners.

Sometimes, but not very often, certain species of *Epilobium* may be found in flower gardens.

One old-fashioned favourite belonging to this family is the **evening primrose**. This belongs to another genus, *Oenothera*, and the most common species, *O. biennis*, grows sometimes as high as five feet. The flowers are large and primrose-coloured. In fundamentals they are similar to that of *Epilobium*. The plant is called the evening primrose because it opens towards dusk when its delicately scented flowers attract nocturnal moths, the long tubes being suited for insect pollination. So John Clare's reference to its wasting 'its fair bloom upon the Night' is scarcely justified from the plant's point of view:

> When once the sun sinks in the west,
> And dew-drops pearl the Evening's breast;
> Almost as pale as moonbeams are,
> Or its companionable star,
> The Evening Primrose opes anew
> Its delicate blossom to the dew;
> And hermit-like, shunning the light,
> Wastes its fair bloom upon the Night;

The evening primrose is of historical interest to scientists since it was one of the main plants experimented on by a famous pioneer in the scientific study of plant hybridisation and genetics—the Dutchman, Hugo de Vries.

Under cultivation, species of *Oenothera* have become much hybrid-ised, so that now we see evening primroses varying in habit and in

FIG. 55.—Double *Godetia*.

colour, such as white, cream, pale yellow, golden yellow and rose. Some are so small that they make useful rockery plants.

So closely related to *Oenothera* is the plant *Godetia* that some botanists place it in the same genus. *Godetia* is a favourite plant for borders and beds. There are many varieties showing all kinds of distinctive characters. Some bear their flowers in loose sprays, others in close clusters. Some have single flowers and others have double (Fig. 55). The colours are almost legion, being white, pink, rose, red, crimson, mauve, bluish, and a large number are variegated in colour. The genus hails from western America.

Another favourite annual is the genus *Clarkia*, though, alas, the flower-spikes do not last very long. These very charming plants are very like *Godetia*, though the flowers (which are borne profusely) are somewhat smaller; in fact, the general habit of the plant is smaller, but more graceful. It is very difficult to conceive of a more charming range of colour variety than *Clarkia* presents, especially the double examples. They give the gardener a grand opportunity for producing a gorgeous display of colour in his garden during the short summer season. The genus *Clarkia* is North American in origin.

A number of cultivated ornamental flowers are members of the genus *Fuchsia*, though the popularity of these plants seems to be waning. The genus is really a native of Central and South America (where the flowers are frequently pollinated by humming-birds, which live on nectar) and of New Zealand. The species vary from small woody plants to large (usually small-flowered) bushes which are sometimes trained as hedges. Often the sepals of the flower are one colour and the petals a totally different one, such as red and white, blue and white, red and blue and so forth. The flowers are also frequently double.

ECONOMIC PLANTS

Though no members of this family (ONAGRACEAE) are cultivated in Great Britain for economic purposes, some are, or have been, used for food or other culinary purposes.

The rose-bay willow-herb, for example, which grows in many parts of the world, is often eaten in certain areas of North America. The young shoots are sometimes used as substitutes for asparagus. The young leaves and stems are used as pot-herbs in Canada and northern Europe. It has also been said that the dried leaves have been used for adulterating tea.

In Great Britain, the young roots of the evening primrose were once boiled and eaten. In Germany also, they boiled the roots and ate the leaves in green salads.

The fruit of another genus, *Trapa*, which are water plants with floating leaves, is the basis of singhara flour, a valuable food in north-west India and China.

22

MISCELLANY

In the scheme of flowering plant classification which we have adopted here, twenty-five families come between that discussed in the last chapter, and that to be considered in the next. Here we are grouping these twenty-five families under the heading of 'Miscellany', because apart from the first two of them (which are therefore most closely related to the ONAGRACEAE) and another odd one here and there, none of the families is represented in the wild state in Great Britain, and only about half a dozen have been introduced into our cultivated gardens. None of the families is very large, but they are all native to other lands, chiefly the tropics.

MARE'S TAIL AND WATER MILFOIL

Of this group of 'miscellaneous' families, the HALORRHAGACEAE is most closely related to the ONAGRACEAE. It consists of herbs and under-shrubs, many of which are aquatic in habit—in fact, all British members are. Those found growing wild in this country are the mare's tail and the water milfoil.

The **mare's tail** (*Hippuris vulgaris*) may frequently be found growing in ponds and ditches, bearing insignificant flowers during June to August.

It is a strange-looking plant. The finely cut leaves are borne in whorls (Fig. 56). In fact, the mare's tail is similar in general appearance to the horse-tail; but it must not be confused with it, for the latter is not even a flowering plant. The mare's tail spreads by means of creeping stems below the water, and these give off aerial shoots which project above the surface. Those leaves which are submerged are longer and more flaccid than those which are borne on the aerial shoots. The stem of this plant contains very large air-spaces to assist respiration under difficult conditions.

The flower of the mare's tail is very much reduced and insignificant, and is therefore wind-pollinated. There are no petals; the sepals are represented by a mere rim around the ovary; there is one stamen and one carpel. So the flower could not be reduced very much more.

FIG. 56.—Mare's Tail growing in Water.

Harold Bastin.

The **water milfoil** (*Myriophyllum spicatum*) is not very common in most parts of the country, though it can be found in some ditches and ponds. The leaves are very finely divided especially when submerged. The inflorescence projects above the surface of the water. The flowers, like those of the mare's tail, are very much reduced; but here they are unisexual, though both sexes are borne on the same plant. In the male flower there is a four-lobed calyx, two to four petals, and eight stamens. In the female flower the calyx is also four-lobed, the petals are minute and the ovary consists of four fused carpels with four separate styles.

A genus not wild in this country, but also belonging to the same family, is *Gunnera*, a genus distributed throughout the southern hemisphere. Unlike its relative this plant has enormous leaves, sometimes as much as five feet in diameter. It is cultivated on occasions beside pools and lakes, chiefly because of its impressively large leaves.

WATER STAR-WORT

Very closely related to the HALORRHAGACEAE is the family CALLITRICHACEAE: so closely, in fact, that some botanists prefer to place the two families together under the former name. To the CALLITRICHACEAE belongs the **water star-wort** (*Callitriche verna*), another plant to be found growing in ditches. The vegetative habit of this plant is different from that of its two relatives already described. The submerged leaves are long and narrow, whereas the aerial leaves are lance-shaped and borne in opposite pairs. At the top of the aerial shoot they form a rosette.

FIG. 57.—Spurge Laurel.

The flowers of the water star-wort are insignificant and unisexual. The male flower is composed of one bract and one stamen; the female of two carpels fused to form a four-chambered ovary with two separate styles.

SPURGE LAUREL

The family THYMELAEACEAE, is represented by the familiar **spurge laurel** (*Daphne laureola*) of damp copses and woods (Fig. 57). This plant is poisonous. A close relative is the **mezereon** (*D. mezereum*).

The shrubby spurge laurel has handsome leaves, lance-

Harold Bastin.

shaped and borne alternately. The plant is perennial and the leaves are evergreen. The flowers are borne in greenish bunches in the axils of the leaves. Each flower has a four-lobed tubular calyx, no petals, eight stamens and one carpel which, after fertilisation, ripens into a black, poisonous berry. The leaves of the mezereon are deciduous, and the flowers are pinkish and produce red berries.

Both the spurge laurel and the mezereon are sometimes cultivated, because the flowers, though never very conspicuous, are sweet-smelling. The flowers of the cultivated species may be white, rose pink, red or purple.

ABRONIA AND GREVILLEA

The next fourteen miscellaneous families are not native to this country, though some are cultivated. The NYCTAGINACEAE, for example, is represented in some flower gardens by *Abronia umbellata*, which has verbena-like, rose-coloured flowers and, owing to its trailing habit, is suitable for rock gardens.

The Australian and South African family PROTEACEAE is represented by several cultivated species of *Grevillea*, which are warmth-loving plants—indeed, some flourish best in greenhouses. The flower is often curiously claw-shaped, and varies in colour with the species—yellow, through orange to red. There are no members of this family indigenous to this country.

ROCK ROSE

The only other family in this miscellany native to this country is CISTACEAE, to which the rock rose belongs. This plant, which must not be confused with the true rose, belongs to the genus *Helianthemum*. There are three wild species of rock rose, but the only species frequently found growing in chalky places and flowering in the late summer (July to September) is the **common rock rose** (*H. vulgare*) (Plate 2). This plant is of a trailing habit, and has simple leaves borne in pairs.

The large yellow flowers are slightly irregular in that there are three large and two small sepals. The five petals are large, heart-shaped and yellow. There is an indefinite, but large, number of stamens. The carpels are fused to form a three-chambered ovary with a single style which has a three-lobed stigma. The fruit is a capsule which eventually splits into three valves (Plate 2).

The flowers of the rock rose close during inclement weather.

Cultivated varieties of the rock rose are favourites with rock gardeners. They are perennials and present various bright colours—white, pale yellow, orange, pink, amber and crimson.

PASSION FLOWERS

The only other family in this group which is at all known in this country, since it is a garden introduction, is the PASSIFLORACEAE, to which belong the **passion flowers** (*Passiflora* and *Tacsonia* species). These are beautiful outdoor and greenhouse climbers, with either blue or whitish flowers. Most of these plants are of American origin. In the New World and the islands around stretching into the Pacific, many members of this family supply edible fruits; for example, *Passiflora edulis*, the **passion fruit**; *P. maliformis*, the **sweet calabash**; *P. quadrangularis*, the **granadilla**; and *P. laurifolia*, the **water lemon.**

23

THE MELON FAMILY
(*Cucurbitaceae*)

A casual glance at the white bryony, a very common hedgerow climbing plant, would scarcely call to mind the vegetable marrow or cucumber plants, yet all three are members of the same family, and are, apart from dimensions of the various parts, very similar indeed.

The melon family (CUCURBITACEAE) is a large family, comprising more than seventy genera; but most of these are unknown in this country. Although the family is widespread throughout the world, except in the very cold regions, there is only one wild species native to Great Britain, and that is the white bryony. Most members of the family are climbers, usually developing tendrils for the purpose, and they show very rapid growth with an abundance of sap in their tissues, especially the fruit.

Nearly all members of the family are unisexual.

WILD PLANTS

The **white bryony** (*Bryonia dioica*), a plant familiar all the year round for its lovely green, handsome leaves and greenish-white flowers in the summer and its clusters of bright red berries in the winter scrambles all over the hedges by means of tendrils (Plate 5). It may be found growing in most parts of the country, and though it prefers to climb over hedges, it is sometimes found in thickets and copses. The flowers appear during May to September (Plate 5).

The white bryony must in no circumstances be confused with the black bryony, which is also a climber but is a totally different plant (Chap. 65); in fact, it is a monocotyledon.

The beautiful leaves of the white bryony are shaped like the palm of the hand with the five lobes somewhat indented (Plate 5).

> And scallop'd briony mingling round her bowers,
> Whose fine bright leaves make up the want of flowers.
> *Sundry Walks*: JOHN CLARE

The unisexual flowers are borne on different plants. The male flower has five united sepals, five greenish-white petals (arranged like a star), and three stamens. The female flower is superficially similar, but, of course, it has no stamens and is also distinguishable from the male flower in that it has a swollen ovary below the sepals. The ovary is composed of three chambers containing many seeds, and the style is divided into three. The fruit is a bright red berry (Plate 5). It is poisonous.

ECONOMIC PLANTS

Though our only native member of the melon family (CUCUR-BITACEAE), and a comparatively small one, is the white bryony, and though no other members have been introduced into our flower gardens, it is scarcely likely that anyone can be unacquainted with the family, for he must have seen certain examples such as marrows, pumpkins and cucumbers, either as the complete plant in the kitchen garden, frame or greenhouse, or represented by their fruits in the greengrocer's shop.

The **vegetable marrow** is a member of the genus *Cucurbita* (*C. pepo*). It is very similar in fundamental structure to the white bryony. Both these plants climb by means of tendrils; the leaves are very similar and so are the flowers; and in each case the fruit is a berry, though that of the marrow, having a tough rind, is sometimes called a pepo. The leaves of the vegetable marrow are, of course, much larger than those of the white bryony, and are not so deeply indented. Tendrils are present, but they are not often used, for the plant under cultivation does not usually climb but trails along the ground.

The male and female flowers of the vegetable marrow are large and yellow, the male flower being borne on a long stalk. The berry-like fruit is very large and elongated. The three-chambered nature of the ovary becomes very evident when the fruit is cut across.

There are several well-known varieties of *Cucurbita pepo*. The original is probably the **pumpkin,** with its large, nearly spherical fruit. The vegetable marrow is one variety of this, and the **squash** is another. The **giant pumpkin** (*C. maxima*) is cultivated in North America, and a single fruit has attained a weight of 240 lb. The **gourds** cultivated in British gardens are varieties of this.

Several species of a closely allied genus, *Cucumis*, also bear edible fruit. The species most familiar to us is the **cucumber** (*Cucumis sativus*), which is cultivated either trailing in garden-frames or trained and climbing in greenhouses (Fig. 58). The cucumber has been cultivated since very early times. The true **gherkin** is a West Indian fruit produced by another species, *C. anguria*; but in this country the gherkins used in pickles are usually the immature fruit of certain varieties of cucumber.

FIG. 58.—Leaves, Flowers, Tendril and Fruit of Cucumber.

The **melon** and the **cantaloupe melon** are two varieties of *Cucumis melo*. These are natives of Asia, but later became known to the Egyptians and the Romans, and now they are popular in both the Americas.

The **water melon** belongs to a different genus (*Citrullus vulgaris*). It is native to tropical and southern Africa, but it also has now found its way to the Americas.

The flask-shaped **calabash cucumber** (*Lagenaria vulgaris*), of the tropics, is of economic value in that the outer layers of the fruit are hard and woody, and when dry the whole makes a useful vessel.

The **squirting cucumber** (*Ecballium elaterium*), of the Mediterranean region, is interesting since its ripe fruit is very highly turgid, that is, it has become swollen and very tight. So when it drops, a hole is pierced in the lower surface and the fruit-wall collapses and squirts out the watery contents containing the seeds. Thus are the seeds dispersed. This plant is also of value, for a purgative (elaterium) is prepared from the fruit.

The **chocho** (*Sechium edule*), of tropical America, is an edible fruit and is unique in that it contains only one seed and that is enormous.

Luffa cylindrica, another genus of tropical regions, is of economic value, for apart from its use as food it supplies the loofah of the bathroom. Examination of a complete loofah shows it to be cylindrical, but in section it encloses three chambers. This is due to the fact that it is actually the woody vascular network of the fruit of *Luffa*.

24

SOME HANDSOME EXOTICS

(*Begoniaceae* and *Theaceae*)

BEGONIAS

No species of the BEGONIACEAE are to be found growing wild in this country, yet we must pause for a while to examine the lovely species and varieties of **begonia** so frequently found adorning parks, gardens, and greenhouses.

The family is mainly tropical and sub-tropical—chiefly South American and Indian. Most species belong to the genus *Begonia*.

Begonias present not only enchanting flowers but also handsome foliage which is frequently variegated. Most of them are perennial herbs, and a large number have thick roots or tubers. Some climb, like the ivy, by means of adventitious roots.

The leaves of begonia are usually large. Each leaf is lop-sided, the part on one side of the mid-rib being larger than its counterpart on the other side. This explains the name ' elephant's ear ' which is sometimes given to the plant (Fig. 59). The surface of the leaf easily becomes wet, but since it usually hangs downwards and has an extended tip, the rain drips off easily. This is very important to tropical plants.

The begonia has a curious method of vegetative reproduction which is frequently used by horticulturists for the production of new plants. If a leaf is cut and the cut parts are placed on the soil in suitable

FIG. 59.—Single and Double *Begonia*.

growing conditions, adventitious buds arise from the callus which forms over the surface, and these form new plants.

Frequently, too, tubers may be found growing in small groups in the axils of the leaves. The axillary branch does not develop, but itself bears these tubers. The tubers are another means of vegetative reproduction. But in cultivation, new plants are obtained either from seeds or from leaf-cuttings.

The flowers of the begonia are sometimes borne in clusters : more frequently they are borne more or less solitary and are very large and handsome. They are unisexual, but flowers of both sexes are borne on the same plant.

In the male flowers there are usually two sepals, two to five petals, and numerous stamens. The female flower is similar to the male except that there are, of course, no stamens, but two or three carpels joined to form a two- or three-chambered ovary. The fruit may be a capsule or a berry, containing many very minute seeds.

The variety of begonias found under cultivation is profuse. There are the tuberous-rooted species and the fibrous-rooted species. The size of the flower varies from half an inch in diameter to six or seven inches. The flowers may be single or double (Fig. 59). The petals may be entire, frilled or picotee and present the most charming range of colour—white, yellow, orange, pink, scarlet and crimson.

CAMELLIAS

To the family THEACEAE belong such beautiful flowers as the camellia and a very important economic plant, the tea plant.

All members of this family are either trees or shrubs and all are natives either of China and Japan or the sub-tropical areas of the south-eastern United States. The tea plant has, however, moved westwards under cultivation, and is now an important crop in India and Ceylon.

The leaves of all genera of this family are simple.

The flowers of THEACEAE are hermaphrodite. There are five to seven sepals, usually five petals, numerous stamens and several free carpels.

Among the ornamental plants of this family, the **camellia** ranks high. Like the tea plant, it has, under cultivation, spread from its native areas (India, China and Japan). It is now cultivated in most warm parts of the world, and in greenhouses in temperate regions. It was introduced into Britain in 1739. The favourite examples are varieties of *Camellia japonica* and other species. These may either be single or double (the latter being the most common) and the most frequent colours are pure white, pink, salmon red and crimson.

Other genera of this family, cultivated as evergreen shrubs or for their flowers, are *Eurya* and *Stuartia* (or *Stewartia*), the former from South America and the latter from North America and Japan.

The **tea** plant is another species of the genus *Camellia* (*C. thea*). Reference to this plant as an economic product is made on p. 2. The leaves are simple and the flower resembles a small white single camellia flower.

25

THE ST. JOHN'S WORTS
(*Hypericaceae*)

The St. John's worts are characterised by bright yellow flowers. All are members of the genus *Hypericum*, which belongs to the family HYPERICACEAE. There are several other genera distributed in the southern hemisphere. A number of species of *Hypericum* are cultivated for ornamental purposes, but not one of the species has any economic value.

WILD PLANTS

Characteristic of the genus *Hypericum* is the **perforated St. John's wort** (*H. perforatum*), sometimes found growing in thickets and flowering during July to September. The plant is called ' perforated ' because its leaves contain minute oil-glands which look like fine pale-green pin-pricks, and when the leaf is held up to the light they appear as perforations. The oil of these glands gives the plant its characteristic smell.

The stem has two longitudinal ridges.

The leaves are small and lance-shaped, and are borne in opposite pairs. The flowering branches are borne in pairs in the axils of the leaves, the upper branch blossoming first.

The flower is like a yellow star (Plate 2). There are five small sepals and five oval and pointed petals. The stamens are numerous, but they are joined to form three bundles—a curious characteristic. They enhance the beauty of the flower, for they are deep orange in colour.

The fruit is a multi-chambered capsule which, when ripe, is long, pointed and golden brown in colour (Plate 2). It eventually splits to release its many seeds.

Like several other introductions, this plant is now proving to be a bad weed in Australia.

The **imperforate St. John's wort** (*H. dubium*) is not so common. Its stem has four ridges, and as its name implies, there are no oil-glands in its leaves.

The **square-stalked St. John's wort** (*H. quadrangulum*) has a four-ridged stem and there are oil-glands in its leaves. It frequents moist places.

The **small St. John's wort** (*H. pulchrum*) has a round stem and oil-glands. It grows on commons and flowers during July and August.

The stem of the **trailing St. John's wort** (*H. humifusum*) is procumbent. There are no oil-glands.

The stem of the **hairy St. John's wort** (*H. hirsutum*) is covered with hairs and the leaves contain oil-glands.

The **tutsan** (*H. androsaemum*) is not common, but it may sometimes be found flowering during June to August in hedges and thickets. It is interesting in that it has deciduous petals and its numerous stamens are fused into five (and not three) bundles.

ORNAMENTAL PLANTS

Several species of *Hypericum* are cultivated. *H. calycinum*, for example, is a dwarf shrub with yellow flowers three to four inches in diameter. *H. polyphyllum* is a charming trailing species to be seen in rock gardens. *H. reptans* does not trail, but is a useful dwarf in rockeries. *H. moserianum* and *H. prolificum* are taller shrubs.

Certain other genera of this family yield useful resins.

———

Leading on from the HYPERICEAE in this scheme of plant classification are several families which contain trees and shrubs of considerable economic importance. Since it is proposed to deal with trees in a separate book in this series, no detailed consideration of them will be undertaken here. A few are worthy of mentioning, however.

EUCRYPHIACEAE is a family of ornamental trees and shrubs with showy flowers. They are natives of Australia and Chile, but some are cultivated in this country.

GUTTIFERAE is mainly tropical and comprises several useful trees and shrubs supplying timber, resins and tropical articles of diet.

TILIACEAE comprises genera and species of trees and shrubs distributed throughout the world. Many of them produce valuable timbers or fibres. The most common in this country is the **lime tree** (*Tilia vulgaris*). Closely related to it is the American **basswood** (*T. americana*). The Indian **jute plants,** *Corchorus capsularis* and *C. olitorius* supply the valuable fibre, jute.

STERCULIACEAE is an economically important family because it comprises the cocoa-producing trees. The **cacao tree** (*Theobroma cacao*) is a native of tropical America, though it now forms the basis of a staple industry in the Gold Coast. The hard berries produce the cocoa and chocolate of commerce, and the pressed seeds yield cocoa-butter. *Cola vera,* an African genus, produces kola nuts, which, since they contain caffeine, have sustaining qualities, and are often chewed by the Negroes.

BOMBACACEAE is another family of tropical trees, the stems of which often bulge to store water. Several members of the family produce useful substances. The **baobab** (*Adansonia digitata*) is an African native, and is one of the largest of trees, often attaining a diameter of thirty feet in the trunk, though the tree is not especially tall. The woody fruit has a mucilaginous edible pulp. The bark yields a fibre from which rope and cloth are made. The huge trunks are frequently excavated by the natives to make houses. The **cotton tree** (*Bombax malabaricum*), of India and Ceylon, produces seeds covered with hairs which are sometimes used as a fine cotton. Dug-out canoes are made from the bark. The **silk-cotton tree** (*Ceiba pentandra*), of tropical America, also produces fine hairs inside the capsules which are used for stuffing cushions.

26

THE MALLOW FAMILY
(*Malvaceae*)

All members of the mallow family (MALVACEAE), especially those cultivated, have large handsome flowers ; only one member of the family is of economic value, but that is of outstanding importance— namely the cotton plant.

WILD FLOWERS

There are only two wild genera, namely *Malva* and *Althaea*, which are native to this country. *Malva* comprises three species of mallow.

The **common mallow** (*Malva sylvestris*) is a frequent inhabitant of waste places, hedgerows and roadsides, where its purple flowers make a striking display during the months of June to September. (The Latin term *Malva* is the origin of the word ' mauve '.)

The plant is strong and sturdy with handsome foliage (Plate 5). The stem and leaves are hairy. Each leaf is divided, though not very deeply, into five lobes, and each lobe is somewhat toothed.

The flowers are borne singly on stalks which grow from the axils of the leaves.

To each flower there are five united sepals, and on the outside of these there are three bracts, usually called the epicalyx. The five purple petals are heart-shaped and comparatively large (Plate 5). There is an indefinite number of stamens. The carpels form a bun-shaped ring, and

I

these, after fertilisation, form a ring of fruit, arranged like wedge-shaped cheeses, and, since they are edible, country-folk call them ' cheeses ' (Plate 5).

> The sitting down, when school was o'er
> Upon the threshold of the door,
> Picking from Mallows, sport to please,
> The crumpled seed we called a cheese.
>
> JOHN CLARE

The flower of the common mallow makes certain of cross-pollination by preventing self-pollination. This is how it is done. The stamens stand upright and ripen first. After they have shed their pollen on to the body of a visiting insect, they bend outwards and downwards, and the styles grow in length and occupy the original position of the stamens and are then ready to collect the pollen from the body of a later insect visitor.

The **dwarf mallow** (*M. rotundifolia*) is smaller in general habit than the common mallow, and its stem is prostrate. It grows in similar situations and blooms during the same season. As its flowers are much smaller, however, the dwarf mallow can ill afford to insist on cross-pollination since it is not so attractive to insects, so, although its stamens and styles go through the same movements as the common mallow, if no insect visitor has called, then the styles bend and twist among the curved stamens and pollinate themselves.

The **musk mallow** (*M. moschata*) is not very common. It grows in dry meadows and flowers during July to September. Its flowers are large and rose-coloured.

The **marsh mallow** belongs to a different genus (*Althaea officinalis*). It is not very common either, but it is interesting, for it is related to the garden hollyhock. It may be found flowering during July and August. It has five united sepals surrounded by an epicalyx of six to nine united bracts. The leaves are thick, heart-shaped and lobed. The flowers are large and rosy.

ORNAMENTAL PLANTS

The family MALVACEAE gives us some of our most attractive and showy garden flowers.

Several species of *Malva* with flowers of pink or white are cultivated. The **musk mallow** (*M. moschata*) is one favourite.

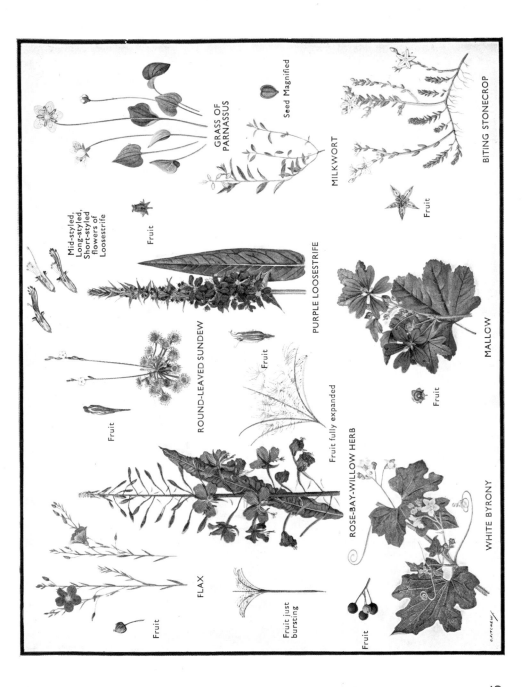

GRASS OF PARNASSUS

Seed Magnified

MILKWORT

Fruit

BITING STONECROP

Mid-styled,
Long-styled,
Short-styled
flowers of
Loosestrife

Fruit

PURPLE LOOSESTRIFE

Fruit

ROUND-LEAVED SUNDEW

Fruit

Fruit fully expanded

MALLOW

Fruit

ROSE-BAY-WILLOW HERB

Fruit

FLAX

Fruit just
bursting

WHITE BYRONY

Fruit

PLATE 5

The **hollyhock** (*Althaea rosea*) needs no introduction. It has been a favourite in cottage gardens for centuries, and its tall and lavish growth and large flowers make it a useful background to herbaceous borders. There are single and double varieties (Fig. 60), with a variety of colours—white, yellow, pink, salmon-red, scarlet and crimson. It is a mistake to derive the word 'hollyhock' from 'holy-oak', for it is really derived from the old Anglo-Saxon word *holi-hōc*, meaning marsh mallow.

Hibiscus is another genus of the mallow family. Some species make useful greenhouse and conservatory plants, for the genus is, in the main, tropical. The most favourite ornamental species are the **shoe flower** (*H. rosa sinensis*), and the **flower of an hour** (*H. trionum*). The flowers may be white, bluish-mauve, yellow or dark rose.

Lavatera produces flowers in profusion. To this genus also belongs the **tree mallow** (*L. arborea*), found wild around our coasts. One of the most popular garden species is *L. rosea*, which is a large, tall, border plant having rose-pink flowers which produce an impressive effect by their very profusion (Fig. 61). Other genera are also cultivated. The genus is native to the Mediterranean region, Asia and Australia.

FIG. 60.—Double Hollyhock.

FIG. 61.—*Lavatera.*

Sidalcea is an American genus sometimes cultivated in this country. The plant is like a diminutive hollyhock.

Abutilon is another conservatory decoration, either as a potted plant or a trained climber. It is useful in bouquets. The genus is tropical, and some species are visited by humming birds.

ECONOMIC PLANTS

Some members of the mallow family are edible, though few are cultivated for this purpose. Certain tropical species of *Hibiscus* have edible fruit, used in jellies and soups.

The most important member of this family from the economic point of view is the **cotton plant** (*Gossypium barbadense* of tropical America, *G. arboreum* and *G. herbaceum* of the Old World. Several other species have now been developed, chiefly by hybridisation, especially in the New World). The whole plant is characteristic of the family (Fig. 62). The seeds are covered with hairs from which cotton is manufactured. The seeds are crushed in order to extract cotton-seed oil, and the residual 'cake' is used, like that of the flax seed (p. 96), for feeding cattle.

Following on the MALVACEAE and leading up to the EUPHORBIACEAE are several plant families, none, however, having any representation in this country. Yet there is one which must be mentioned (ERYTHROXYLACEAE) because it contains the genus of plants which produce cocaine.

The **coca plant** (*Erythroxylon coca*) is the source of cocaine—a drug valuable to doctor and dentist and a hideous curse to the drug addict. The plant is native to Bolivia and Peru, but is also cultivated in Java. The drug is prepared from the leaves of the coca plant.

FIG. 62.—Leaves, Flowers and Fruit of Cotton.

27

A VERY USEFUL FAMILY
(*Euphorbiaceae*)

The family EUPHORBIACEAE is widespread throughout the tropics and the temperate regions. Its members may be trees, shrubs or herbs, and some contain a milky juice which, in certain cases, forms the raw material of valuable economic products. Although the British species are herbs, there are many trees in this family. Many members of the family are poisonous.

In most cases, the flowers are borne in inflorescences of varying design. The flowers themselves are very much reduced. Invariably they are unisexual, and in most cases both male and female flowers are borne on the same plant.

WILD PLANTS

There are only two wild genera belonging to the EUPHORBIACEAE which are native to this country, namely, *Euphorbia* (the spurges) and *Mercurialis* (dog's mercury).

The genus *Euphorbia* also inhabits arid regions, such as deserts, especially in the United States and South Africa, and there the species are modified for storing water, and thus, apart from their flowers, closely resemble the cacti.

The British examples of *Euphorbia* are the spurges, some of which are very common. They all have smooth leaves, and these and the stems contain a poisonous juice.

The inflorescence of *Euphorbia* is very unusual ; in fact it is characteristic of the genus. It takes the form of many male flowers, each insignificant and yellowish-green, together with one female flower, the whole enclosed in a four- or five-toothed bract. Between each two adjacent teeth of the bract is a crescent-shaped gland. Thus the complete inflorescence looks like one flower.

This resemblance is due to the sheath of bracts, which looks like a whorl of greenish-yellow petals ; but it is further enhanced by the fact that the twenty or more male flowers have only one stamen each and all these surround one female flower in the centre which is composed of three carpels united to form a three-chambered ovary with three separate styles.

The **wood spurge** (*E. amygdaloides*) is common in woods and copses. It is an early-flowering plant (March to May), and grows about a foot high. The **dwarf spurge** (*E. exigua*) is a garden and farm weed. It flowers much later (July to November) and attains a height of only six inches. The stem is much branched. Two spurges of waste places, the **sun spurge** (*E. helioscopia*) and **petty spurge** (*E. peplus*) flower about the same time as the dwarf spurge. There are several other rarer species.

The sub-tropical genus *Poinsettia* has bright red upper bracts which render the inflorescence conspicuous. For this reason it is often cultivated in this country.

The other wild genus of this interesting family is *Mercurialis*, whose sole representative in this country is the **dog's mercury** (M. *perennis*). This plant is very commonly found in shady places, sometimes carpeting woods and thickets, and growing along tall hedgerows. It is very poisonous, but contains no milky juice. It also is an early flowering plant (March and April). It spreads by means of underground stems.

The stem of the dog's mercury is about eighteen inches high, bearing oval and pointed leaves in opposite pairs. The two sexes of flowers grow on different plants, which is unusual in this family. The male flowers are borne in spikes which grow from the axils of the leaves. Each male flower has three sepals, but no petals, and eight to twenty stamens. The female flowers are borne in clusters hidden among the leaves of the female plants. Each flower has two reduced sepals and two carpels joined to form a two-chambered ovary with two styles.

ECONOMIC PLANTS

The family EUPHORBIACEAE is very important for the useful plants it contains, and this applies especially to the **rubber** plants.

Rubber is the product of the milky juice or latex of a large number of plants. In fact, it would surprise many people to know how many plants produce a milky juice which contains rubber ; but in the great majority the percentage of rubber is so small as to render extraction uneconomic. This can be said, for example, of the dandelion in Great Britain, though the Russian species of dandelion yields sufficient quantities to warrant commercial exploitation.

The most important rubber-yielding plant belongs to the genus *Hevea*, a member of this family. The best rubber (caoutchouc rubber) is obtained from the **rubber plant** (*Hevea brasiliensis*), a native of Brazil, which has been transported and cultivated in Malaya, Ceylon, etc.

Ceara rubber is obtained from another genus of the same family— *Manihot glaziovii*, of the Argentine.

Other species of the genus *Manihot* are used for food. *M. utilissima* is the **bitter** and *M. aipi* the **sweet cassava** of Brazil. Both plants have small roots and tuberous roots which contain much starchy reserves of food. From the small roots, cassava meal or Brazilian arrowroot is prepared. From the tuberous roots, tapioca is manufactured after they have been dried and the poisonous element thus removed.

Ricinus communis, the **castor-oil plant,** is a tropical shrub. The castor-oil, used as a lubricant and in medicine, is extracted from the seeds. This plant is frequently cultivated in pots in greenhouses for its very handsome foliage.

28

CURRANTS AND GOOSEBERRIES
(Grossulariaceae)

Although both currants and gooseberries are sometimes found growing wild in thickets and woods in this country, they are most frequently seen under cultivation.

Waterers
Fig. 63.—Flowering Currant (*Ribes sanguineum*).

Both the currant and the gooseberry belong to the genus *Ribes*, which is the only genus in the family Grossulariaceae. Some Floras include the genus in Saxifragaceae (Chap. 13). Certain species of *Ribes* make handsome early-flowering shrubs for the flower garden and shrubbery.

ORNAMENTAL PLANTS

Perhaps the most familiar member of the *Ribes* genus which is used as an ornamental shrub in our parks and gardens is the **flowering currant** (R. *sanguineum*) (Fig. 63). This plant is a sturdy shrub, with large leaves, five-lobed and with slightly toothed edges. The veins are very pronounced.

The flowers are rather small but make a handsome show since they are borne in drooping trusses. They are pinkish-purple when young, but darken as they grow older.

The colour of the flower is due to the five comparatively large petalloid sepals. The five petals are reduced in size within the whorl of sepals. There are five stamens and two carpels joined to form a single-chambered ovary with a large style.

Several other species closely related to R. *sanguineum* are cultivated. Some have more deeply coloured flowers. Another species, R. *speciosum*, makes a good wall climber.

The so-called **American currant** (R. *americanum*) has small yellow flowers, and its green foliage turns a striking crimson towards the end of the summer. The **Buffalo currant** (R. *aureum*) has lovely yellow flowers, slightly tinted red. They change to carmine as they get older. There are several other cultivated species and hybrids. The species R. *alpinum* is unisexual, each sex being borne on a different plant.

The fruits of the above species of *Ribes* are berries, but they are of no use for human food as their taste is unpleasant.

ECONOMIC PLANTS

The cultivated forms of currant are so well known as to need little description. The **red currant** (R. *rubrum*) is cultivated in most parts of the country ; the **white currant** is a variety of the red. The **black currant** (R. *nigrum*) is noted for the high vitamin C content of its berries.

The stems of the **gooseberry** (R. *grossularia*) bear protective spines. This plant frequently reproduces itself vegetatively by means of so-called stolons. These are the branch stems which bend to soil-level. The lower part of the stem which touches the ground gives off adventitious roots ; adventitious buds also arise, and thus new plants are formed.

29

HYDRANGEA AND 'SYRINGA'
(*Hydrangeaceae*)

Though not a single member of the family HYDRANGEACEAE is native to this country, there are several cultivated genera which are so popular that the family cannot be passed over altogether. HYDRANGEACEAE comprises trees and shrubs native to north temperate and subtropical regions.

The flowers are usually very conspicuous, and are frequently borne in large, close inflorescences. In the case of *Hydrangea*, these are either flat or almost spherical.

Hydrangea is a cultivated indoor and outdoor genus ; some species are climbers. The outer flowers of the species, with flat-topped inflorescences, are frequently larger than the inner ones. In the wild species, these outer flowers are sterile, that is, they have neither stamens nor carpels. In the majority of the species cultivated in this country, all the flowers are sterile ; so reproduction of the plants is perforce vegetative, chiefly by means of cuttings.

The conspicuousness of the flowers is due to the petaloid sepals.

There are some very lovely species of white *Hydrangea* ; the climbers are also white. Other familiar shades are pink, carmine,

Harold Bastin

FIG. 64.—*Philadelphus.*

red and blue. The blue shade is not natural to *Hydrangea,* but is induced by varying soil conditions. In horticultural practice a special 'blueing' mixture is recommended for forking into the soil around the plant.

Philadelphus is a genus of charming hardy deciduous shrubs of great floral beauty. Sometimes they achieve a great size. Frequently these plants are called 'orange blossom', which, of course, they are not; also they are often named '*Syringa*', which again is a misnomer, for *Syringa* is the generic name of the lilac, which belongs to a totally different family, namely, OLEACEAE.

Philadelphus has large, oval, pointed leaves, also with pronounced veins. The flowers are conspicuous and strongly scented (Fig. 64). An unusual feature of the axillary buds is that they are protected by the leaf-bases, through which they frequently have to break when about to open. The flower has a large number of stamens (twenty to forty). In all species, the flowers are cream or white; they may be single or double.

Several other genera of flowering shrubs belonging to this family are cultivated in this country, for example, *Deutzia, Jamesia* and *Carpenteria.*

30

THE ROSE FAMILY
(Rosaceae)

And the rose, like a nymph to the bath addrest,
Which unveiled the depth of her glowing breast,
Till, fold after fold, to the fainting air,
The soul of her beauty and love lay bare.

The Sensitive Plant : SHELLEY

Some of the loveliest and most welcome of our countryside flowers, such as the dog rose, belong to the rose family (ROSACEAE), the cultivated species and varieties of which find favour with everybody. This family also produces an exceptionally large number of delicious edible fruits.

The rose family is rather cosmopolitan in world distribution; though most of its members are restricted to the north temperate regions. It comprises trees, shrubs and herbs. Although trees in general are being left for consideration in another book, the trees belonging to this family can scarcely be ignored here, since their flowers are almost always conspicuous. Within the family, too, there are several very common means of vegetative reproduction, frequently utilised by the horticulturist, together with the more artificial means of grafting (of fruit trees) and budding (of roses) (Fig. 65).

You see, sweet maid, we marry
A gentler scion to the wildest stock,
And make conceive a bark of baser kind
By bud of nobler race : this is an art
Which does mend nature, change it rather, but
The art itself is nature.

A Winter's Tale, Act 4, Sc. 3 : SHAKESPEARE

Examples of the natural means of vegetative production are the strawberry (runners), raspberry (suckers) and the blackberry (stolons).

The flowers of most members of the rose family are similar in fundamental structure; vegetative habit and fruit structure are the most frequent bases for generic and specific differentiation.

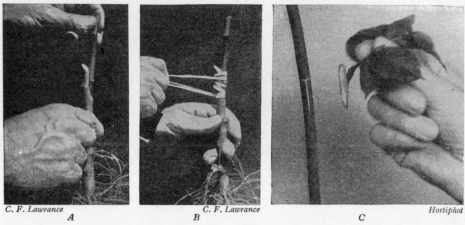

C. F. Lawrance   C. F. Lawrance   Hortiphot

A   B   C

FIG. 65.—*A* and *B*, Grafting ; *C*, Budding.

The flower usually has five sepals, five large, free petals, many stamens, and, since we already know that the fruits show considerable variation, so therefore must the carpels. These may be only one or they may be indefinite in number, either free or united and either situated above the point of insertion of the other floral whorls or below it. This variation, which is reflected in the fruit, is due chiefly to variations in shape and size of the receptacle on which the floral organs are inserted.

WILD FLOWERS

The rose family is well represented among the wild flowers of this country. In fact, it is one of our largest flowering plant families, and for convenience may be divided into three groups—shrubs, trees and herbs.

SHRUBS

There are several species and hybrids of wild roses in this country belonging to the genus *Rosa*, but the most common is the **dog-rose** (*R. canina*), whose pink flowers bedeck the hedgerows during the summer (June and July). This plant is called ' dog-rose ' because since the days of the Ancient Greeks and Romans it was believed to cure the bite of a mad dog, as is mentioned in Pliny's *Natural History*. It scrambles over the hedges, and its profusion of very lovely flowers never fails to arrest

Harold Bastin

FIG. 66.—Dog-Rose.

our attention (Fig. 66). Some people consider the dog-rose more lovely than the garden species.

> The roses that in yonder hedge appear
> Outdo our garden buds which bloom within ;
> But since the hand may pluck them every day,
> Unmarked they bud, bloom, drop and drift away.
> *The Four Bridges*   JEAN INGELOW

The leaves of the dog-rose are compound, being divided into seven serrated leaflets and having two pronounced stipules at the base of the leaf stalk (Plate 6). The stems and leaf stalks are covered with prickles which, unlike the thorns of the hawthorn, are produced from the outer layers or skin of the stem, and are not modified complete stems.

The flower of the dog-rose is typical of the genus (Plate 6). The receptacle is deep and hollow. Around the rim of this receptacle the five sepals, five petals and many stamens are inserted. The sepals curve backwards, and are sometimes toothed. The petals are large, heart-shaped, tissue-like and pink. There are many free carpels which are partially sunk in the hollow receptacle, and each carpel has a long style. These are insect-pollinated, though roses do not secrete honey. The insects are attracted by the delicate perfume of the flower (Fig. 18). After fertilisation, each carpel forms a small dry fruit covered with stiff hairs. These are called achenes, and are very like those of the buttercup (p. 38). As these ripen, the receptacle swells and encloses the fruit. Meanwhile the former turns red, and thus produces the well-known ' hips ' of the rose which, therefore, are not true fruit, but are swollen receptacles each enclosing several fruit in the form of achenes. (Plate 6.)

The hips of the dog-rose contain a high content of vitamin C, so today rose-hip syrup is a valuable preparation, especially for growing children.

There are several other wild roses, but none of them deviates from the dog-rose to any considerable degree. Some have white flowers, and others have smaller flowers. There are, for example, the **burnet rose** (R. *spinosissima*) with globular, black hips, the **sweet briar** or **eglantine** (R. *rubiginosa*) with leaves having a hairy under-surface, the **trailing rose** (R. *arvensis*), with styles united to form a column, and so forth. Several roses which have hitherto all been grouped under the species *Rosa canina* are now separated by botanists into distinct species.

Another genus of shrubby scramblers belonging to the rose family is that of *Rubus*, which includes the **bramble** or **blackberry** (R. *fruticosus*) (Plate 6) of which there are many varieties. This familiar plant scrambles and climbs by means of hooks on its stems and leaves, and it frequently reproduces itself vegetatively by means of stolons, as the gooseberry does (p. 127). So persistent is the bramble in this means of vegetative reproduction that it often becomes a weed, especially on arable land, for the scrambling branches are difficult to remove, since one often finds that they themselves have taken root where they touch the soil. In New Zealand especially, the bramble has proved to be a pest : it has been estimated that over there from a single plant 250 miles of brambles originated. There are many hybrids of this species even in this country.

The bramble was once used to bind down graves, to keep the grass in shape and protect it from browsing animals. The custom is mentioned several times in literature.

> [Little Nell] loitered from grave to grave, now stopping to replace with careful hands the bramble which had started from some green mound it helped to keep in shape.   *The Old Curiosity Shop* : DICKENS

The leaf of the bramble is divided into three leaflets (Plate 6), and on its stalk there are many hooks : frequently, also, these hooks appear on the backs of the veins of the leaflets.

The flowers are white or pink. They appear during July and August, borne in clusters towards the ends of flowering stalks which also are hooked.

The receptacle of the bramble flower, in contradistinction to that of the dog-rose, is slightly elevated. There are five free sepals, five free petals, many stamens and many carpels. The sepals, petals and stamens are inserted at the base of the slightly raised receptacle, so that the carpels come above them, which is the opposite to their position in the dog-rose.

After fertilisation, each carpel becomes covered with a soft, juicy covering and is called a drupe. Each fleshy drupe contains one seed. The whole familiar blackberry fruit is therefore a collection of drupes, which are at first hard and green, then softer and red and eventually juicy and black (Plate 6).

This luscious fruit is used for dessert, jams and jellies.

Closely related to the blackberry is the **dewberry** (R. *caesius*), each fruit of which is a collection of larger though fewer drupes, which are often covered with a bloom like that of the black grape. The **wild raspberry** (R. *idaeus*) differs in that its floral receptacle is more conical, and the drupes are red when ripe. There are several other wild relatives of the bramble, some of which are also cultivated (p. 145).

FIG. 67.—Blackthorn in Bloom.

TREES

Several wild genera of the rose family take the form of trees. These include the crab-apple, hawthorn or may, and the blackthorn or sloe.

The **blackthorn** or **sloe** belongs to the genus *Prunus* (P. *communis*). This tree is seen sometimes growing alone or in groups, but more often in hedgerows (Fig. 67). Its leaves are elliptical and simple, and the

Harold Bastin

stem bears thorns. The white flowers are usually born in pairs during April and May. The flower buds are formed during the August and September of the previous year, which explains why the flowers are open before the leaves appear. The same applies to the cultivated members of this genus, such as plum, cherry and almond.

The flower of the blackthorn is comparatively small, but similar to that of the rose, except that there is only one carpel in the sunken receptacle. After fertilisation, this ripens into a large, fleshy, black drupe, and the remains of the hollow receptacle wither away. The fruit is usually covered with a bloom. It is sometimes used for making jellies, and also in the preparation of the liqueur sloe gin. The dried leaves have been used for adulterating tea.

Related to the blackthorn is the **bird cherry** (*P. padus*), with flowers borne in pendulous clusters, sometimes found in woods, as is the **wild cherry** (*P. cerasus*) (Fig. 69), the forerunner of the cultivated cherry (p. 145). In early summer (April to June) these trees are an enthralling vision of white blossom.

> Loveliest of trees, the cherry now
> Is hung with bloom along the bough,
> And stands about the woodland side
> Wearing white for Eastertide.
>
> And since to look at things in bloom
> Fifty springs are little room,
> About the woodlands I will go
> To see the cherry hung with snow.
> *The Shropshire Lad*: A. E. HOUSMAN

The **hawthorn** or **may** is one of our most common hedgerow trees, though it is so often cut and trimmed as to take the form of a bushy shrub. When growing alone it attains the habit and height of a tree. It belongs to the next genus of rosaceous trees (*Crataegus*), and is the only wild representative of the genus in this country (*C. oxyacantha*). Some botanists recognise two British species of *Crataegus*. The wood of this plant is sometimes used as a substitute for box wood in engraving.

The thorns of the hawthorn are really modified branches, and are sometimes so large that they themselves bear lateral leaves. The leaf is simple, though very deeply indented. The flowers are white and borne in dense clusters. They make a lovely scene in the hedgerows during May and June (Fig. 68). The word 'hawthorn' signifies 'good hope', for the plant in flower signifies that summer is at hand.

Harold Bastin

FIG. 68.—Hawthorn or May.

Gives not the hawthorn-bush a sweeter shade
To shepherds looking on their silly sheep
Than doth a rich embroider'd canopy
To kings that fear their subjects' treachery ?

III Henry VI : SHAKESPEARE

K

Each flower has five sepals, five white petals, many stamens and one or two styles. The fruit is composed of a stony seed surrounded by the swollen receptacle which eventually turns dark red. It is sometimes called a 'haw'. Though edible, these haws are dry-eating and not very palatable; yet children sometimes eat them, and in certain parts of the United States they are used in jellies.

It is still believed by many that if the hawthorn haws and rose hips are borne in profusion then a hard winter lies ahead—and this in spite of no meteorological confirmation. But this lore is hundreds of years old.

> The thorns and briars, vermilion-hue,
>   Now full of hips and haws are seen;
> If village prophecies be true,
>   They prove that winter will be keen.
>
> *Autumn*: J. CLARE

The famous Glastonbury Thorn is a variety of the hawthorn (*C. oxyacantha* var. *praecox*), which flowers both in winter and in early summer. Legend has it that the original Glastonbury thorn sprang from the staff of Joseph of Arimathea who planted it in the grounds of Glastonbury Abbey, when he visited the Abbey with his eleven followers.

> Glastonbury, where the winter thorn blossoms at Christmas, mindful of our Lord.
>
> *The Holy Grail*: TENNYSON

This thorn is, however, probably nothing but a 'sport' from the common thorn, for, though cuttings from the original Glastonbury Thorn still bloom twice a year, those plants produced from its seeds revert to the ordinary type and bloom only once a year—in early summer.

An important genus in the rose family is *Malus*, which counts among its wild species the **crab-apple** (*M. pumila*), found growing in woods and hedges and flowering during May to August. The leaves are simple (Plate 6).

The flowers are pink and very lovely and are borne in clusters on short branch shoots.

> The apple blossoms' shower of pearl,
>   Though blent with rosier hue,
> As beautiful as a woman's blush,—
>   As evanescent too.
>
> *Apple Blossoms*: LETITIA E. LANDON

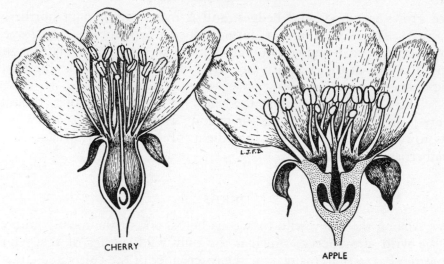

FIG. 69.—Sections through Cherry (left) and Apple (right) Flowers.

To each apple flower there are five sepals, five, free petals which are heart-shaped (Plate 6), many stamens and five carpels joined to form an ovary embedded in the base of a slightly hollow receptacle (Fig. 69). There are usually five styles.

The fruit is very well known (Plate 6), for the crab-apple is the direct forerunner of the many kinds of cultivated apple, which are only varieties of it. It is actually formed from the five joined fertilised carpels, which have horny walls enclosing the seeds (constituting the apple core), and the receptacle, which has swollen to form the fleshy edible part of the fruit. This fruit is called a pome.

Wild crabs are usually too acid to eat raw, but they make delicious jelly. In earlier days, crab-apples were used more often than now. They were often served in hot drinks and punches.

> When roasted crabs hiss in the bowl
> Then nightly sings the staring owl.
> *Love's Labour's Lost* : SHAKESPEARE

> And sometimes lurk I in a gossip's bowl
> In very likeness of a roasted crab.
> *Midsummer Night's Dream* : SHAKESPEARE

A common wild plant belonging to the genus *Sorbus* is the **rowan** or **mountain ash** (*S. aucuparia*), whose flowers are borne in dense clusters taking the form of round, flattened inflorescences. This tree grows in woods and hedges, and is more common in northerly regions. The flowers appear during June to September. The leaves are characteristic, being compound with leaflets arranged in six to eight pairs like that of the ordinary ash. The clusters of fruit take the form of conspicuous red berries.

These berries are seldom used now as an article of diet, though there is an old Scottish recipe for making a kind of marmalade which has rowan berries as its main ingredient. Birdlime is also made from the berries.

HERBS

Among the many wild rosaceous herbs, one of the most common is the **wild strawberry,** which is the only wild species of the genus *Fragaria* (*F. vesca*). This plant is the forerunner of the cultivated strawberry. In fact, the most familiar cultivated strawberries are nothing but enlarged varieties of the wild species (Fig. 70).

FIG. 70.—Wild Strawberry Plant showing Leaves, Flowers, Fruit and Runners—one forming a new Plant.

Harold Bastin

The wild strawberry grows on moist banks and on the edges of woods. The plant is a small herb, with characteristic leaves, each divided into three toothed leaflets (Plate 6). It reproduces itself vegetatively by means of runners. These are branch stems. The runner becomes elongated, and where a node touches the ground it gives off adventitious roots, while the axiliary bud grows into a new, upright shoot. Thus a new plant is formed. Gardeners take advantage of this, and often guide the runner on to a pot and peg the node down to the soil. Once the new plant has become established in the pot, the runner can be severed and the new plant transplanted as required.

The flowers of the wild strawberry open during May to July. There are five large sepals, and alternating with these are five smaller ones collectively forming what is called an epicalyx (p. 119). The five petals are white. The stamens are numerous; so are the carpels. The arrangement of the carpels is almost the opposite of that in the rose, so that the resulting 'fruit' structure is also. In the rose, the receptacle is hollow, whereas in the strawberry it is raised and conical. The carpels of the rose ripen into small, hard achenes, and so do those of the strawberry; but in the latter they are borne on the outside of a swollen receptacle, whereas in the former they are enclosed by the receptacle. The receptacle of the strawberry eventually becomes juicy and red. Therefore the so-called strawberry 'fruit' is not a true fruit, but is the swollen, juicy, receptacle bearing many small hard fruits (not seeds) in the form of achenes on its surface (Plate 6).

The 'fruit' of the wild strawberry, though small, is delicious to eat.

Closely related to the genus *Fragaria* is the genus *Potentilla*, which contains several common wild plants such as the barren strawberry, silver-weed, creeping cinquefoil, tormentil, and so forth. In all these cases, the main difference between them and the wild strawberry is that the receptacle is small and dry. Apart from this, the plants are very similar to the wild strawberry, though the leaves vary somewhat, and the flowers are most often yellow.

The **barren strawberry** (*Potentilla fragariastrum*) grows on dry banks and produces its white flowers early (March to May). It has no runners.

The **Silver-weed** (*P. anserina*) grows in very dry situations. In fact it can sometimes be seen actually growing in the roads and lanes, but it is more frequently seen growing in waste places.

This plant reproduces itself by means of creeping stems (Plate 6). The leaves are divided into many leaflets each of which is also finely divided so that the whole leaf resembles a fern (Plate 6). On the under surface of the leaf there is a soft, silky hairy covering giving the silvery appearance which explains the common name of the plant. The flowers are yellow and appear during June and July, the fruit are achenes, and the receptacle dry (Plate 6).

The roots of silver-weed, when roasted or boiled, are like parsnips. Treated in this way they are frequently eaten in the Hebrides.

The **creeping cinquefoil** (*P. reptans*) has a flower and fruit very like those of the silver weed (Plate 6). It also reproduces itself vegetatively by means of creeping stems. The leaf is divided into five

toothed leaflets arranged like the palm of a hand (Plate 6) : this explains
the common name. The creeping cinquefoil grows in meadows and
waysides and flowers during June to September.

The **tormentil** (*P. tormentilla*) grows on moors and heaths. Its
leaves are divided into three leaflets (rarely five). The flowers are borne
in loose inflorescences. The number of petals is four—an exception in
this family.

The **salad burnet,** commonly found growing in dry pastures,
belongs to a genus of its own (*Poterium sanguisorba*) since it has unisexual
flowers, though both male and female grow on the same plant, all together in a roundish head, the upper, female flowers showing crimson
tufted styles, and the lower, male, flowers having long stamens. The
leaves are very like those of the silver weed. A near genus is represented by the **great burnet** (*Sanguisorba officinalis*) of moist meadows.
Some Floras place both the burnets in the genus *Sanguisorba*, and in this
case salad burnet is designated *S. minor*.

The leaves of both burnets make excellent green salads.

The **common agrimony** (*Agrimonia eupatoria*) is the only wild
member of this next genus. It grows on banks and in hedgerows and
exhibits attractive spikes of yellow flowers during June to August
(Plate 6). It has certain medicinal virtues and at one time was used for
the treatment of many complaints.

The leaf of the agrimony is strange in that it is composed of seven
to nine large, toothed leaflets, and interspersed between these on the
same leaf-stalk are several small ones of varying size (Plate 6).

The small yellow flowers are borne on a stiff, long, pyramidal
spike, the lower flowers opening first (Plate 6). The flower is similar
in structure to that of the rose, but it has only one or two carpels.
The resulting fruit is surrounded by a tuft of hooks growing out from
the edge of the receptacle (Plate 6), and by means of these hooks the
fruit clings to browsing animals and is thus distributed.

Closely related to *Agrimonia* is the genus *Geum*, to which belong
the wood avens or herb Bennet and the water avens.

The **wood avens** or **herb Bennet** (*Geum urbanum*) is a tall plant,
frequently seen growing in hedges and flowering during June to
August. The leaves are large, deeply toothed and lobed (Plate 6).
There are usually five sepals with an alternating smaller epicalyx, five
bright yellow petals, many stamens and many carpels. After fertilisation, the carpels develop into dry, hairy achenes, each with a long
hooked awn at its tip (Plate 6). This awn is curious : in the unfertilised

carpel it is extended but with a kink in it, but after ripening, that part above the kink drops off (Plate 6).

Water avens (*G. rivale*) is a larger plant which grows in marshy places and on river banks. The flowers are larger than those of the wood avens and they droop. The petals are orange-bronze, and the sepals purple.

The purplish roots of the water avens are aromatic, and in parts of the United States they are used as a substitute for cocoa. For this reason the plant is sometimes called ' chocolate root ' by Americans.

The genus *Alchemilla* comprises plants which bear their minute flowers in large, densely packed inflorescences. There are a few wild representatives of the genus in this country, two of which are **lady's mantle** (*A. vulgaris*) of hilly pastures, and **parsley piert** (*A. arvensis*) of fields and woods. The lady's mantle was the alchemist's plant (hence its generic name), and was so called because the alchemists collected the dew from it for their experiments.

The rose family contains the true *Spiraea* genus (see p. 77). The wild representative of this is the lovely **meadow-sweet** or **queen of the meadow** (*S. ulmaria*) (Plate 6). This is a tall plant, usually found growing in dense masses by the sides of rivers and ponds or in ditches or on the edges of very damp woods. It flowers during July to September.

The stem of the meadow-sweet is stiff and reddish in colour, often attaining a height of four to five feet. The leaf, like that of the agrimony, is subdivided into large toothed leaflets, interspersed with some much smaller ones (Plate 6).

The flowers are very small and cream or white. They are borne in dense inflorescences which collectively are very conspicuous. The flower emits an overpowering perfume which is the means of attracting insects, for there is no nectar. The carpels ripen to form follicles which are capable of splitting to release the enclosed seeds.

The **dropwort** (*S. filipendula*) is not so common. All its leaflets are uniform and the clustered flowers are yellowish cream.

ORNAMENTAL PLANTS

SHRUBS AND TREES

The ornamental members of the rose family are probably known to more people than are the wild ones, for they are such great favourites, not only in our parks and gardens, but also for indoor and personal adornment. To many, the garden rose is the queen of flowers.

> The cowslip is a country wench
> The violet is a nun ;
> But I will woo the dainty rose,
> The queen of every one.
>
> *Flowers* : HOOD

So universal a favourite is the **garden rose** (Fig. 71) that it is not possible to consider here all the species, subspecies and varieties of it which are now under cultivation. These could only be considered in a book specially written on them, just as very often a part of the garden is set aside specially for their cultivation. The many British garden roses probably originated from about twelve species. There are standard, bush, climbing and rambling roses, some single, but most of them double, and the shades of colour are legion. Some are delicately perfumed, others are not. Frequently in the rose can one see transitional stages between sepals and petals, petals and stamens—a phenomenon often occurring in cultured so-called ' double ' flowers. The artificial method of vegetative reproduction, namely, budding, is practiced in rose culture more than in the cultivation of any other plant (Fig. 65). The briars on which buds are usually grafted are those of the dog-rose (*Rosa canina*).

Attar of roses is extracted from the species R. *damascena* (the **damask rose**), cultivated in fields, chiefly in Balkan countries. Rose water also is prepared from this species and from the old-fashioned white cabbage rose (R. *centifolia*).

Certain species of *Rubus* are also sometimes cultivated for ornamental purposes.

Several genera and species of trees of the rose family are grown solely for their beauty.

Included in the genus *Prunus* are the **cherry laurel** (*P. laurocerasus*) and other species of laurel. These are usually cultivated in shrubberies for their handsome habit and foliage. The variegated Japanese laurel (*Aucuba*) must not be confused with the true laurels, for it belongs to a different plant family (CORNACEAE). Other early-flowering species of *Prunus* frequently seen in parks, gardens and town streets are the many varieties of single and double **almonds** (*P. amygdalus* varieties), the **Japanese cherry** (*P. serrulata*), other flowering cherries, and so forth. The double flowering cherries in Kew Gardens make a never-to-be-forgotten sight when in bloom.

Fig. 71.—Garden Roses.

Among the species of *Malus* are the **flowering crabs** (*M. pumila*) of which there are several varieties. Then the **mountain ash** (*Sorbus aucuparia*) makes a handsome tree, and its red berries are a welcome sight during the drabness of winter. Its leaves also frequently turn bright red. Closely related species which are sometimes found wild, but more often cultivated, are the many varieties of **service tree** (*S. torminalis*) and the **white beam** (*S. aria*). The very attractive **japonica**, frequently seen displaying its scarlet or crimson flowers against walls, is *Chaenomeles japonica*.

The **hawthorn** or **may** is another garden favourite, usually grown separately or in hedges, and displaying masses of red or white single or double flowers.

Cotoneaster is a genus which, though seldom seen wild in Great Britain, has given several species and varieties to our flower gardens. The shrubs or trees may be deciduous or evergreen. They are of particular value because their clusters of flowers give very conspicuous bunches of red berries to adorn the winter garden. Some weeping varieties of this genus are also cultivated.

The genus *Amelanchier* comprises several species of trees and shrubs which bear white flowers and crimson or purple fruit.

HERBS

Outstanding among the cultivated ornamental genera of rosaceous herbs is *Geum*. The species and varieties of this are favourite border plants, having large red, yellow or orange flowers. Some of them are partially double.

Some species of *Potentilla* are cultivated, usually in rock gardens. Their flowers are either red or yellow. The related *Poterium obtusum* has lovely rose-coloured flowers.

Other genera have been imported into our gardens from other lands.

Species of *Acaena*, from Mexico and California, make good carpet plants, having reddish flowers with attractive foliage—bluish-green, orange or purplish in colour.

ECONOMIC PLANTS

Most of the economic plants of the rose family belong to the genera *Malus*, *Pyrus*, *Prunus*, *Rubus* and *Fragaria*. Here again, as in the case of

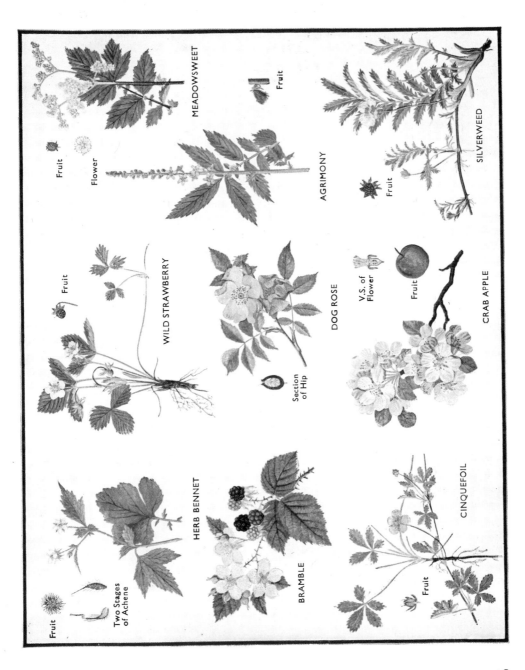

MEADOWSWEET

Fruit

Flower

AGRIMONY

Fruit

SILVERWEED

Fruit

WILD STRAWBERRY

DOG ROSE

Section
of Hip

V.S. of
Flower

Fruit

CRAB APPLE

Fruit

Two Stages
of Achene

HERB BENNET

BRAMBLE

CINQUEFOIL

Fruit

PLATE 6

roses, so important has the culture of these plants become that a detailed consideration of the subject would demand a book in itself.

Then there are the **pear** (*P. communis*) and the **medlar** (*Mespilus germanica*). The latter is not so popular now as it was at one time, though sometimes it is used in making jellies. The apple (*Malus pumila*) is very popular.

All are used as dessert and for other table purposes. From certain varieties of apple, cider is made, and perry is made from the pear.

Eric Hosking

FIG. 72.—Apple Blossom.

Among members of the genus *Prunus* are the **plum** (*P. domestica*), **damson** (*P. inistitia*), **sloe** (*P. spinosa*), **cherry** (*P. cerasus*). Other familiar fruit belong to this genus, but they are exotics, and, except in some greenhouses, are seldom seen under cultivation in Great Britain, though outdoor peaches will thrive if placed in well-protected positions. They are the **prune** (a variety of *P. domestica*), **peach** (*P. persica*), **apricot** (*P. armeniaca*) and **sweet** and **bitter almonds** (*P. amygdalus*).

The **blackberry** (*Rubus fruticosus*), though wild, is often cultivated in this country. Other cultivated species of *Rubus* are the **dewberry** (*R. caesius*), the **raspberry** (*R. idaeus*), which reproduces itself by means of suckers which are shoots given off from the creeping roots, and the **loganberry**, which is considered to be a hybrid of the blackberry and raspberry, though some doubt has been cast on this.

Perhaps the most favoured of all rosaceous edible fruits are those of the **strawberry** (*Fragaria vesca*).

One of the chiefest doctors of England was wont to say that God could have made, but God never did make, a better berry.

Key into the Language of America : ROGER WILLIAMS

Dr. William Butler's botany was at fault, for the fruit of the strawberry is not a berry (p. 139). But no doubt many will agree with the sentiment. Alas, this 'fruit' has a very short season, and will not keep except as a preserve.

31

THE PEA FAMILY
(Leguminosae)
(see frontispiece)

Like that of the rose family, the pea family (LEGUMINOSAE) is a very large one. It is also very cosmopolitan in distribution; in fact, more so than the rose family, for many of its members are tropical, whereas few of the rose family are. Most members of the pea family bear very handsome flowers; some people, indeed hold the sweet pea in higher esteem than the garden rose. Again, like the rose family, the pea family gives us a number of important food plants; but although the parts of the plant eaten are the same as those of the rose family, namely, the fruit, and sometimes the seed, whereas the rosaceous fruits are treated as such and served as dessert or sweet or some other confection, the leguminous fruits and seeds are treated as 'vegetables' from the culinary point of view.

The greatest distinction between the pea and the rose lies in the flower. Whereas that of the rose is regular, that of the pea is irregular in that it can be divided into two symmetrical halves along one plane only. All members of the pea family found growing wild in this country are irregular like this, but certain tropical members have regular flowers.

The flowers of all British members of the pea family are based on a common plan, described on pp. 23 and 24 and illustrated in Fig. 13. There are five united sepals separating into five teeth at the tips. There may be five regularly arranged teeth, or the calyx may be two-lipped, with two teeth at the top and three at the bottom. The petals show the greatest irregularity, having a large standard at the back, two side wings, and two smaller petals forming the keel at the bottom. This floral form gives a butterfly effect, so all very irregular members of the family are sometimes placed in a sub-family called the PAPILIONACEAE.

There are ten stamens united along about two-thirds of their length and forming a tube around the carpels, as in the broom and gorse; in other genera nine of the stamens are so joined, but the tenth—the upper one—is free along its entire length, as in the bird's-foot trefoil and the vetches (Fig. 17).

The single carpel contains one to several ovules, and the fruit formed after fertilisation is the very characteristic pod or legume. The legume splits in varying ways to eject the ripe seeds.

The roots of most members of the pea family exhibit extraordinary swellings called tubercles or nodules (Fig. 73). These are of considerable value to the plant, for they contain millions of microscopic bacteria which are capable of 'fixing' atmospheric nitrogen (obtained from the air-spaces in the soil) and converting this into nitrogen compounds, chiefly nitrates,

By courtesy of U.S. Bureau of Plant Industry

FIG. 73.—A Clover Plant showing Root Nodules.

which the plant is then able to absorb for its own use. The ordinary green plant, though it needs nitrogen, is unable to absorb the free nitrogen from the atmosphere and has to depend on getting it from the nitrates present in the soil. For this reason, leguminous plants, especially clover, are frequently planted on arable land and in gardens, and when they are at their best are dug into the soil, thereby enriching it with a supply of more nitrates.

WILD PLANTS

All British wild members of the pea family are either herbs or shrubs (chiefly the former), and all of them belong to the sub-family PAPILIONACEAE, that is, their flowers are very irregular.

The **common broom** (Plate 7) belongs to the genus *Cytisus*, which is indigenous to Britain. The broom is *Cytisus scoparius*.

It is a handsome, quick-growing shrub inhabiting heaths and hillsides, and bearing its golden yellow flowers during May and June. The leaves are small, the lower ones being compound and composed of three leaflets (trifoliate); the upper ones are simple.

The calyx of the flower is two-lipped. The standard of the petals is comparatively large. All ten stamens are joined. The flower contains no honey, but bees visit it for its pollen. The bee alights on the keel and pushes the petals apart, and in so doing receives a shower of pollen from the stamens. After its visit, the petals remain apart with the withered style and stamens exposed. Thus the next potential insect visitor is warned in time that there is no pollen to be had there.

The pod is black or reddish-brown (Plate 7), and when ripe it splits open suddenly, thus releasing the seeds.

The only common wild member of the next genus, *Ulex*, is the **gorse, furze** or **whin** (*U. europaeus*) (Fig. 74). This is a shrub which adorns our heaths, hillsides and railway embankments, its masses of golden blossom making a brave show during two seasons of the year, namely, February and March, August and September, though frequently

Eric Hosking

FIG. 74.—A Gorse Bush in Flower.

one sees some flowers in bloom all the year round, hence the saying, 'When the gorse is out of bloom, kissing's out of fashion'. The sight of masses of golden gorse on sometimes the most barren heath must have brought pleasure to thousands. It is said that Linnaeus when he visited England was so overcome by a scene of gorse blooming on a common that he fell on his knees and thanked God.

> Mountain gorses, since Linnaeus
> Knelt beside you on the sod,
> For your beauty thanking God,—
> For your teaching, ye should see us
> Bowing in prostration new !
> *Lessons from the Gorse* : E. B. BROWNING

The gorse is curious in that it seems to decide to protect itself from browsing animals rather late in its individual life. The leaves of the young seedling are trifoliate, like those of the broom (Plate 7) ; but, as the plant grows, all its leaves are modified to spines and even bear branch spines in their axils. Thus we have branches of spines borne in the axils of lateral spines (Plate 7). This reduction of the leaves to spines is of double advantage, for not only does it mean an effective protection to the plant against animals, but it also means a diminution in water-loss—of considerable benefit to a plant which grows in dry situations.

The flowers and the fruit of the gorse are similar to those of the broom. The pods split with a distinct ' pop ' to eject their seeds ; this ' popping ' can be easily heard during a hot, dry summer day—for the pods must be dry in order to split (Plate 7).

> Love you not, then, to list and hear
> The crackling of the gorse-flower near,
> Pouring an orange-scented tide
> Of fragrance o'er the desert wide ?
> *A June Day* : W. HOWITT

The **needle-whin** belongs to a different genus (*Genista anglica*) (Plate 7). It has very small leaves, and its flowers are borne in rather dense inflorescences at the ends of the stems, while those of the gorse are more distributed. The plant has needle-shaped spines. Closely related to it is the **dyer's green weed** (*G. tinctoria*), found growing in thickets and having lance-shaped leaves with flowers borne in slender inflorescences, each flower in the axil of a bract. There are no spines. A yellow dye is obtained from this flower, and when it is mixed with woad (*Isatis tinctoria*, see p. 63), it gives the valuable green dye known as Kendal green.

There are many different vetches, and most of them belong either to the genus *Vicia* (p. 153) or to the genus *Lathyrus* (p. 154) : but there are some vetches sufficiently different from either of these two genera to warrant being placed in two other genera. The **milk vetch** (*Astragalus glycyphyllos*) grows in fields and copses and flowers during June to September. The leaf is compound, with leaflets arranged in about eleven pairs along a common leaf-stalk. The flowers are borne in compact inflorescences and are cream in colour. The tenth stamen of the flower is free. A related species (*A. hypoglottis*) is not so common. It grows on heaths and bears its purple flowers in dense spikes. Certain other species belonging to this genus which grow wild in the United States (but not in this country) are sometimes eaten. In some cases, the whole green pod is boiled and served as a green vegetable ; in others it is boiled and spiced, then used as a pickle.

The **kidney vetch** belongs to another genus (*Anthyllis vulneraria*). It is common and blooms on dry pastures during June to August (Plate 7). The leaf of this plant also has about four pairs of leaflets and a terminal one. The pale yellow flowers are borne in dense heads at the ends of long flower-stalks. The dense inflorescence is supported by two deeply serrated bracts (Plate 7). The tenth stamen is free, and the fruit is a one-seeded pod. Note that, unlike most of the other vetches, neither the kidney nor the milk vetches are climbers and therefore they have no tendrils.

To the genus *Ononis* belong the two species of rest-harrow. The only difference between the two species is that the **spiny rest-harrow** (*O. spinosa*) has some spines and the stem is erect, whereas the **common rest-harrow** (*O. arvensis*) has no spines and the stem is decumbent. Sometimes both species are found growing together on heaths and moors and displaying their lovely pink, pea-like flowers during June to September. The leaves are simple or trifoliate (Plate 7). All ten stamens are joined. The pod is swollen and contains a small number of seeds.

Several fodder crops belong to the genus *Medicago*, which is represented in the wild state by the **medick** or **nonsuch** (*M. lupulina*). This plant also makes good fodder. It is small and grows in profusion in fields and waste places. The flowers are small and yellow and are borne in compact, almost spherical heads. The explosive pod contains only one seed. The Californian Indians relish the seeds of the nonsuch.

The fragrant **tall melilot** (*Melilotus officinalis*) is an attractive plant, and is frequently found growing in fields and along waysides. The yellow flowers appear in long inflorescences during June to August (Plate 7). The leaf is trifoliate and has two stipules at its base (Plate 7). The flower contains much nectar. The tenth stamen is free. The pod is green and somewhat hairy and is covered with reticulate markings (Plate 7). A white variety of this plant (*M. alba*) may also be found growing wild, but it is rather rare.

In the very important genus *Trifolium* are the clovers and most of the trefoils.

The two most common clovers are the **red clover** (*T. pratense*) and the **white** or **Dutch clover** (*T. repens*). Both are common meadow plants (Fig. 75) and spread vegetatively. They are valuable fodder crops. Both flower during May to September, and apart from the fact that the white clover is of a somewhat smaller habit of growth and has white instead of purple flowers, both plants are similar (Plate 7).

The foliage leaf is typically trifoliate, and this is the reason why the clover is sometimes called the shamrock. Tradition has it that St. Patrick used the three leaflets to illustrate the Trinity; but more people favour the association of the wood sorrel with this tradition than the clover (see p. 97). Some of the leaves grow from ground-level, others from the flower-

Henry Irving

FIG. 75.—White or Dutch Clover, a good Fodder Plant.

L

stalks. Paler green bands appear on each leaflet. There are two stipules at the base of the leaf-stalk. The leaflets close up at night (p. 97).

The flowers of the clover are borne in dense, almost spherical heads. The wings and keel of the flower together form a tube at the base, so that only long-tongued insects such as bees are able to get at the nectar situated at the base of the flower (Plate 7). The supplies of nectar in the clover are especially high. Children frequently suck the ends of the flowers because they are so sweet.

> The pedigree of honey
> Does not concern the bee;
> A clover, any time, to him
> Is aristocracy.
> *Poems*: EMILY DICKINSON

Other species of clover and trefoil are: the **hare's-foot trefoil** (*T. arvense*), having cylindrical pink heads and growing in dry pastures; the **slender yellow trefoil** (*T. filiforme*), with yellow flowers in a loose head, also of dry pastures; the **hop trefoil** (*T. procumbens*), with yellow flowers borne many together in hop-like heads, also of dry pastures; the **lesser yellow trefoil** (*T. minus*), of pastures; the **strawberry clover** (*T. fragiferum*), with red flowers in small spherical heads, of meadows and ditches; the **knotted clover** (*T. striatum*), with small, pale red flowers in ovoid heads, also of dry pastures.

The well-known **bird's-foot trefoil** belongs to a different genus (*Lotus corniculatus*), which must not be confused with the true lotus of the water-lily family (p. 50). Neither must it be associated with the lotus eaters of Homer's *Odyssey*, for their fruit came from a tree. The bird's-foot trefoil is a very graceful plant and grows in fields and along waysides, presenting its golden-yellow flowers during July and August. The leaves are trifoliate (Plate 7). The yellow flowers are borne in loose heads, with five to ten flowers to each head (Plate 7). The tenth stamen is free (Fig. 17). The keel is united above and below with a small apical opening. The pollen is shed while the flower is still in bud. Then, as the flower opens, the filaments of five of the stamens begin to swell and act as a piston in pushing the mass of pollen out through the apical opening of the keel, thus smothering the stigma of the style. Self-pollination is therefore ensured, but cross-pollination sometimes also takes place. The pods when ripe hang from the old flower-head in a way resembling a bird's foot. This plant is known in some localities as **Tom thumb** and **fingers and thumbs.**

There is a rarer **narrow-leaved bird's-foot trefoil** (*L. major*) the stems of which are erect whereas those of the ordinary bird's-foot trefoil are procumbent.

Most of the many vetches in this country belong either to the genus *Vicia* or the genus *Lathyrus*. Both these genera are important because they are the forerunners of some of our kitchen and flower garden inhabitants, for example, the broad bean and the sweet pea. Both genera produce tendrils by which the plants climb.

FIG. 76.—Tufted Vetch.

The genus *Vicia* has compound leaves with several opposite pairs of lateral leaflets and the terminal leaflet (sometimes including some lateral leaflets) modified to a tendril like that of the garden pea (*Pisum*) (Fig. 13). In the genus *Lathyrus*, the number of leaflets is sometimes reduced and the rest of the leaflets (including the terminal one) modified to form several tendrils; sometimes the whole leaf is modified to form tendrils, and the stipules enlarged considerably in order to carry on the main functions of the leaf blade; again, in certain cases, the leaflets have disappeared altogether and there are no tendrils, but the leaf-stalk becomes flattened and looks like a leaf-blade.

In the flowers of *Vicia*, the tenth stamen is free, and the style is hairy. The pollen is shed in the flower at an early stage, and the hairy brush on the style forces the pollen out on to the body of the insect visitor as it depresses the keel when it alights.

Many common vetches belong to the genus *Vicia*: the **common vetch** (*V. sativa*) is a good fodder plant, with large blue flowers borne in pairs, seen growing in fields and blooming during May and June. The **bush vetch** (*V. sepium*) is a conspicuous and common hedgerow climber, displaying its purple flowers during May to August. The **wood vetch** (*V. sylvatica*) shows its white flowers with blue veins during June to August. The **tufted vetch** (*V. cracca*), of hedges and fields, bears its blue flowers in dense inflorescences during June and July (Fig. 76). The **hairy tare** (*V. hirsuta*) also appears at this time with long inflorescences of few flowers. There are several other common vetches.

> And where profuse the wood-vetch clings
> Round ash and elm, in verdant rings,
> Its pale and azure-pencilled flower
> Should canopy Titania's bower.
>
> *Rokeby* : SCOTT

The American Indians relish some vetches. Both they and some Europeans eat the seeds, even raw.

The genus *Lathyrus* contains plants with leaves showing varying degrees of modification. The flowers in general resemble those of *Vicia*, and may be purple or yellow. The **meadow vetch** (*L. pratensis*) grows in meadows and in hedges, and its yellow flowers appear during June to September. There is one pair of leaflets and one pair of large stipules, and the rest of the leaf takes the form of short tendrils. The **grass vetch** (*L. nissolia*) is rare, but it is interesting because its leaflets have completely disappeared and the leaf-stalks have become flattened expansions. Thus it resembles some species of *Acacia* (p. 159). Its flowers are purple. The **tuberous bitter vetch** (*L. macrorrhizus*) appears in bloom during May to July in thickets and copses. There are two or four pairs of leaflets and some tendrils. The flowers are crimson and borne on long-stalked inflorescences.

ORNAMENTAL PLANTS

In flower gardens, parks and greenhouses we are able to see not only the papilionaceous members of the pea family (PAPILIONACEAE), but also some of those with regular flowers, such as the *Mimosa* (sometimes placed in the sub-family MIMOSACEAE), and others whose flowers are not quite regular but very nearly so, such as *Caesalpinia* (placed in the sub-family CAESALPINIACEAE).

PAPILIONACEAE

The mere mention of ornamental peas conjures up into the mind visions of the very lovely **sweet pea**. This plant belongs to the genus *Lathyrus*, and its seductive perfume obviously inspired its specific name (*L. odoratus*). The butterfly-like character of the flowers, the tall nature of the whole plant, and the clinging habit of the tendrils inspired the poet to describe them thus :

FIG. 77.—Sweet Pea.

Here are sweet peas, on tiptoe for a flight;
With wings of gentle flush o'er delicate white,
And taper fingers catching at all things,
To bind them all about with tiny rings.

I Stood Tiptoe upon a Little Hill : KEATS

The sweet pea is an annual and is typical of the genus *Lathyrus* (p. 154) (Fig. 77). The flowers vary in size and number in each inflorescence; but the gardener seeking blooms for exhibition usually goes for the largest flowers with the greatest number per stalk. There are smooth-edged, frilled and picotee varieties. The many shades of colour are well-known to most of us.

The **everlasting pea** (*L. latifolius*) is not so popular now as it used to be, though it is still seen growing in cottage gardens. It is even more like an enlarged vetch, with big, many-flowered purple inflorescences. It is not much perfumed. It spreads rapidly.

The popularity of the perennial garden **lupin** (*Lupinus* species) has increased considerably during the last several decades, so that hybridisation and other experiments have produced some very lovely varieties of this border plant. Most perennial lupins are varieties of the species *Lupinus polyphyllus*. The genus is closely related to that of the medick (*Lotus*), and the explosive mechanism of the pod is similar. The flowers are borne in long, very dense, conspicuous spikes, and when cultivated *en masse* they present a striking picture (Fig. 78). Not satisfied with the very lovely shades of lupin they have already given us, the

FIG. 78.—A Border of Lupins.

horticulturists have now produced specimens with flowers of one colour, such as red or blue, at the base of the spike, shading to white or other colours at the top. Others have two or more different colours in each flower, such as a red standard and blue wings and keel, or white standards with blue wings and keel, and so forth. Unfortunately, many of these hybrids revert to the old blue type after a few generations.

There are also several species of annual lupins of different hues and delicately scented. Then the tall, perennial tree lupin (*L. arboreus*) grows to a height of six feet with yellow or mauve flowers.

Several species of *Genista* are cultivated. Most of them are of shrubby habit and bear yellow flowers. Some species of *Trifolium*, too, are grown in the flower garden.

Many species and varieties of broom (*Cytisus*) are to be found growing in gardens and parks. Some of these shrubs are so densely covered with flowers as to make veritable clouds of colour, which range from white through shades of yellow, orange and crimson to garnet.

Though there are no leguminous trees growing wild in this country, several very familiar forms are to be seen under cultivation. Perhaps the most common is the **laburnum** (*Laburnum anagyroides*), whose

FIG. 79.—*Wistaria.*

lovely yellow flowers hang in long pendulous inflorescences often called ' golden chains '. The flower is similar to that of *Trifolium*. All parts of this tree are poisonous.

A rarer tree is that of the curious *Cytisus adami*, which is actually a graft-hybrid. The stock was that of *Laburnum anagyroides* and the scion of *Cytisus purpureus*. The result is that there are yellow and purplish flowers growing simultaneously on the same tree.

One of the most beautiful deciduous climbing trees in existence is *Wistaria sinensis*, which was originally imported from China (Fig. 79). Some varieties of this plant can be trained as standard weepers. The flowers are similar to that of the laburnum except that they are mauve, purple or white according to the species, and their long chains exude a seductive perfume especially in the evening. Some of these chains attain a length of two to three feet.

The **locust** or **false acacia** (*Robinia pseud-acacia*) is also now finding much favour among gardeners and park-keepers. The flowers hang in pendulous chains, frequently sweet-smelling and varying in shades of white and pink according to the variety. The two stipules at the base of the compound leaves are modified into spines. Other species of *Robinia* are now cultivated here.

CAESALPINIACEAE

Certain members of this sub-family, with flowers much less irregular than that of the pea, are now cultivated in Great Britain, either in sheltered positions or in greenhouses. *Caesalpinia japonica*, a deciduous shrub from Japan, has branches covered with spines, graceful fern-like foliage, and masses of golden yellow flowers. The five petals are heart-shaped, but the upper one is inside the rest and somewhat larger. The **peacock flower** or **Barbados pride** (*C. pulcherrima*) is also sometimes cultivated for its ornamental beauty.

Species of *Gleditschia*, from sub-tropical Asia and America, are sometimes grown for their long fern-like foliage which turns yellow in the autumn. These plants are covered with true thorns, which are really branch stems borne in the axils of leaves. The plants make useful hedges provided they are in a sheltered position. The North American **honey locust** (*G. triacanthos*) bears characteristic reddish-brown three-forked thorns. The brown pods are more than a foot long, and between the many seeds is a succulent sweet pulp, which is **edible**.

MIMOSACEAE

This is the sub-family of the LEGUMINOSAE with quite regular flowers. To it belongs the genus *Mimosa*, one species of which (*M. pudica*) is the **sensitive plant,** sometimes found in greenhouses. Its leaves are very sensitive to external stimuli such as touch or heat. Each leaf-stalk has four secondary leaf-stalks on which are borne several pairs of leaflets. If one leaflet is touched, or a lighted match brought near it, the pairs of leaflets begin to close upwards, then the four secondary leaf-stalks close upwards, and eventually the main leaf-stalk bends downwards through an angle of about 60°. All this takes place in a matter of seconds. Later the leaf regains its original position provided the stimulus has been removed. The leaf moves in this way under the stimulus of intensity of light also, so it is closed at night.

The **mimosa** which is seen in shops with masses of small yellow flowers and compound leaves composed of many small leaflets is not a true *Mimosa*, but the true *Acacia*. The most favoured species is *A. dealbata*, the Australian **silver wattle**. Its leaves are silvery and fern-like ; the flowers small, yellow, and sweetly scented. Each flower is quite regular, with usually many stamens.

ECONOMIC PLANTS

An exceptionally large number of members of the pea family are cultivated for various economic purposes, chiefly for human or animal food ; in fact, so many different edible leguminous plants are cultivated throughout the world that we must confine ourselves mostly to those with which we are familiar in this country.

The **garden pea** belongs to still another genus, *Pisum*, and the one most commonly cultivated in our gardens is *Pisum sativum*. All varieties are annual, some fruiting early and others late ; some are dwarf and need no support, others are medium and need short support, while others are strong, tall climbers, which need supports five to six feet high. The leaves are similar to those of some species of *Vicia* (Fig. 80), with two to four pairs of large leaflets and several tendrils. The greenish-white flowers are similar in structure to that of the purple *Lathyrus*. In fact, on very rare occasions, purple pea flowers may appear. The fruit-pods, if allowed to ripen, split and then each half suddenly makes a spiral twist, thus ejecting the seeds.

FIG. 80.—Garden Pea in Fruit
(Sutton's 'Foremost')

The **broad bean** is closely related to the *Vicia* vetches; it actually belongs to the same genus—*Vicia faba*. There are many varieties, in all of which the flowers are white with black patches on them. The seeds are about seven to a pod and are flat and kidney-shaped.

The Mexican genus, *Phaseolus*, though not native to this country, has supplied some popular kitchen-garden examples, such as the **scarlet runner bean** and **haricot bean**, and the **French, kidney** or **dwarf bean.** Runners and haricots are varieties of *P. multiflorus*, whereas the dwarf is a variety of *P. vulgaris*. The leaves of this genus are compound and trifoliate, each leaflet being very large, heart-shaped and pointed at the tip (Fig. 81). The flowers may be scarlet or white. These plants have no tendrils, but some climb by twining.

Various species of clover (*Trifolium*), chiefly the red and the white clover, are cultivated for fodder, and frequently stored in silos for the winter and early spring. This underlies the expression ' he is in clover ' meaning to be prosperous, like cattle feeding in a clover field. The medick (*Medicago lupulina*) and the lucerne (*M. sativa*) are also cultivated for fodder. The latter is the familiar **alfalfa** of the United States. **Sainfoin** (*Onobrychis sativa*) (Plate 7) is another useful fodder plant. This was introduced into Britain from the Continent in the seventeenth century and now may sometimes be found growing wild. The name is derived from the French and means ' wholesome hay '.

A host of different leguminous plants are cultivated in other lands. The **soy bean** (*Glycine max* and *G. hispida*) is of Japanese origin; but varieties of it are now cultivated in other countries, especially the United States, where it is of great economic value. The seeds are eaten and produce a valuable flour which is now being utilised in this country,

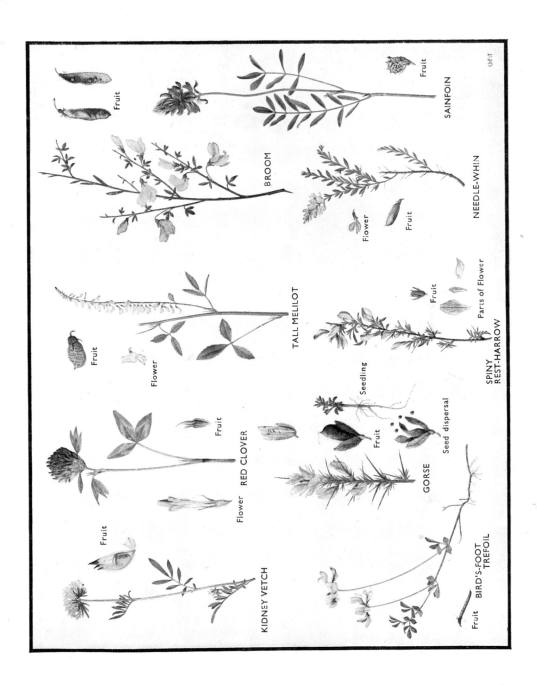

FruitFruitFruitFruit

SAINFOIN

BROOM

FlowerFruit

NEEDLE-WHIN

Fruit

Flower

TALL MELILOT

Fruit

Parts of Flower

SPINY
REST-HARROW

Seedling

Fruit

RED CLOVER

Flower

Fruit

Flower

Fruit

Seed dispersal

GORSE

Fruit

KIDNEY VETCH

Fruit BIRD'S-FOOT
TREFOIL

PLATE 7

even in sausages. Oil is also extracted from them. Furthermore, the green stems and leaves are used as fodder.

Phaseolus mungo, and its variety *radiatus,* are the highly valued **pulses** (or **grams**) and horse-food of India.

The **lentil** (*Lens esculenta*) of the Mediterranean regions and of West Africa, is a food-plant of great antiquity.

The **pea-nut** (*Arachis hypogaea*) of Brazil and Paraguay, and now grown also in Africa (sometimes called the **ground-, earth-,** or **monkey-nut**) is most curious, for it sows its own seeds

FIG. 81.—Dwarf French Bean.

before they are ripe. The flower, after fertilisation, bends over and its stalk lengthens, thus forcing the developing fruit below the surface of the soil where it ripens.

The drug senna is the dried pods of the **Alexandrian senna** (*Cassia acutifolia*), the **Italian senna** (*C. obovata*), and other species.

Gum-tragacanth is extracted from the Australian species, *Astragalus gummifer* by wounding the stems. From the thick unground stem of the south European plant *Glycyrrhiza glabra,* Spanish liquorice is obtained.

The tropical *Indigofera tinctoria* and other species furnish an indigo dye. The young green plants are steeped in water, and a yellow dye is exuded : this turns deep blue on oxidation.

Many other leguminous plants, too numerous to mention, are cultivated for various economic purposes.

32
SOME USEFUL TREES AND SHRUBS

At this point in our scheme of flowering plant classification there occur several important families of trees and shrubs, which can only receive a brief mention here.

ORNAMENTAL AND ECONOMIC EXOTICS

Though the family HAMAMELIDACEAE is sub-tropical in distribution, several genera and species are now being widely grown in this
country in ornamental woods, shrubberies and avenues. *Parrotia persica*,
a native of Persia, presents beautiful foliage which turns gold and
crimson in the autumn. *Fothergilla major*, a North American shrub, is
a slow-growing plant, usually with the habit of a shrub in this country.
It has fragrant white flowers and its foliage turns golden in the autumn.
Distylium racemosum is a Japanese evergreen shrub with graceful glossy
leaves. *Sycopsis sinensis* is native to China. It is an evergreen shrub
which attains a height of about ten feet. Several other cultivated species
of this genus are Japanese in origin. Certain species of the genus
Corylopsis, which come from China and Japan, can now be found in
shrubberies in this country. They all bear fragrant yellow flowers.
Hamamelis virginiana, the ' **witch** ' **hazel,** is an American import, bearing
red or yellow flowers which open before the leaves develop. *Liquidambar*
is a widely spread genus, being native to the Mediterranean regions and
to America. The species, *L. styraciflua* is the **sweet gum** of North America
which supplies the well-known satin wood. Other species yield fragrant
balsams.

BOX

The family BUXACEAE contains the very familiar **box** tree (*Buxus
sempervirens*). In some schemes of classification, this genus is placed in
the EUPHORBIACEAE (p. 123). Sometimes the box is found growing wild
in this country, but it is so very often cultivated that it seems best now to
look upon it as such. The plant may be seen growing with a tree-like
habit alone or in shrubberies, but more often it is trained as a hedge. It
is often cut into rather fantastic shapes, especially in so-called Italian
gardens. There are several species of box, some of them with yellow
leaves, and some variegated. The leaf of all species is small, thick, oval
and evergreen. The wood of the trunk is very close-grained, and is
frequently used in wood engraving.

PLANE

PLATANACEAE is a family closely related to the BUXACEAE. It is
composed of one genus only, *Platanus*, and the most familiar member
of it is the **London plane** tree (*P. acerifolia*), commonly grown in

London parks and streets. This plane tree is said to be a hybrid between the **oriental plane** (*P. orientalis*) and the **western plane** (*P. occidentalis*), and is not found in the wild state.

POPLARS AND WILLOWS

The family SALICACEAE contains the willows and the poplars. These form the basis of the two genera of the family. The genus *Populus* comprises the wild species **black poplar** (*P. nigra*), **white poplar** (*P. alba*) and the **aspen** (*P. tremula*). All these trees are also cultivated in this country, together with other exotic species. The **Lombardy poplar,** that tall handsome tree which, usually growing in groups, contributes to the attractiveness of any landscape, is a variety of the black poplar (*P. italica*). The genus *Salix* comprises several willows, about a dozen of which are native to this country. The **white willow** (*S. alba*) grows along river banks. It is often pollarded about eight feet from the ground. The **goat willow** (*S. caprea*) grows in woods. It produces a useful timber. This willow is often called **sallow** or **palm,** and has very handsome catkins. The catkin-bearing twigs make useful decorations. The **crack willow** or **withy** (*S. fragilis*) is one of our commonest tree willows. The **cricket-bat willow** (*S. coerulea*) has a light but tough and elastic wood from which cricket bats are made. The **osier willow** (*S. viminalis*) is usually pollarded near ground-level, and the resulting long branches are used in the making of baskets and other wicker-work. *S. babylonica* is the beautiful **weeping willow**, also found growing along river banks, though it is not a native. These species of willow already mentioned, together with other species, are frequently cultivated in this country for economic or ornamental purposes.

The family GARRYACEAE is a Californian family. The genus *Garrya* is a useful evergreen shrub which is sometimes cultivated in this country. It bears long yellowish-green catkins.

ALDER AND BIRCH

The *birch* and the *alder* are members of the family BETULACEAE. The common wild **alder** (*Alnus glutinosa*) frequently grows along river and canal banks. The **birch** (*Betula alba*) has attractive leaves and conspicuous catkins. *Betula alba* is now considered to comprise two species, namely, *B. pendula* and *B. pubescens*. Several species of birch are common in North America, and supply the bark from which the Indians make their canoes. A number of other species are cultivated. Dense tufts of twigs called ' witches' brooms ' frequently grow on these trees.

HAZEL AND HORNBEAM

To the family CORYLACEAE belong the familiar hazel and hornbeam. The **hazel** (*Corylus avellana*) produces a popular edible fruit, the hazel nut. The filbert is a variety of this. Early in the year, the lovely catkins, which are really the inflorescences of male flowers, make a charming sight in the countryside (Fig. 82). The **hornbeam** (*Carpinus betulus*) is a common tree in this country ; but its timber is not used very much. Both the genera of this family are cultivated, the hazel for its nuts, and both trees for their handsome habit.

FIG. 82.—Hazel in Bloom.

Harold Bastin

OAKS, BEECHES AND ELMS

To the family FAGA- CEAE belong some of our most common forest, park- land and countryside trees, namely, oak, beech, Spanish chestnut and elm. Among the oaks are several species which are found growing wild, and several more which are cultivated. The **British oak** (*Quercus robur*) is the most common ; then there is another, namely, *Quercus petraea*. The evergreen **holm oak** (*Q. ilex*), of parks and gar- dens, hails from southern Europe. The **cork oak**

(*Q. suber*), supplies the cork of commerce. *Fagus sylvatica* is the common **beech,** and *Nothofagus cunninghami* is the **myrtle** tree, which also gives good timber. The **Spanish chestnut** (*Castanea vulgaris*) yields the edible chestnuts. Only two elms are commonly found in this country, namely, the **common elm** (*Ulmus procera*) and the **wych elm** (*U. glabra*), but there are several varieties and hybrids. Many of the trees of the family FAGACEAE are cultivated in horticulture and in forestry.

TROPICAL ECONOMIC TREES

Among the family MORACEAE are several genera of economic importance, most of which are tropical and sub-tropical in native distribution. The **india-rubber tree** (*Ficus elastica*) yields a kind of rubber. It is often cultivated in this country, sometimes even in pots, for its handsome foliage. In the tropics, this plant and related species form the so-called banyan forests. The aerial branches give off adventitious roots which hang downwards and eventually reach the ground. There they take root, and then gradually thicken to form secondary trunks, so that any one tree may be composed of one main trunk and hundreds of satellite trunks. *Artocarpus*, a related genus, is sometimes cultivated in this country. *A. incisa* is the tropical **bread-fruit** tree. The fruit has the texture of bread and is roasted and eaten. The genus *Morus* contains the mulberry trees, namely **white mulberry** (*M. alba*) and **black mulberry** (*M. nigra*). The leaves of the latter are utilised in the feeding of silkworms and therefore cultivated in many parts of the world, especially China, Japan, India and Mediterranean regions. The characteristic red fruits are sometimes eaten by man. This very handsome tree is frequently cultivated in British parklands.

33

NETTLES
(*Urticaceae*)

Few people are unfamiliar with stinging nettles, but not many could describe their flowers.

The stinging nettle belongs to the family URTICACEAE, which comprises several genera (not grown in this country) supplying useful fibres.

Willam Camden, so far back as the sixteenth century, wrote that the Romans brought the seed of nettles to this country in order to chafe their limbs when they came in contact with the cold of Britain. If true at all, this probably applies to the Roman nettle (see below).

There are only two genera of the nettle family found growing wild in this country. In fact, the nettle is an agricultural pest, and the farmer has still to learn of a really effective means of getting rid of it, for it reproduces itself very efficiently by means of strong underground stems. The only means of keeping this weed down at present is to place pieces of rock salt among the clumps, and then allow cattle to lick the salt and in doing so trample the nettles to destruction.

> The stinging nettle only
> Will still be found to stand :
> The numberless, the lonely,
> The thronger of the land,
> The leaf that hurts the hand.
>
> It thrives, come sun, come showers,
> Blow east, blow west, it springs ;
> It peoples towns, and towers
> Above the courts of kings,
> And touch it and it stings.
>
> *More Poems* : A. E. HOUSMAN

There are three species of wild stinging nettle. All belong to the genus *Urtica* and are : the **common nettle** (*U. dioica*), the **small nettle** (*U. urens*) and the **Roman nettle** (*U. pilulifera*). The last-named is not common.

The common nettle is a tall, handsome plant, sometimes achieving a height of four feet. It grows in dense clusters in waste places, along roadsides and in fields. The leaves are heart-shaped and pointed and are borne in opposite pairs. These, like the younger parts of the ridged stems, are covered with the all-too-familiar stinging hairs. The sting is a single, superficial cell which has become elongated and tapering, with a bulbous base. The tip contains silica and is therefore brittle. When touched, the tip breaks off, and the sharp point of the hair enters the skin. The pressure thus set up causes the poisonous liquid in the bulbous part to be ejected into the puncture. At one time it was believed that the poison was formic acid like that of the bee and wasp, but it is now found to be a protein of unknown composition. It can now be seen why one gets stung only if one touches the nettle gently, for if it is firmly grasped, although the tips of the hairs may break off the rest of the long hairs are bent over and crushed before they are able to effect a puncture.

> Tender-handed stroke a nettle,
>   And it stings you for your pains ;
> Grasp it like a man of mettle,
>   And it soft as silk remains.
> 'Tis the same with common natures ;
>   Use 'em kindly, they rebel ;
> But be rough as nutmeg-graters,
>   And the rogues obey you well.
>   *Verses Written on a Window in Scotland* : AARON HILL

The leaves of the dock (p. 86) are popularly supposed to cure the sting of a nettle.

The flowers appear during June to September. They are unisexual, and in the common nettle the sexes are borne on different plants. The male flowers hang in long greenish inflorescences borne in the axils of the upper leaves. There are no petals, but each flower has four joined insignificant sepals and four stamens. The latter, when unripe, are bent in the flower-bud ; but when they ripen they spring up violently and their heads at the same time turn inside out. Thus the powdery pollen is suddenly ejected into the air and is carried by the wind to the styles of the female flowers. The female flowers are borne in denser but less pendulous inflorescences. The female flower has one to three small sepals and the single carpel contains one ovule and a brush-like stigma which is well constructed to catch the air-borne pollen. The fruit is an achene, containing, of course, one seed.

The small nettle grows about a foot and a half high, and is found in places similar to the haunts of its greater relative. It also flowers at the same time. Both male and female flowers are borne not only on the same plant, but also in the same inflorescences.

Sometimes the young leaves of nettles are cooked and eaten like spinach. An infusion called nettle tea, supposed to have medicinal properties, is sometimes made by country-folk. The fibres also used to be extracted from the stems.

The other genus of the nettle family found growing wild in this country is *Parietaria*, to which belongs the **pellitory of the wall** (*P. officinalis*). As its name implies, this plant grows on old walls and blooms during June to August ; but it is not very common. The stem is brittle and reddish. It is covered with silky hairs, but they do not

M

sting. The leaves are lance-shaped and alternately arranged. The greenish flowers are borne in dense clusters and they are hermaphrodite. Each cluster of flowers is supported by three to six united bracts. In each flower there are four united sepals, but no petals, four stamens and a single style. The plant ensures cross-pollination by ripening its style first, and this protrudes. The four stamens, when ripe, suddenly jump out, like those of the nettle. They can be made to do this by gently pushing a pencil-point into the centre of an unfertilised flower.

Among the plants of economic value belonging to the nettle family, is the genus *Boehmeria*, cultivated in China for its fibres, which are the longest, toughest and most silky in the vegetable world. But they are difficult to prepare.

In some countries, certain species of *Urtica* are cultivated for their fibres. *Maoutia puya*, of tropical Asia, also yields good fibres.

The root of another genus, *Pouzolzia tuberosa*, is eaten in India.

34

HOPS AND BEER: HEMP AND HASHISH

(Cannabinaceae)

Hops very frequently festoon the hedges with their long, climbing stems and their handsome leaves; particularly attractive are they during July and August when their large, bright green catkins appear.

The hop is so very similar in fundamental structure to the nettle that it is placed in the same family (URTICACEAE) in some schemes of plant classification; it is, however, considered in others to be sufficiently different to merit a separate family—CANNABINACEAE, to which also belongs the hemp which supplies the well-known fibre and various drugs.

The hop belongs to the genus *Humulus*. Since it is used in the making of a beverage that is a world-wide favourite, beer, it is cultivated in many countries. The **European hop** is *Humulus lupulus* and the **American hop** is *H. americanus*.

The stem of the plant is very long and is so rough as to be almost prickly. It is thus enabled to scramble over hedges where it grows

Harold Bastin

FIG. 83.—Hop.
Above, male inflorescence; below (left), female in flower; below (right), fruit ripening.

wild. The leaves are borne in opposite pairs: they are deeply serrated and the lower ones are divided into three, five or seven lobes, whereas the upper ones are not so divided but are heart-shaped (Fig. 83).

The small greenish male and female flowers are borne in separate inflorescences; the male is a loose branched spike, and the female a loose catkin (Fig. 83). The male flower has five small united sepals, no petals, and five stamens. The female has a calyx formed of one enlarged bract which encloses a single ovary bearing two long styles. The enveloping bracts give the whole female inflorescence the catkin-like appearance (Fig. 83). The fruit is an achene.

Cultivation of the hop for brewing ale or beer began in Asia and spread westwards to the New World. There is evidence that prehistoric man was able to brew beer. It was certainly known in ancient Babylon and was a common drink in ancient Egypt; in both areas it was used as a medicine as well as a beverage. The Greeks and Romans were also very fond of it. During medieval times, both in Great Britain and on the Continent, the value of yeast in both brewing and baking was known, and to this day in the monasteries the brewery and the bakery are frequently next door to each other. Today, beer-making is practised all over the world—even among savage tribes. The fundamental plant in brewing is the barley. The grain of this plant is used. The barley grains are soaked and then allowed to germinate. Now the barley grain contains much starch, and as it germinates this starch is converted into the sugar glucose, which is the very thing required for fermentation in the brewing process. The germination is allowed to go on for about a fortnight at about 100° F. Then the heat is increased, either under the floor of the malt-house or by passing hot air through it, and so the barley seedlings are killed. The resulting mixture is called malt. The malt is dried and ground, and is then placed in water to form what is called wort. This is then boiled to kill any ferments present and also any contaminating bacteria. The fruit-catkins of the hop are then added, with the object of imparting flavour. (This was not always the case, for at one time spices were added instead.) The mixture of wort and hops is allowed to stand for a few days after boiling. Then the hops are removed, and the wort is cooled to about 60° F. To this is added the yeast which causes fermentation, a process which is allowed to go on for several weeks. Eventually the yeast is removed and the resulting ale or beer stored in vats to mature.

> Say, for what were hopyards meant,
> Or why was Burton built on Trent?
> Ah many a peer of England brews
> Livelier liquor than the Muse,
> And malt does more than Milton can
> To justify God's ways to man.

Ale, man, ale's the stuff to drink
For fellows whom it hurts to think :
Look into the pewter pot
To see the world as the world's not.
A Shropshire Lad : A. E. HOUSMAN

Barley is grown in many parts of Great Britain, but especially in Scotland. The cultivation of hops is confined chiefly to Kent for the plant is very sensitive to climatic changes.

The hop of commerce is propagated by means of cuttings taken from the lower parts of the previous year's vines.

Some species of Japanese hops are cultivated for ornamental purposes and allowed to climb over hedges or verandahs for their decorative effect. Some have variegated leaves—silver and creamy white.

To the family CANNABINACEAE belongs also the genus *Cannabis* and one of its most important constituent species is the **hemp** (*C. sativa*). This plant is a native of Central Asia, where it still grows wild ; but it is also now cultivated in southern Europe and in the United States.

The valuable hemp fibre is obtained from the inner bark of the stem.

The hemp plant also exudes a resin from which drugs and stimulants are made. From the female flowering shoot exudes a resin from which the Indian drug ganja is extracted. The resin knocked off the twigs is the basis for the preparation of the drug charas. A third drug is obtained from the wild plant in Asia, and therefore traffic in it is difficult to control. This is the drug bhang which is extracted from the resin in the leaves.

Asiatics make use of hemp as a narcotic or intoxicant. They smoke it either by itself or mixed with tobacco. They make from it such drugs as bhang and hashish, which are smoked, chewed, drunk, and even eaten. A close check has to be kept on the sale of these drugs, and the strictest control is essential, for, though in small doses they create a pleasant sensation, larger doses cause delirium and even catalepsy. The health of a drug addict, of course, eventually becomes seriously, if not hopelessly, impaired.

The hemp drugs are known in other countries in different forms as gunga, kif and marijuana. The last-named is used for making cigarettes which are proving to be a curse, especially in South America. The hemp has been known to be grown in American backyards for this purpose.

35

HOLLY: THE HOLY TREE
(*Aquifoliaceae*)

There is surely no-one in this country who could not identify a twig of holly, whether in flower or in fruit, or with neither. The holly is frequently seen cultivated in gardens and parks, either growing alone as a tree or trained as a hedge. When bedecked with its scarlet berries, it is a favourite Christmas decoration.

It may seem strange, but its Yule-tide companion the mistletoe, belongs to a family not very far removed from it in this scheme of plant classification. For that reason, although the holly is really a tree, it is being considered in this book.

Holly belongs to the family AQUIFOLIACEAE, in which there are three genera, *Ilex* being the most important. The holly is *Ilex aquifolium*.

In this country it is more often a small bush or hedge, for it is tolerant of constant clipping; but sometimes under cultivation, and certainly in the wild state, it can attain the habit and height of a tree. If left alone it has been known to attain a height of 60 to 80 ft. In fact, there are some holly trees in Shropshire with trunks 14 ft. in circumference several feet from the ground. The holly is often used as a hedge, and a very effective one it makes. There was a holly hedge in Evelyn's garden in Deptford 400 ft. long, 9 ft. high and 5 ft. wide. It suffered considerably when the house was let to Peter the Great of Russia, who amused himself by driving furiously along the top of the hedge mounted on a wheelbarrow.

The holly leaf scarcely calls for description. It is leathery and shiny, and the margins and tip have some strong spines. All this is necessary, because the plant is an evergreen and requires protection against inclement winter weather and browsing animals (Fig. 84). In some trees, the uppermost leaves have no spines except perhaps at their tips. It has been suggested that only the lower ones need the spines, for they are the only ones that animals can reach; but this does not explain why in many cases the uppermost leaves are spiny, and in others the lower ones bear no spines.

The flowers appear during May to August, and they may be

unisexual or, more rarely, hermaphrodite. Frequently the female flower can be mistaken for a hermaphrodite one, for it often has four large stamens, but these are sterile. The flowers are borne in loose inflorescences growing from the axils of the leaves.

In each flower there are four united sepals and four white petals slightly united at the base. The male flower has four white stamens, and the female flower four to six carpels joined to form a four- to six-chambered ovary. There are no styles, but the stigmas are fixed direct on to the top of the ovary. The fruit is a fleshy drupe containing one to six stones. It is usually scarlet in colour, but there are some varieties of holly which bear yellow or even black

Harold Bastin

FIG. 84.—Holly in Fruit.

fruits. Birds eat the fruit, but since the stones are indigestible they are excreted, and in this way the holly is distributed.

The use of holly as an indoor decoration dates back to antiquity. The Romans used it for their festivals, as did the Greeks. The old Teutons used it in the belief that it would keep away evil spirits. Its use in churches, halls and homes at Christmas-time is as old as Christianity itself. The name 'holly' is derived from 'holy tree' for obvious reasons. In Germany and Scandinavia it is known as 'Christ's Thorn' from its use in church decorations and putting forth its fruit at Christmas time. The early Christians called it the 'Righteous Branch'. One old legend claims that the holly was used for the crown of thorns placed on Christ's head, and that the fruits became coloured by His blood.

The evergreen character of holly adds point to the old Border proverb about a persistent liar : ' He lees never but when the hollen is green'.

Many interesting superstitions about holly have naturally developed through the ages, since it has been used for so many festivals. In some parts it is considered unlucky to bring it into the house before Christmas Eve, and in many parts it is thought unlucky to take it down again until

Old Christmas Day (January 6). In a few rural districts, the spiny holly is called ' he ', and the spineless holly ' she ', and whether the man or the woman shall rule the house during the coming year depends on which type of holly was used for Christmas decoration.

The species *Ilex paraguensis* yields the very popular yerba maté or Paraguay tea, largely consumed in South America. The leaves are dried and broken up and the tea is then brewed just as we brew our tea.

Closely related to the holly family (AQUIFOLIACEAE) is the family (CELASTRACEAE) to which belongs the **spindle tree** (*Euonymus europaeus*), and other species. This tree has handsome foliage and lovely pink fruit which make an attractive sight in the autumn. For that reason, this and other species are often cultivated. Some trees under cultivation have silver or even purple foliage.

A related genus sometimes found in parks is *Celastrus*, which contains some climbers with conspicuous scarlet or golden fruit.

36

MISTLETOE: THE GOLDEN BOUGH
(*Loranthaceae*)

The mistletoe hung in the castle hall,
The holly branch shone on the old oak wall.
The Mistletoe Bough : T. H. BAYLY

Thoughts of Christmas bring to mind another plant, namely, the **mistletoe,** which, like the holly, has been used on festive occasions from time immemorial.

Sir James Frazer has concluded from his exhaustive researches through the literature of magic, mythology and folk-lore, that the mistletoe is the ' Golden Bough ' of many legends. His tentative theory that the name was given because the mistletoe turns a golden colour after hanging for some time seems, however, too simple to explain its true origin.

The name ' mistletoe ' is derived from a biological misconception. The word ' mistletoe ' is a corruption of *mistel-ta* : *mist* in German means 'droppings of a bird'; *ta* is from *tan* (Old Norse, *toin*) meaning 'plant' or 'shoot'. It is true that the plant is distributed through the agency of birds. The white berries attract the birds which eat them, but the enclosed stones are covered with a slimy, glutinous material which the birds cannot master. They therefore scrape them off their beaks, usually against the tree on which they perch, and there the new plant grows and makes its home. But at one time it was thought that birds ate the whole of the mistletoe fruit and, as in the case of the holly, passed the stones out again unharmed in their excreta. It was this misunderstanding which has given the plant its common name.

Harold Bastin

FIG. 85.—Mistletoe growing on a young Apple Tree.

Before considering the part played by this extraordinary plant in folk-lore, let us examine it biologically.

The mistletoe is not really a parasite as it is so often described, for a plant parasite absorbs all its food from another plant, called the host, on which it lives. A true parasite therefore has no green leaves, since it does not make any food of its own. Examples are considered in Chaps. 42 and 60. But the mistletoe is green and is able to manufacture its own food; it does, however, absorb water and mineral salts from the tree upon which it grows (Fig. 85). It is therefore a semi-parasite.

In this country, the host tree of the mistletoe is usually the poplar or apple, though it is frequently found growing on oak, hawthorn and other trees. When the seed has been sown by the bird, it eventually germinates and sends out a sucker which penetrates the host and grows down into the wood up which the sap composed of water and dissolved salts is passing. Once this sucker has become established, the semi-parasite develops its own leaves and is then in a position to manufacture its own food. The sucker acts in almost the same way as the roots of a normal plant growing on the soil.

The mistletoe belongs to the family LORANTHACEAE, most members of which are semi-parasites, though the majority of them are natives of tropical regions. The only representative genus in this country is *Viscum*, and the only species belonging to it is the mistletoe (*V. album*).

The plant branches repeatedly in a characteristic, dichotomous manner ; that is, the tip of each branch sends out two branches forming a Y, and the two branches of the Y send out two more branches, and so forth. Each branch bears two opposite, greenish-yellow, leathery leaves, and this represents one year's growth.

The flowers are unisexual and are borne in groups usually of three in the forks of the branches, each group containing one sex of flower only. The flowers appear during March to May.

There are four, six, or eight small greenish sepals, and in the male, a corresponding number of stamens, but no petals. In the female flower the ovary is single-chambered. The fruit contains one seed. The white, juicy part of the fruit is really the swollen receptacle.

The rich store of folk-tales and legends about the mistletoe provides fascinating study in itself.

The Druids of Ancient Gaul and England esteemed nothing more sacred than the mistletoe, provided always that it grew on an oak, for they revered the latter also. They believed the mistletoe to be heaven-sent and able to make barren animals fertile and to be a remedy against all poisons. The Aryans and the Teutons also revered the oak, and therefore they wove all kinds of legends around the mistletoe which was associated with it.

In Old Norse mythology, the mistletoe was held in high esteem. It was believed to take care of the life of the oak on which it was borne. This belief might be due, as Sir James Frazer has pointed out, to the observation that the mistletoe continues leafy and alive when the oak is leafless and apparently dead. Sir James makes a further suggestion that the mistletoe, growing neither on the earth nor in heaven, is therefore in a safe place and is itself fitted to preserve life. Hence the rule in ancient folk-medicine that the mistletoe should never be allowed to touch the ground.

According to an old Norse legend, Balder, the Apollo of Scandinavian mythology, dreamed heavy dreams which foreboded his death. The other gods were alarmed and took counsel together. Then the goddess Frigg, Balder's mother, took an oath from fire and water, iron and all metals, stones and earth, all trees, all sicknesses and poisons, all beasts, birds, and creeping things, that they would not hurt Balder. After this oath was given, the gods surrounded Balder and amused themselves by shooting at him, hewing at him with their weapons and even stoning him, but all without effective results. But Loki, the god of mischief, who had power over the earth, became jealous and angry, and persuaded the blind god Hother to shoot an arrow of mistletoe at Balder. The mistletoe killed Balder. Some say that the gods were able to restore him to life ; others that his body was put on board his ship, which was set on fire to be his funeral pyre, and vanished with him out at sea, after the custom of the old Vikings. But whatever happened, Frigg took care of the mistletoe and placed it high upon a tree, never again to touch the earth—the empire of Loki the god of evil. And so today, the mistletoe is suspended from the ceiling, or anywhere well above the ground, and under it people give each other the kiss of peace and love.

> So on the floor lay Balder dead ; and round
> Lay thickly strewn swords, axes, darts and spears,
> Which all the Gods in sport had idly thrown
> At Balder, whom no weapon pierced or clove ;
> But in his breast stood fixed the fatal bough
> Of Mistletoe, which Lok the Accuser gave
> To Hoder, and unwitting Hoder threw—
> 'Gainst that alone had Balder's life no charm.
>
> *Balder Dead* : MATTHEW ARNOLD

37

GRAPE AND OTHER VINES
(*Ampelidaceae* (*Vitaceae*))

Most members of the grape family are climbing vines or small trees, usually the former. None is to be found growing wild in this country, but the cultivated grape and the ornamental Virginian creeper are so well known that we cannot omit reference to them.

In Great Britain, the **grape vine** is cultivated solely for its dessert fruit. One of the largest and most famous is that at Hampton Court Palace. In the very south of England, grapes will sometimes ripen satisfactorily in the open ; but elsewhere they are cultivated outside

R. A. Malby & Co.

FIG. 86.—Muscat Grape.

for their ornamental value only. They are good climbers and have handsome foliage, and are therefore useful for covering old walls, arches and cloisters. Many species, other than that of the grape vine, are cultivated for this very purpose, because they produce such beautifully coloured foliage, some very rich red in colour, and most turning to lovely shades in the autumn.

The grape vine belongs to the family AMPELIDACEAE (usually known as VITACEAE in other schemes). Most genera of the family are tropical or sub-tropical. The genus containing the grape, *Vitis*, is perhaps the most important one. The grape vine is *Vitis vinifera*.

The flowers are borne in large, comparatively loose inflorescences, and since the plant climbs by means of tendrils, these are produced by the modification of some inflorescences.

The flower is regular and usually hermaphrodite. There are four or five sepals forming a cup, the same number of petals which unite at their tips and fall off like a hood after fertilisation, the same number of stamens, and two carpels joined to form a single ovary containing usually two ovules. The fruit is a berry with two hard seeds.

The edible fruit produced in this country is invariably used as dessert, and is especially useful for invalids because of the large amount of energy-producing grape sugar or glucose it contains. The varieties of grape cultivated for dessert in this country today are the black varieties, such as, Black Cluster and Black Prime, and the white or muscat (Fig. 86) such as Pitmaston White Cluster and Royal Muscadine.

The grape vine is, however, cultivated in many of the warmer parts of the world, for the purpose of wine-making. For this reason, the vine has been celebrated in song, verse and prose, times out of number. It also forms the motif for many designs, architectural and otherwise. It is interesting to note that grape seeds have been found in the tombs of the Pharaohs. The ancient Greeks and Romans also made extensive use of wine.

> A man cannot make him laugh ; —but that's no marvel,
> he drinks no wine.
> > *II Henry IV* : SHAKESPEARE

> Sing ! Who sings
> To her who weareth a hundred rings ?
> Ah, who is this lady fine ?
> The vine, boys, the vine !
> The mother of the mighty Wine,
> A roamer is she Oer wall and tree,
> And sometimes very good company.
> > *A Bacchanalian Song* : B. W. PROCTER

> Inflaming wine, pernicious to mankind,
> Unnerves the limbs, and dulls the noble mind.
> > *Iliad*, VI : HOMER (POPE)

Wine is the fermented product of freshly gathered grapes, cultivated in the large vineyards of warmer climes. It is produced by crushing the grapes and then allowing fermentation to take place. In beer-making, it is necessary to add the yeast for this purpose ; but in the case of wine-making this is not necessary because the yeast grows on the grape's skin while it is still on the vine. Red wines are more or less the pure product of this fermentation. In the case of port wines, extra alcohol is usually added. White wines are the red fermented juice treated in various ways to remove the colour. Sparkling wines differ from still wines in that the former are bottled before fermentation has ceased, with the result that the carbon dioxide gas given off during the fermentation process remains dissolved in the wine under pressure. When the cork is drawn this pressure is removed, and the dissolved carbon dioxide is released in sparkling bubbles. In the making of wines, the whole fruit, including the skins, are used. On the other hand, champagne is prepared entirely from the juice of the grape.

A by-product of wine-making is malt vinegar. This flavouring liquid is also obtained during the preparation of cider from apples. There is little doubt that vinegar was first produced, probably by the ancient Greeks and Romans, by the natural souring of cheap wines; but vinegar-making began as a separate industry in France during the seventeenth century. The main action is the production of acetic acid in the wine, for this acid is the basis of vinegar. It is produced from the wine by the action of certain bacteria added specially for the purpose.

Glucose or grape sugar is also a product of the grape.

The dry currants of commerce, muscatels, raisins and sultanas, are all fruit products of varieties of *Vitis vinifera*. The vines producing dried currants are grown chiefly in Greece, the Ionian Islands and other parts of the eastern Mediterranean. They are also now cultivated in California, Australia and South Africa. Sultanas are a seedless variety of grape.

Another familiar genus of the grape family is *Parthenocissus*, to which belong the **Virginian creepers** (*P. tricuspidata* and *T. quinquefolia*). The first-named species has a simple, oval, pointed and deeply serrated leaf. It climbs walls and trees by means of branched tendrils which are modified stems. At the tip of each branch tendril is an adhesive disk by means of which the stem adheres to the wall. The leaf of the second-named species is compound and divided into five very large leaflets. The leaves of both species turn to beautiful golden and scarlet shades during the autumn.

38

ORANGES AND LEMONS
(Rutaceae)

Oranges and lemons are not seen growing outdoors in this country, though the trees are sometimes cultivated, and even bear small fruit in conservatories. No members of the family, RUTACEAE, are native to Great Britain; but the fruit are so popular and valuable that they cannot be overlooked entirely. The chief genus of

RUTACEAE is *Citrus*, which is cosmopolitan in distribution, but thrives outdoors only in very warm temperate, sub-tropical and tropical regions.

All citrus fruits are useful as dessert or for making preserves such as marmalade, and their consumption, especially among children, should be encouraged, for they have a very high vitamin C content.

All species of *Citrus* are either trees or shrubs : some have simple and others have compound leaves, all of which contain aromatic oil-glands. Similar oil-glands are present in the skin of the fruit. The fruit is a large berry subdivided into sections by pulp-masses which grow inwards from the leathery skin or peel.

The most important citrus fruits are : the **citron** (*Citrus medica*) and its varieties **lemon** (*C. medica* var. *limonum*) and **sweet lime** (*C. medica* var. *limetta*) ; the **orange** (*C. aurantium*) and its varieties, **Bergamot orange** (*C. aurantium* var. *bergamia*), from which a perfume is extracted, the **bitter** or **Seville orange** (*C. aurantium* var. *amara*) used for making marmalade ; the **grape fruit** (*C. decumana*) ; the **mandarin** or **tangerine orange** (*C. nobilis*), and several others. All these are cultivated in the warmer regions of the Old and the New Worlds.

Other members of the family RUTACEAE are grown in this country since they are able to tolerate the climate. Even some species of *Citrus* are thus cultivated and display inflorescences with handsome white flowers. The leaves contain oil-glands which can be seen if the leaf is held up to the light. Another related genus is *Choisya*, to which belongs the **Mexican orange blossom** (*C. ternata*)—a very beautiful evergreen shrub with masses of white flowers.

Following the family RUTACEAE come several important families of trees and shrubs.

BURSERACEAE contains some well-known oil- and resin-secreting trees and shrubs, for example, **frankincense** (*Boswellia carteri*) and **myrrh** (*Balsamodendron* species).

MELIACEAE is a family of tropical and sub-tropical trees, some of them supplying important timbers such as **mahogany** (*Swietenia mahogani*).

SAPINDACEAE is represented in this country by the **horse-chestnut** (*Aesculus hippocastanum*). The tree *Koelreuteria*, a native of China, is said to have inspired the original willow pattern. It is sometimes cultivated in this country.

ACERACEAE contains the familiar **sycamore** (*Acer pseudoplatanus*) and the **maple** (*A. campestris*). The **sugar maple** (*A. saccharum*) of eastern North America is a source of sugar supply. Many species and varieties of *Acer*, chiefly of Japanese origin, are cultivated for their dwarf habit and their coloured or variegated foliage.

39

IVY

(*Araliaceae*)

The **ivy** is another plant which has now become established as a favourite in folk-lore and in art design, chiefly, perhaps on account of its handsome foliage leaves. It used to be dedicated to Bacchus, since it was supposed to prevent drunkenness, but whether the Dionysian ivy was the same as ours of today or not is a moot point. At one time an ivy bush was used as a sign for a tavern. In Christian art, the ivy is the symbol of everlasting life, owing to its evergreen habit. More recently the ivy has been used for sombre occasions and, like the bramble (p. 132) used for binding grave mounds.

The ivy is a very common plant, and it grows almost everywhere—in town and in country. It belongs to the family ARALIACEAE, and is, indeed, the chief representative of the most important genus (*Hedera helix*).

It is a root climber in that its stems give off adventitious roots by which it climbs almost everywhere—over walls, woodwork and tree trunks. The stems are thus able to grow almost interminably, for by these roots they are able to absorb water from anything up which they are climbing.

The leaves, too, are interesting in that they are very variable (Fig. 87). There are pointed heart-shaped leaves and palmate, five-lobed leaves, and every gradation between the two (Plate 8). Those leaves of ivy growing on the ground and under hedges are usually beautifully lobed and arranged in such an efficient mosaic that each leaf gets the maximum of sun and air. The leaves are leathery and shiny like most evergreen leaves which have to withstand winter conditions.

The ivy is one of the latest flowering plants of the year, for the flowers appear in October and November, thus giving nectar-seeking insects (chiefly wasps and flies) their last chance. The nectar is freely exposed. The flowers appear in inflorescences of about a dozen flowers

FIG. 87.—Different Leaf-forms of Ivy.

to each, and all the flowers of any one inflorescence are borne on separate
stalks which come off from a common point on the main inflorescence
stalk (Plate 8). Each flower is greenish, with five united sepals, five
reflexed petals, five to ten stamens and five carpels united to form an
ovary with several chambers and five joined styles. The fruit is a
black berry (Plate 8), enclosing three to ten seeds. Though birds eat
these berries, they are poisonous to man.

Many species and varieties of ivy are cultivated in gardens, shrubberies and parks, and a large number are trained over buildings, etc.
There are some kinds of tree ivy, but most are climbers and may have
green, gold, silver or variegated leaves.

Related to the ivy family is the family CORNACEAE, to which belongs
the **Japanese laurel** (*Aucuba japonica*), which is readily recognised by
its large, leathery, lance-shaped leaves covered with blotches of pale

N

yellow. Sometimes, even on the same plant, some leaves are entirely green and others entirely yellow. The Japanese laurel must not be confused with the true laurels (p. 47).

A wild member of this family is the **dog-wood tree** (*Cornus sanguinea*).

40

THE PARSLEY FAMILY
(Umbelliferae)

The parsley family of plants (UMBELLIFERAE) is an extraordinary one, for though there are many wild representatives growing in this country and throughout north temperate regions, few are used for ornamental purposes, probably because their flowers are insignificant except *en masse*, and also in general they are not fragrant—in fact, some have a repugnant smell. Furthermore, compared with the pea and rose family, not many are of great economic value, though an exceptionally large number are used for flavourings, especially in confectionery.

The main characteristic of the family is the structure of the inflorescence from which it derives its name. The flowers are arranged in groups of seven to twelve, each flower being on a long stalk, and all the stalks coming away from the main stalk at the same point. This type of inflorescence is called an umbel. A more frequent arrangement is one in which this conception can be carried the next step further, where roughly ten to twenty umbels are arranged in a fashion similar to the single flowers, thus giving an umbel of simple umbels, or, in other words, a compound umbel. Frequently bracts are inserted where the stalks of the flowers meet and where the stalks of the simple umbels meet (Fig. 88).

The flowers are usually small and white or cream; some are yellow. Each is usually

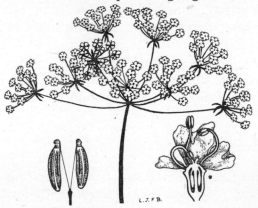

FIG. 88.—Typical Umbellifer. Showing the inflorescence, fruit (left) and flower (right) with stamen pollinating stigma.

regular, having five free sepals, five free petals (which soon fall), five stamens and two carpels which are united and have two short styles. The fruit also is very characteristic of the family. It is a splitting schizocarp. When ripe, it splits into two halves, both of which hang from a central stalk, and each is called a mericarp (Fig. 88). The fruit-wall is usually ridged and longitudinal canals containing oil are frequently present (Fig. 88). In some species this oil is poisonous.

The flower is usually cross-pollinated by flies, but if this fails self-pollination is effected by the stamens turning inwards towards the short styles which turn outwards (Fig. 88).

The leaves of most genera and species are finely divided, though there are some exceptions to this.

The stem is usually hollow except at the nodes, where a partition of pith extends across the central hollow channel.

WILD PLANTS

The parsley family is composed of about a hundred genera, and thirty or more of these are represented in this country.

The beaked parsley is a very typical umbellifer. There are two species, the **wild beaked parsley** (*Anthriscus sylvestris*) (Plate 13) and the **common beaked parsley** (*A. vulgaris*). Both grow along waysides and both flower at about the same time (April to June). The umbels of both are compound. The former, however, is three to four feet high, and though the stem is mainly smooth it is hairy below ; the latter only grows two to three feet high and is entirely smooth.

The **fool's parsley** (*Aethusa cynapium*), known in the West of England as **snake's food,** grows in waste places and frequently in large masses, making an arresting display. The plant is covered profusely with finely divided leaves, though not so finely divided as those of the beaked parsleys. At the common point of the flower-stalks of each umbel there are three long pendulous bracts. The plant is poisonous.

The **hedge parsley** (*Torilis anthriscus*), which exhibits its compound umbels during July to September, can be distinguished by its hooked fruit. There are no ridges. Another species (*T. nodosa*) is one of the few umbellifers having simple umbels.

The **common hemlock** (*Conium maculatum*) (Plate 13) cannot be mistaken, for it is the only umbellifer with a smooth spotted stem. The spots are deep purple. The plant grows in waste places to a height of two to six feet, and blooms during June and July. It is very poisonous. The fruit has many oil-channels and thick ridges. It is this plant which probably supplied the poison by which Socrates met his death. The shepherd's pipes of Pan were also made from its hollow stems.

The **wild angelica** (*Angelica sylvestris*) grows in moist woods, and blooms during July and August.

The **wild parsnip** (*Peucedanum sativum*), sometimes found growing on waste places, is the forerunner of the cultivated parsnip. It has yellow flowers which appear during July and August, but only during its second year, because it is a biennial.

The **cow-parsnip** (*Heracleum sphondylium*) is a tall plant, sometimes attaining a height of five feet or more. The stems are very furrowed, and the flowers, which appear during June, are unusually large (Fig. 89) and the outer ones of the compound umbel are irregular in that their outermost petals are larger than the inner ones. The species *H. giganteum* is sometimes cultivated in damp, shaded positions and grows to a height of nine feet, producing umbels as large as umbrellas.

The **wild carrot** (*Daucus carota*) is the forerunner of the cultivated carrot. It grows in pastures. The fruit is covered with long prickles (easily seen on the carrot ' seed ' supplied by the seedsman).

The **shepherd's needle** (*Scandix pecten-veneris*), of cornfields, has a beak on its fruit sometimes three inches long. The outer flowers of its umbel are also irregular. This plant is sometimes known as **Venus's comb**.

FIG. 89.—Cow-parsnip.

The **rough chervil** (*Chaerophyllum temulum*) grows to a height of three feet along waysides. It has long fruit. The **sweet Cicely** (*Myrrhis odorata*), of pastures and river-sides, also has long fruit. It is so-named because the whole plant, especially the fruit, is aromatic. The fruit of the **coriander** (*Coriandrum sativum*) is globular. The plant sometimes appears in waste places, flowering during June.

The **pignut** (*Carum bulbocastanum*) is not common. The flowers appear during June and July. The root has a solitary tuber. The pignut is closely related to the caraway and the garden parsley.

The dropworts may be distinguished by their long fruits still surmounted by the styles. They are all water-loving plants and belong to the genus *Oenanthe*. There are four fairly common species : **water dropwort** (*O. fistulosa*) of ditches ; **hemlock dropwort** (*O. crocata*) of marshes and ditches (poisonous) ; **parsley dropwort** (*O. lachenalii*) of fresh and salt marshes ; and the **fine-leaved dropwort** (*O. phellandrium*) of ponds and streams (also poisonous).

The **water parsnip** (*Sium angustifolium*) grows, as its name implies, in wet places. The leaves are not so finely divided as those of previously described genera.

The **burnet-saxifrage** (*Pimpinella saxifraga*) grows in dry pastures and flowers during July to September. Its leaves also are not so finely divided, especially those which grow from ground-level.

The **earth-nut** (*Bunium flexuosum*), which grows in fields, has a large root tuber more than an inch in diameter.

The marsh-worts, too, bear leaves which are not so finely divided. The **lesser marshwort** (*Helosciadium inundatum*) grows in wet places, and has few aerial leaves but many submerged, the latter being more finely divided, as one would expect. The **procumbent marshwort** (*H. nodiflorum*) has a creeping stem.

The **celery** (*Apium graveolens*) is not usually found growing wild, but it does occur in salt marshes. Here again, its leaves are not so finely cut.

The **hare's ear** (*Bupleurum rotundifolium*) derives its common name from the shape of its leaves, which are not at all like the usual umbelliferous type (Plate 13). They are roughly oval, and the lower parts completely encircle the stem. The plant is not common, and has yellowish flowers.

The **Alexanders** (*Smyrnium olusatrum*) also has yellow flowers. It is not common either ; but sometimes it may be seen flowering in waste places during April to June. It was formerly used like celery.

The last three wild genera of the UMBELLIFERAE family to be considered have inflorescences in the form of simple umbels. The **marsh pennywort** (*Hydrocotyle vulgaris*) has about five greenish flowers to each head. The **wood sanicle** (*Sanicula europaea*) has hooked fruits. The **sea holly** (*Eryngium maritimum*) is perhaps the most unusual umbellifer (Plate 13). It is a very prickly plant and grows on seashores. The blue flowers are borne in dense umbels, each of which is surrounded by five to eight large bracts, each bract being shaped somewhat like a holly leaf. The foliage leaves are also spiny, and all are covered with a waxy bloom as a protection against excessive loss of moisture.

Species of the sea holly are sometimes cultivated in flower gardens. The roots at one time were candied and used as a confection.

ECONOMIC PLANTS

The most important food plants of the family UMBELLIFERAE are the **carrot** (*Daucus carota*), **celery** (*Apium graveolens*), and the **parsnip** (*Peucedanum sativum*), and all of these have their wild forerunners already described. The carrot is of exceptional value in that it contains the red colouring matter, carotene, which is the precursor of vitamin A. This means that although man, like most animals, is unable to manufacture the necessary vitamins in his own body but has to absorb them from the plant and animal foods he eats, if he does absorb a vitamin precursor, then his own body can build up the appropriate vitamin from it. Vitamin A is very necessary to growing children and to all of us in helping the body to resist bacterial infection. Carotene is also connected with the visual purple of the eye, and therefore aids in night blindness and helps the normal eye to function better in the dark.

Other genera of this family supply flavourings and herbs, such as **parsley** (*Petroselinum crispum*), **caraway seeds** (*C. carvi*), **aniseed** (*Pimpinella anisum*), **coriander seeds** (*Coriandrum sativum*), **fennel** (*Foeniculum capillaceum*), **angelica** (*Angelica officinalis*) the leaf-stalks of which are used in confectionery, **chervil** (*Anthriscus sylvestris* and *A. cerefolium*), **samphire** (*Crithmum maritimum*), and others.

PART III

DICOTYLEDONS

II. FLOWERS WITH UNITED PETALS

The rest of the dicotyledonous families, to be considered in this Part, have their petals united with each other, and frequently exhibit highly specialised mechanisms for ensuring pollination. These families are more advanced than those with free petals dealt with in Part II.

41

MOUNTAIN AND MOORLAND PLANTS

(*Ericaceae* and *Vacciniaceae*)

We have now arrived at the first flowers in our scheme which have united petals.

The first two families (ERICACEAE and VACCINIACEAE) in this section contain some plants very commonly found on heaths, moorlands, hillsides and mountains; indeed, members of both families are frequently discovered growing together.

HEATH AND HEATHER

The two most important wild genera of the ERICACEAE are *Calluna* and *Erica*. To the genus *Calluna* belongs the common ling or heather, and to the genus *Erica* belongs the cross-leaved heath and the fine-leaved heath. There seems to be some confusion as to whether the ling or the heath is the true heather, but most people nowadays favour the former.

WILD PLANTS

The **common ling** or **heather** (*Calluna vulgaris*) is a woody shrub frequently seen flowering in rosy purple masses on mountain and moorland during July to October. The leaves of this plant are very small and closely overlapping like tiles on a roof—a useful precaution for a plant growing in such exposed positions. The flowers are very small, and it is only because they grow in profusion on long spikes that the plants *en masse* look so bold and colourful (Plate 12).

Each flower has four sepals, which are rosy purple like the four shorter joined petals. Below the sepals are four greenish-purple bracts. There are usually four stamens and the ovary is composed of four united carpels, with a common long style. (Plate 12). The fruit is a capsule (Plate 12), and when ripe the withered remains of the style and the sepals are still attached to it.

The flowers of the wild heather are sometimes white, but these are rare. They are considered to be lucky; but many of the sprigs offered for sale in the streets are actually purple sprays which have been bleached.

The nectar of the heather flower is more easily available to the visiting bee than that of the heath. The flower may also be wind-pollinated. From the heather a specially delicious honey is made, highly flavoured and much darker in colour than normal yellow honey.

Heather is common on the mountains and moorlands of England, but more so even in Scotland. In fact, it is distributed throughout northern Europe, Greenland and Newfoundland, and is the only common member of the family in North America.

> No more these simple flowers belong
> To Scottish maid and lover;
> Sown in the common soil of song,
> They bloom the wide world over.
>
> .   .   .   .
>
> Wild heather-bells and Robert Burns!
> The moorland flower and peasant!
> How, at their mention, memory turns
> Her pages old and pleasant!
> *On Receiving a Sprig of Heather in Blossom*: WHITTIER

The **cross-leaved heath** (*Erica tetralix*) is often seen growing among heather. It is a smaller plant, but it has larger flowers borne in denser spikes (Plate 12). The plant derives its name from the fact that the small leaves are arranged in whorls of four equally spaced along the stem.

Each flower is bell-shaped and pendulous. The visiting bee, in struggling to get at the nectar at the base of the flower (which in this case is uppermost), must perforce shake it, and thus brings showers of pollen tumbling on to its own body. By this means the flower is pollinated. The heath flower has four sepals, but not four outer bracts as the heather has. The petals are much more closely united, and there are five small points only to mark them. There are eight stamens, and the style protrudes beyond the bell of petals.

The **fine-leaved heath** (*E. cinerea*) bears its leaves in whorls of three.

The heath of the south of France and North Africa (*E. arborea*) grows several feet high, and from its root-stocks 'briar pipes' are made. The word 'briar' is from *bruyère*, the French word for heath.

The **lesser wintergreen** (*Pyrola minor*) also belongs to this family, and is found growing in similar places to its relatives, though it also inhabits woods, and blooms during June and July. It is not a very common plant. The flower is white, tinged with pink, and is usually half an inch in diameter. It also is globose and borne in pendulous inflorescences. There is no nectar. The wintergreen is evergreen and has a creeping underground stem. There are several other species of wintergreen native to Britain, though they are not common. *Pyrola uniflora* bears solitary terminal flowers. *P. rotundifolia* is similar, having pure white flowers and almost round leaves.

ORNAMENTAL PLANTS

Among the ERICACEAE there are some very lovely garden and parkland plants, chiefly shrubs, such as species of *Rhododendron* and *Azalea*.

The home of the *Rhododendron* is east Asia, from Japan and China to the Himalayas. It is from such places that explorers of the past and the present have enriched and are enriching our own garden flora with this genus. (There is a smaller group native to North America.) As a result we have today a particularly rich collection of species and varieties of *Rhododendrons* and *Azalea* in this country, many of which delight the eye either by their clouds of colour on the bushes, or the floral beauty when viewed separately. The *Rhododendron* is evergreen ; the *Azalea* is deciduous.

The flower is very large, but closely similar to that of heather, except that it is slightly irregular. In the *Rhododendron* flower especially it can be very easily seen how the stamen and the style curve upwards

Eric Hosking

FIG. 90.—*Rhododendron.*

in order to touch the under surface of the body of a visiting insect (Fig. 90).

There are literally hundreds of different genera, species and varieties of *Rhododendron* in varying habits and indescribably lovely shades, and the same can be said of *Azalea*. Those who have the opportunity should not miss the show of these lovely genera in Rhododendron Dell at the Royal Botanic Gardens, Kew.

Arbutus is another cultivated ericaceous genus. The **strawberry tree** from the south of Europe has white, bell-shaped flowers and brilliant fruit like spherical strawberries. There is a variety having red flowers.

Many species of *Erica* are also cultivated, and they are very popular around Christmas-time as potted plants, with comparatively large rose or white flowers. .In fact, the family ERICACEAE seems to have provided more than its share of beautiful ornamental plants, for there must be nearly twenty other genera which, though not native to this country, are sufficiently beautiful to inspire the horticulturist to grow them in his outdoor garden or his conservatory.

BILBERRIES AND CRANBERRIES

All wild members of the family VACCINIACEAE, so closely related to the family ERICACEAE, are frequently found growing among their relatives.

WILD PLANTS

The family contains the bilberry (or whortleberry), the cowberry and the cranberry—all members of the genus *Vaccinium*, the only wild genus of the family to grow in this country.

The **bilberry** or **whortleberry** (*V. myrtillus*) is a shrub growing about a foot or so high. It has deciduous, oval, toothed leaves. The rose-coloured flowers are similar to those of the heather, but they are borne in the axils of the leaves. The fruit is the well-known edible blue-black berry.

The **cranberry** (*V. oxycoccus*) has a creeping stem with ovoid or egg-shaped evergreen leaves. The flowers are pale pink and the fruit is red. The American species of cranberry is *V. pennsylvanicum*, usually called the **blue huckleberry** and is a very popular fruit.

The **cowberry** (*V. vitis-idaea*) is very similar to the cranberry and is often mistaken for it. One distinction, however, may be detected in the leaves. Both are ovate, but that of the cranberry has the broader part of the leaf-blade near the stalk whereas in the cowberry it is the reverse.

ORNAMENTAL PLANTS

Some species of *Vaccinium*, especially imported from America, have now been established in British gardens. They have the habit of procumbent shrubs and give beautiful foliage and fruit effects, especially on peaty soils. It need scarcely be said that most of their fruit can be preserved for kitchen purposes.

42

A PLANT SAPROPHYTE
(*Monotropaceae*)

Evolution is not always progressive, neither has it always been so in the past. Now and then some individual or group seems to take a retrograde step, and then degenerate into a mere caricature of what it would have been had it kept on progressing like its relatives at the same stage of evolution.

All parasites—whether fish, flesh or fowl, plant, animal or man—are degenerates. Some plants, however, though they are not green and therefore cannot make their own food, are yet not parasites. They live on dead and decaying plant and animal material, such as dung, humus, etc. These plants are called saprophytes, and are also degenerate.

Richard Morse

FIG. 91.—Yellow Bird's Nest.

We now come to our first plant saprophyte (formerly considered parasitic) to be found growing wild in this country, though earlier in this scheme there have been others, chiefly of tropical regions.

The present saprophyte belongs to a family which had formerly advanced so high in the scale of evolution as to reach the stage achieved by the ERICACEAE and the VACCINIACEAE, and then began to degenerate by becoming saprophytic on humus. This family, MONOTROPACEAE, is so closely similar, especially in the flower, to the ERICACEAE and the VACCINIACEAE that some botanists group them all together. We think, however, that there is sufficient distinction to warrant a separate family. There are several genera, but only one (*Monotropa*) is represented in this country, and that by one species only, namely, the **yellow bird's nest** (*M. hypopitys*).

This extraordinary plant is not common, but it may be found growing in dense fir, birch and beech woods, frequently where the light-intensity is so low that no green plant could possibly grow there (Fig. 91). Normal plants manufacture their own foodstuffs from the raw materials (chiefly water and dissolved substances drawn from the soil by the roots, and carbon dioxide absorbed from the atmosphere by the leaves); but the plant must have light and the green colouring matter of leaves (chlorophyll) in order to carry out this food manufacture. Water and dissolved substances pass up the stem and into the leaf through its veins. Carbon dioxide from the atmosphere is absorbed by the leaf through its pores, which are situated mainly on the under-surface. In the leaf, the carbon dioxide and water unite, through the agency of the chlorophyll and the light of the sun, to form the sugar glucose. Proteins, fats, and other food substances are then synthesised from this.

Now the bird's nest is a saprophyte. It lives saprophytically on the humus in the soil where it grows. Its roots are covered with a fungus which helps it to extract food from the humus of decaying leaves in which the soil of woods is particularly rich. Thus it does not need to manufacture its own food, and so green leaves are unnecessary. Accordingly the plant has none. The stem is stout and fleshy, about ten inches high. The leaves are reduced to brownish scales. The flowers are pendulous and borne in terminal spikes. Each flower is rather large, ericaceous in structure, and yellowish-brown in colour. The fruit is a capsule.

One very interesting example of a completely *parasitic* flowering plant is *Rafflesia*. This plant belongs to the family RAFFLESIACEAE, which had not progressed along the road of evolution as far as had MONOTROPACEAE. In fact, it follows closely on the water-lilies. All species of this family are natives of Malaya. The plant is parasitic on the roots of vines. It is parasitic to such an extent that the whole plant body, including roots, stems and leaves, has all been reduced to straggling threads which grow through the soil and pierce the roots of their vine hosts to extract food. The flower, on the other hand, is far from being reduced. The species R. *arnoldii* has, in fact, the largest flower of any plant in the world (Fig. 92). It is brilliant red in colour, measures thirty inches across and weighs about fifteen pounds. It has a repulsive smell.

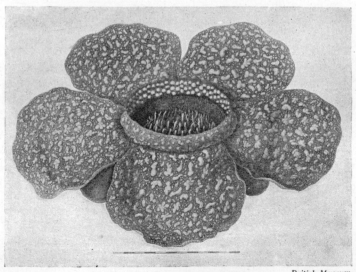

British Museum

FIG. 92.—Flower of *Rafflesia arnoldii*.
The scale represents twelve inches.

43

PERIWINKLES

(*Apocynaceae*)

The lesser and great periwinkles belong to the family APOCYNACEAE, a large family, fairly widely distributed, chiefly in the tropics. Many members of the family are climbers, especially the genus *Vinca*, to which the periwinkles belong. Some of the tropical genera yield rubber.

WILD PLANTS

The **lesser periwinkle** (*V. minor*) cannot be misidentified when its lovely sky-blue flowers are peeping out from its dark foliage during April and May. The plant trails thickly over banks and in thickets. It is chiefly by its creeping stems (Plate 8) that it reproduces itself (vegetatively), for the flowers do not often set seed.

> Through primrose tufts in that green bower,
> The periwinkle trailed its wreaths ;
> And 'tis my faith that every flower
> Enjoys the air it breathes.
> *Lines written in Early Spring* : WORDSWORTH

The leaves are simple and lance-shaped, and the stems are tough and pinkish in colour.

The flowers are large, blue and solitary, borne on long axillary stalks. Each flower has five united sepals, five large petals united towards their bases and easily deciduous. Each of the five stamens is joined to a petal near its base. There are two carpels united and having a common style. The flower ensures cross-pollination (if it occurs at all) by keeping the nectar accessible to long-tongued insects only. This is done by a rampart of silky hairs in the throat of the petals, which prevents small insects from crawling in. The fruit is composed of two follicles which split to release their seeds (Plate 8) ; but these are not easily found.

The **great periwinkle** (*V. major*) is not very different from the lesser, except that it is somewhat larger in general habit, and the leaves tend towards the shape of a heart with a distal point. It is possible that this species is not indigenous but is a garden escape.

ORNAMENTAL PLANTS

Both species of periwinkle are frequently cultivated : there are white and purple varieties, some of them double.

A greenhouse favourite belonging to this family is the **oleander** (*Nerium oleander*). This is a native of Mediterranean regions and is of a tall shrubby habit. The leaves are lance-shaped and thick and are arranged in opposite pairs. They exude a milky juice if pricked or cut. The pores on the lower surface of the leaf are sunk in deep pits and surrounded by microscopic hairs to prevent excessive loss of water.

The flowers are borne in terminal inflorescences and when growing wild are usually pink, though sometimes white. The cultivated varieties show various shades of colour, and some have double flowers.

44

SOME GARDEN FLOWERING SHRUBS
(*Loganiaceae* and *Oleaceae*)

Here we come to a pair of flowering plant families which have given us several of our most popular cultivated shrubs together with some economically useful plants ; but, though the second family contains the ash tree, neither includes any wild herbs or shrubs native to Britain.

LOGANIACEAE

This family is mainly tropical and sub-tropical, but it does contain a very showy cultivated shrub familiar in this country, namely *Buddleia*. Many tropical genera are climbers. In most of the flowers there are four or five sepals, petals and stamens, and two carpels. All the floral whorls are united. The fruit is a berry or drupe.

Buddleia is a handsome deciduous shrub (Fig. 93), its constituent species often giving bold effects with masses of mauve, rose, purple or orange-yellow flowers. The long arching sprays of B. *alternifolia* are particularly striking.

Another attractive shrub, not so frequently grown in Britain, is *Desfontainea spinosa*, a native of Chile. It is a holly-like shrub, with trumpet-shaped flowers, yellow and crimson in colour.

A very useful genus belonging to this family is *Strychnos*, most species of which are tropical climbers, except perhaps the most important of all, namely *S. nux-vomica*, a tree native to India and Ceylon. The fruit of this species is a berry, the flesh of which is quite harmless, but the seeds of which are very poisonous since they contain strychnine. It is from these seeds that this important drug is chiefly obtained. The South American species *S. toxifera*, contains the deadly curare poison with which the South American Indians poison their arrows.

OLEACEAE

To this family belongs the **ash** (*Fraxinus excelsior*), but here we are only interested in the flowering shrubs, such as privet, lilac and jasmine.

Privet (*Ligustrum vulgare*) is sometimes seen growing wild in woods, but it is one of the most commonly cultivated shrubs in this country because it is tolerant of constant clipping and therefore makes good hedges. The privet may be looked upon as being a semi-evergreen, because though it is never without leaves, it is more thickly covered with them in summer than in winter. The leaves are simple, lance-shaped and borne in opposite pairs, and are frequently variegated in colour. Others are completely yellow or golden.

FIG. 93.—*Buddleia alternifolia.*

Waterers

The flowers appear during May to June in dense inflorescences. Each flower is rather small, having four sepals united to form a four-toothed tube, four petals forming a tube with four comparatively large lobes, two stamens and two carpels united to form a two-chambered ovary. The fruit is a large black berry.

Ligustrum vulgare is the common European privet; sometimes one sees under cultivation the so-called **Californian privet**

(*L. ovalifolium*), which is really a native of Japan.

The genus *Olea* contains the very important **olive tree** (*O. europaea*), a native of south-east Europe and Asia Minor, but now cultivated in many other parts of the world for its fruit. This is a large drupe with oily flesh. Sometimes the whole fruit is pickled and served in hors d'oeuvres. But it is more important for the olive oil which is extracted by bruising and pressing the fruit.

Lilac and jasmine are the two most common ornamental shrubs in this family.

Lilac is the true *Syringa* (*S. vulgaris*). The beauty of its large pyramidal inflorescences, and the seductive perfume of its small flowers need no description here; Walt Whitman did it well enough :

R. A. Malby & Co.

FIG. 94.—Jasmine (*Jasminum nudiflorum*).

> The lilac-bush tall-growing with heart-shaped leaves of rich green,
> With many a pointed blossom rising delicate, with the perfume
>   strong I love,
> With every leaf a miracle.
> *When Lilacs Last in the Dooryard Bloom'd* : WHITMAN

In fundamental structure, the lilac flower resembles that of the privet, but it is larger and far excels the privet in colour and perfume. There are flowers of purest white, others of cream, and the lilac shades vary between pale mauve and deep crimson-purple. Both white and lilac shades are presented either by single or double flowers.

The climbing **jasmine** or **jessamine** (*Jasminum*) is equally as lovely as the lilac both in its floral beauty and its perfume (Fig. 94). There are two colours of jasmine—yellow (*J. fruticans*, *J. nudiflorum*, etc.) and white (*J. officinale*, etc.).

O

Jas in the Arab language is despair,
And Min the darkest meaning of a lie.
Thus cried the Jessamine among the flowers,
How justly doth a lie
Draw on its head despair !
Among the fragrant spirits of the bowers
The boldest and the strongest still was I.
Although so fair,
Therefore from Heaven
A stronger perfume unto me was given
Than any blossom of the summer hours.

Jessamine : C. G. LELAND

The genus *Jasminum* is different from the previous two in that its floral parts are in fives. *J. nudiflorum* is very early flowering, and in this species the flowers appear before the leaves.

Forsythia, a genus which hails from China and Japan, is now a well-established favourite in our gardens. It presents its many blossoms in veritable clouds of yellow, like large jasmine flowers.

45

THE BEDSTRAW FAMILY
(Rubiaceae)

Though this family (RUBIACEAE) is mainly tropical and contains some plants which supply various highly important economic products, such as coffee and quinine, there are several wild members in this country, especially the genus *Galium*, which is also represented as far north as the Arctic.

WILD PLANTS

Most British wild members of this family belong to the genus *Galium*, the bedstraws. It is not easy to mistake this genus, for the small, lance-shaped leaves are borne in characteristic whorls at intervals along the stem.

A very typical species is **cleavers** or **goose-grass** (*G. aparine*), so common in tufted masses in hedgerows. The plant climbs easily, for its square stems and even its leaves are covered with short reflexed hooks

(Plate 8). Thus the long branches can leave the tufts at the bottom of the hedge and scramble all over it.

The leaves are simple and are borne in whorls—six to eight in each whorl (Plate 8). To each whorl there is usually one or perhaps two axillary buds, which grow out to form branch-stems frequently bearing the inflorescences (Plate 8). In each inflorescence there are three to nine small white flowers.

In each flower there are four united sepals so small as to form a mere ring; four white petals joined at their bases and spread out clearly from each other further up; four stamens; two carpels joined and having two separate styles (Plate 8). Nectar is freely exposed.

The fruit of the goose-grass is interesting. It is a schizocarp and is covered with hooks (Plate 8), and so able to cling to passing animals, thus ensuring wide distribution. It is these fruits which so often stick to our clothes during a country ramble.

The common name ' cleavers ' means, of course, ' clingers '. The other common name, ' goose-grass ' was given to this plant because geese like it. In fact, even today, poultry keepers frequently gather it and boil it and add it to mash which is to be fed to geese and turkeys during the fattening period.

A near relative of goose-grass is the **yellow** or **lady's bedstraw** (G. verum) (Plate 8). This plant, however, has no prickles and its flowers are yellow. Its stem is long, thin and weak. The leaves are exceptionally small and are borne in whorls of six to eight. The small flowers appear during June to September, and since they grow in very large and dense inflorescences, both terminal and axillary (Plate 8) they make a striking show on downs and commons and other dry places where the plant grows. The flower, apart from a difference in colour, is similar to that of the goose-grass.

The **great hedge bedstraw** (G. mollugo) is very like both the yellow bedstraw and the goose-grass (Plate 8). It differs from the yellow bedstraw chiefly in that its leaves are larger, the flowers are white and are borne in smaller and less dense inflorescences. Its main points of difference from the goose-grass are that its leaves are smaller and the whole plant is smooth. The plant is to be found growing on the upper banks of hedgerows, and blooms during July and August.

There are about eight wild species of Galium, among them, the **water bedstraw** (G. palustre), having white flowers and growing in marshes, but the three described above are the most common.

Of other wild genera belonging to the RUBIACEAE the **field madder** (*Sherardia arvensis*) is one of the most common. It grows in cornfields and has a long flowering season (April to October). The leaves are borne in whorls of four to six. The flower is lilac-coloured with petals forming a funnel.

The **madder** (*Rubia tinctorum*) is not very common. It is covered with prickles. The flowers are borne in small yellowish cymes, and the fruit is a black berry. Formerly this plant was cultivated for the extraction of the red dye alizarin. This dye was prepared from madder from the time of the Ancients until 1868, when its chemical synthesis was first achieved.

The **woodruff** (*Asperula odorata*) grows in shady woods, and flowers during May and June. Its leaves are borne in whorls of six at the bottom of the stem, and seven to nine nearer the top. The sweet-scented flowers are white and the four petals open out like a salver. The fruit is hooked.

> For, where the welcome sun came through,
> A delicate, rising green was new.
> The crosswise flowers were white and pure,
> And started from a ruff demure,
> And every tiny cluster lent
> A fresh and most entrancing scent.
> This pretty Puritan I claim,
> And Woodruff is its charming name.
>
> JOHN WYNN

ORNAMENTAL PLANTS

The **yellow bedstraw** (*Galium verum*) is sometimes cultivated, because its large, tufted, yellow inflorescences certainly give an attractive display.

Some species of *Asperula* are also cultivated for their show of pale blue flowers over a very long season.

ECONOMIC PLANTS

Several tropical forms of this family (RUBIACEAE) are of considerable economic value.

Coffee is the product of the **coffee plant** (*Coffea arabica*). This species is a native of Abyssinia, but it has now been established in

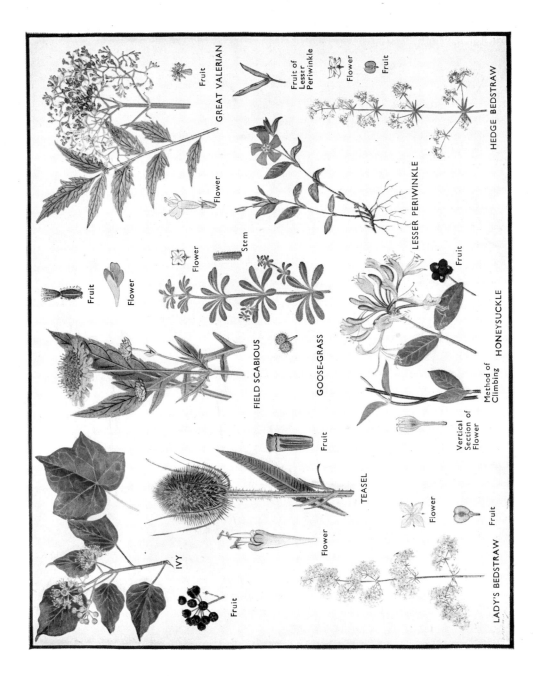

GREAT VALERIAN

Fruit

Flower

Fruit of Lesser Periwinkle

Flower

Fruit

HEDGE BEDSTRAW

LESSER PERIWINKLE

Flower

Fruit

Flower

Stem

Fruit

Flower

FIELD SCABIOUS

GOOSE-GRASS

Fruit

Vertical Section of Flower

Method of Climbing   HONEYSUCKLE

IVY

Fruit

TEASEL

Flower

Flower

Fruit

LADY'S BEDSTRAW

PLATE 8

several parts of the world, and is the staple product of Brazil. Other species are used, but they produce coffee of inferior quality.

The plant is an evergreen shrub attaining a height of about twenty feet. The fruit is a fleshy berry. Inside each berry are two seeds, and it is from these that coffee is made. These seeds are usually referred to as ' coffee beans ' ; but, of course, they are not beans at all, if we are to consider the leguminous beans (p. 160) to be true beans.

We know very little of the early history of coffee, except that it goes back to very remote times ; but it is certain that it was a popular drink in Abyssinia during the fifteenth century. Coffee achieved popularity in Europe during the seventeenth century, when coffee-houses sprang up almost as thickly as the tea-shops in larger towns of the present day. The earliest known coffee-house in England was opened in St. Michael's Alley, Cornhill, London, in 1652.

The genus *Cinchona* contains several small tropical trees which produce quinine—a most important drug, especially in the treatment of malaria.

Quinine is present in the bark of the tree. The earliest record of the medical use of the cinchona bark dates back to 1638, when it was used effectively for curing the Countess of Chinchon, the wife of the Viceroy of Peru, of a fever. From this incident, the plant got its common name, cinchona. The term ' quinine ' is from the native name ' quina-quina '. At that time cinchona trees were grown only in South America ; but gradually the fame of its bark spread and eventually reached Europe. In 1854, the Dutch Government obtained some trees from South America and transplanted them in Java. Five years later, the British Government tried a similar experiment in India and Ceylon. Then the price of quinine decreased from twelve shillings to one shilling an ounce. After this, the attack of the trees by disease caused the cultivation of quinine in Ceylon to die out. So today Java holds the monopoly, though India still cultivates a considerable quantity to supply to the local inhabitants through its public services, including the post office.

The War has sent men of science in quest of substitutes, especially in anti-malarials. The two synthetics, atabrine and plasmochine, are valuable, but we still need all the quinine we can get, for each year several hundred million people are stricken with malaria, which is still a serious menace.

Ipecacuanha is extracted from the root of another genus of plants belonging to this family, namely, *Psychotria ipecacuanha*, a native of Brazil.

46

ELDER AND HONEYSUCKLE

(*Caprifoliaceae*)

Many beautiful ornamental shrubs and climbers, both wild and cultivated, belong to the family CAPRIFOLIACEAE. Most of them have soft wood with broad pith.

WILD PLANTS

The **common elder** (*Sambucus nigra*) is actually a tree, ten to twenty feet high when growing in woods ; but it frequently assumes the habit of a shrub in hedges where it so often grows.

The bark of the twigs is greyish-brown in colour and dotted with very pronounced lenticels or breathing-pores. On the older branches the bark becomes corrugated and rough. The leaf is large and compound, with two to five pairs of lateral leaflets and a terminal one. Each leaflet is lance-shaped and serrated. There are no stipules. In having compound leaves, the elder differs from the rest of the family.

The flowers are very small, but they are borne in dense inflorescences, shaped like large irregular disks, and there are so many of them on a plant that it looks very handsome in June when it is in bloom.

Each inflorescence is composed of five main branches, all of which bear their flowers at the same level, thus giving the disk-shaped effect.

The five sepals of the flower are united, and display five teeth at the upper rim. There are five petals which towards their bases are united to form a tube, but higher up are separate and spreading. The stamens are equal in number to the petals and alternate with them. The three carpels are united and have three stigmas joined immediately on to the top of the ovary, for there are no styles. The fruit is the familiar berry, which contains three to six seeds. The berry is first green, then red and eventually deep purple. Elder berries are edible though neither very palatable nor nourishing. A wine is sometimes made from them. The plant has also been looked upon as having medicinal virtues.

The **dwarf elder** (*S. ebulus*) differs from the common elder in that it grows only two to three feet high, its leaves have stipules, the inflorescences have only three main branches, and the flowers are purplish.

Perhaps the most charming wild member of this family is the **honeysuckle** or **woodbine** (*Lonicera periclymenum*), frequently discovered climbing over hedgerows and displaying its sweet-scented flowers during May to September. (The common name 'woodbine' is sometimes applied to convolvulus.) The plant climbs by twining its long woody stem in a clockwise direction around the stems of the stronger supporting plants.

The leaves are simple and lance-shaped. They are borne in pairs, each pair being at right angles to the adjacent pair.

The flowers are borne several in a head (Plate 8). Each flower is irregular. The five sepals are united and toothed. The five large petals are united into a long funnel-shaped tube, yellowish-pink in colour, which opens out in two large lobes. The five stamens and the style project beyond the petal-tube. This fact, and the deep-seated site of the nectar, both help to ensure pollination by long-tongued night moths, for the flower opens and smells best at night.

> Good Lord, how sweetly smells the honeysuckle
> In the hush'd night, as if the world were one
> Of utter peace, and love, and gentleness.
>
> *Gareth and Lynette* : TENNYSON

The stamens split and expose their dry pollen just as evening approaches, then the flower moves into a horizontal position. At first the style curves downwards, and the visiting moth alights on the stamens while it forces its long tongue down the tube to get at the nectar at the bottom. Then the moth takes its departure. After this the style gradually assumes the horizontal position and the stamens wither and wilt. All this happens before the next evening approaches, for by then more flowers in the head have opened and are ready for the moths. Thus when the moth alights on a flower with its style in the right position the stigma touches that part of its body bearing the pollen from another flower.

The fruits are bright red berries (Plate 8) which are poisonous.

There are several other species of honeysuckle, though these are rare.

Two shrubs, often attaining the size and habits of trees, are the **guelder rose** and the **wayfaring tree**—both species of the genus *Viburnum*. The guelder rose is *V. opulus*, and the wayfaring tree, *V. lantana*.

FIG. 95.—*Viburnum sterile.*

Both these plants are inhabitants of woodlands, the guelder rose flowering during June and July and the wayfaring tree during May and June. The leaf of the guelder rose is five-lobed, whereas that of the wayfaring tree is simple with a downy under-surface. A curious feature of the wayfaring tree is that its buds have no protective bud-scales.

The flowers of both these species are very like that of the elder and they are borne in similar inflorescences. In the case of the guelder rose, the outer flowers of the disk are much larger than the inner ones and are neuter. In both, the fruits are berries—dark red in the case of the guelder rose, and purplish-black in the case of the wayfaring tree.

One wild herb, the **moschatel** (*Adoxa moschatellina*), belongs to this family. It is a strange-looking plant, growing in shady places and bearing its insignificant greenish flowers during April and May. The plant is four to six inches high. Each leaf is divided into three leaflets, and each leaflet is again divided into three deeply toothed lobes.

The flowers are borne in close heads of five each. They are greenish in colour and are regular—in fact, very similar in structure to the elder flower.

ORNAMENTAL PLANTS

All the wild shrubs of this family are also cultivated. Some varieties of cultivated elder have attractive golden foliage. A large number of species of *Viburnum* are cultivated: in most cases all their flowers are neuter. A close relative of the guelder rose is the **snowball tree** (*Viburnum sterile*) with balls of creamy white flowers (Fig. 95).

Another old-fashioned favourite is the **snowberry** (*Symphoricarpus albus*), with unusually large white berries.

Abelia is an Asiatic and Mexican genus which gives us several semi-evergreen shrubs with rosy-purple or pink flowers. *Diervilla* is an Asiatic and North American genus which comprises a large number of species of shrubs with large flowers borne in inflorescences of five to twenty flowers, varying in shades from white to pink and so on to purple.

47

THE VALERIAN FAMILY
(*Valerianaceae*)

The valerian family (VALERIANACEAE) is a small one, but its most outstanding member is a conspicuous common plant. All members of the family are herbs with thick, strong-smelling underground stems.

WILD PLANTS

The **great valerian** (*Valeriana officinalis*) may be seen flowering in moist woods during June to August (Plate 8). The leaves are compound with lance-shaped serrated leaflets. The flowers are flesh-coloured and are borne in large loose inflorescences.

The sepals are reduced to feathery structures collectively forming what is called a pappus which is very common among composite flowers (p. 212). The pappus remains attached to the fruit and by its means the latter is able to parachute through the air and thus become widely distributed. The five petals form a long tube with five irregular lobes at the rim (Plate 8). There are three stamens. The three carpels are united and have a common hair-like style.

Cats are attracted by the scent of this plant, and they delight in rolling in clumps of valerian just as they do in clumps of cat-mint.

The **marsh valerian** (*V. dioica*) has rose-coloured flowers. Its leaves growing from ground-level are oval; those on the flowering stems are simple, but very deeply cut.

The genus *Valerianella* contains the **lamb's lettuce** (*V. olitoria*) a plant sometimes seen growing in cornfields and hedges and flowering during April and June. The flowers are blue and are borne in dense inflorescences.

ORNAMENTAL PLANTS

The genus *Valeriana* is often cultivated in garden borders and frequently grows thickly on old walls. There are deep red, pink and white varieties.

The genus *Centranthus* is also cultivated. It is very similar to *Valeriana*, with bright red flowers, but at the base of the petal-tube there is a long spur. The **red spur-valerian** (*C. ruber*), which is cultivated, may sometimes be found growing wild as a garden escape.

ECONOMIC PLANTS

The genus *Valeriana* has a certain medicinal value, though valerian, which is extracted chiefly from the thick underground stem of *V. officinalis*, is not used in medicine so much today. At one time this plant was known as ' all-heal ', owing to its supposed manifold medicinal properties.

From the fragrant underground thick stems of the Himalayan genus *Nardostachys* (*N. jatamansi*), spikenard is extracted. This perfume was at one time used as a cosmetic, especially by the Ancient Greeks, Romans and Egyptians.

48

THE SCABIOUS FAMILY
(*Dipsacaceae*)

The scabious family (DIPSACACEAE) is entirely an Old World family. Most of its members are herbs.

This family is very different from any other so far considered in that the flowers are small and crowded together in a single head, which, at a casual glance, looks like one large complicated flower. In this respect, the family DIPSACACEAE resembles the next family, COMPOSITAE, which has carried this unique structure of the inflorescence to the farthest extreme among all flowering plants.

WILD PLANTS

One of our most lovely meadow plants is the **field scabious** (*Scabiosa arvensis*), easily recognised by its large disk-shaped flower-heads, with their outer flowers (or florets) a beautiful sky-blue, and the inner ones mauve with golden stamens standing out (Plate 8).

The plant grows in meadows and along river-banks, and its conspicuous flower-heads are at their best during July and August. The leaves growing from ground-level are large, lance-shaped and serrated. Those on the long inflorescence-stalks are deeply divided (Plate 8). The whole plant, especially its leaves and stems, is very hairy.

The inner or disk flowers are small and mauve. Those on the rim (usually called the ray flowers) are large and sky-blue (Plate 8). Surrounding the whole inflorescence is a large number of small green bracts, collectively called the involucre.

In each flower, the sepals are united to form a cup on the rim of which are about sixteen radiating teeth which eventually form a hairy pappus on the fruit (Plate 8). The four petals are joined to form a tube with four lobes, the lobes of the ray flowers being much larger and extended, each petal being unequal in size and forming two lips (Plate 8). There are four stamens, those of the disk flowers standing up like golden pins. The two carpels are joined and have a common style which is as fine as a hair. Each fruit is a small achene crowned by a pappus of hairs formed from the sepals (Plate 8), by which the fruit is distributed.

Cross-pollination is assured because the stamens ripen first while the style remains still undeveloped within the petal-tube. Then the stamens wither and the style takes their place.

There are two other kinds of scabious, both of which belong to the genus *Scabiosa*, namely, the **devil's-bit scabious** (*S. succisa*) and the **small scabious** (*S. columbaria*). The former grows in pastures, and blooms during July to October; the latter is found in drier fields and on banks and has a shorter flowering season—July and August.

The pappus of both these species has a smaller number of hairs than that of the field scabious. The devil's-bit scabious has a pronounced involucre and no large ray flowers. All the flowers are purplish-blue. None of the leaves is divided.

The small scabious has divided leaves both growing from ground-level and on the floral stalks. The petal-tube is five-toothed as against the four lobes of the two other kinds of scabious.

Another genus of the family DIPSACACEAE, namely, *Dipsacus*, contains the **wild teasel** (*D. sylvestris*). This plant grows in waste places, especially along river-banks and in marshes, flowering during August and September, though its dry brown heads remain conspicuous long after the fruit have been distributed (Plate 8).

The wild teasel grows to a height of five to six feet and its stems are covered with strong, sharp bristles. The leaves are large, wavy and lance-shaped: they have no stalks. They are inserted opposite each other on the stem, and the bases of both leaves are fused so that they completely encircle the stem. In the cup thus formed water collects (Plate 8).

The inflorescence of the teasel is different from that of the scabious in that the former is egg-shaped. The involucre of bracts surrounding the flower-head is very pronounced. While the flower-heads are young and green, the green involucral bracts are long and surround the head completely. Then gradually the bracts open out and eventually wither, though a considerable part of each bract remains as a tough brown scale.

On the conical inflorescence, each small flower is subtended by a long, spiny, hooked green bract (Plate 8).

Each flower has four sepals united to form a cup, without teeth on its rim. There are four petals forming a four-lobed tube, the tube part being white and the four lobes at the rim purple (Plate 8). The four stamens are very long and the style simple and short.

FIG. 96.—Double Scabious.

The flowers are pollinated by bees.

After fertilisation, the whole conical flower-head turns brown and tough, thus presenting a brown, cone-shaped structure having a surface covered with sharp hooked spines (the floral bracts), and surrounding the whole head at the base are about a dozen ridged brown involucral bracts. The heads of the **fuller's teasel** (*D. fullonum*) were at one time used for 'teasing' or combing wool. They are still used for raising the nap on cloth, though not to the same extent as when the plant was cultivated for this purpose.

PLATE 9

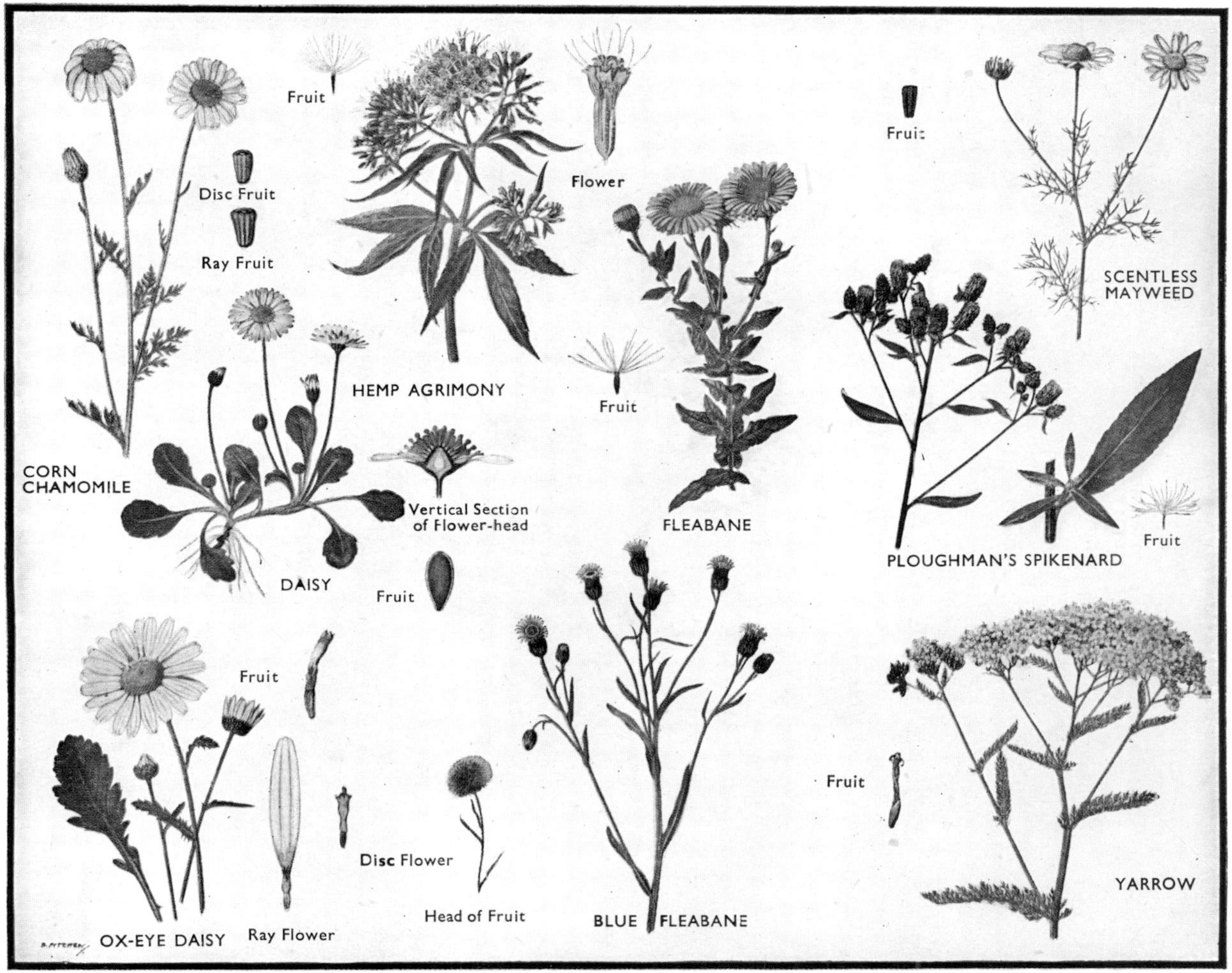

SCENTLESS MAYWEED

Fruit

PLOUGHMAN'S SPIKENARD

Fruit

YARROW

Fruit

FLEABANE

Flower

Fruit

BLUE FLEABANE

HEMP AGRIMONY

Vertical Section of Flower-head

Fruit

Disc Flower

Head of Fruit

Fruit

Disc Fruit

Ray Fruit

DAISY

Disc Flower

Fruit

CORN CHAMOMILE

Fruit

Ray Flower

OX-EYE DAISY

The brown heads, having lost their fruit, are, of course, quite dead, and that is why they can be, and are, used for household decoration without having to be supplied with water. They are often dyed various colours, and are more or less everlasting.

ORNAMENTAL FLOWERS

Scabious is a very popular summer flower in the garden, and its handsome flower-heads on long graceful stalks are favoured for household decoration (Fig. 96). These garden varieties give delicate shades of white, pink, salmon and blue, with darker shades of red, mauve and purple, and are most frequently double.

49

THE LARGEST FAMILY OF ALL
(Compositae)

The COMPOSITAE is the largest of all flowering plant families, comprising about nine hundred genera and fourteen thousand species. That means that more than ten per cent of the wild species of flowering plants belong to this family alone. Furthermore, the family is distributed throughout the world. Yet, in spite of its very large numbers and exceptionally comprehensive and wide distribution, the composite family has such well-marked characteristics that its members cannot be mistaken. Some of its characteristics are unique, though the family does bear a certain resemblance to the family DIPSACACEAE just considered.

Since members of this family are to be found in almost every conceivable situation, we should expect a great variation in vegetative habit, and, indeed, this is so, though it should be noted that nearly all, in fact, about ninety-eight per cent of the members of the family are herbs. The very small minority is made up of shrubs and trees, none of which is to be found in Great Britain. Furthermore, there are very few aquatic and marsh plants, and climbers are rare.

The reason why the COMPOSITAE are so widely distributed is because of the many means of vegetative reproduction, chiefly underground stems, and the presence in many of the fruit of a hairy pappus

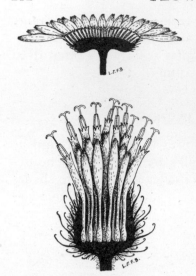

FIG. 97.—Sections through Flower-heads (capitula) of Composites; above, daisy (ligulate and tubular flowers); below, burdock (all tubular flowers).

by which the fruit is disseminated far and wide.

Perhaps the most characteristic feature of all is the unique arrangement of the flowers (almost equalled by one family only, namely, DIPSACACEAE). Each flower-head, such as that of the daisy or the dandelion, looks like one large flower; but actually it is a collection of many separate flowers or florets arranged on a flat or cone-shaped swollen stem. The whole arrangement of flowers is surrounded by an involucre of bracts (Fig. 97). Such an inflorescence is called a capitulum.

The various whorls of floral organs in each flower are usually in fives with the exception of the carpels. In the case of the sepals, the five members are sometimes only represented by a five-toothed rim, though much more often the sepals are modified into a hairy pappus which eventually forms the parachute of the fruit, or instead of a pappus on the fruit there may be hooked bristles. There are five petals, all united in such a way as to make the flower either regular or definitely irregular. The petals may be united along their length, forming a tube around the stamens and carpels and having five teeth at the top rim. This gives what is called a tubular flower, which is regular (Fig. 98). On the other hand, the five petals may be joined to form a strap with five teeth at the top. This gives what is called a ligulate flower, which of course is irregular (Fig. 98).

In different genera the flowers are grouped in all three possible ways. That is, the capitulum may contain nothing but tubular flowers, as in the case of hemp agrimony (p. 213) and the burdock (Fig. 97); or all ligulate flowers, as in the dandelion (Fig. 98); or a mixture of both,

FIG. 98.—Some Composite flowers; left to right, ragwort (tubular), dandelion (ligulate), outer neuter flower of cornflower, inner tubular flower of cornflower.

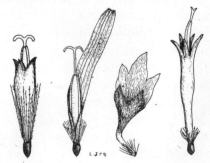

with usually a central disk of tubular flowers (called disk flowers) surrounded by a ray of ligulate flowers (called ray flowers), as in the daisy (Fig. 97 and p. 214).

In a few species, such as knapweed or hard-head and corn-flower, the disk flowers are all tubular and regular, whereas those on the rim of the inflorescence are tubular but much larger, irregular and usually neuter (Plates 10 and 11 and Fig. 98).

Those composite plants which have inflorescences containing tubular flowers only or tubular and ligulate flowers together are usually grouped in the sub-family *Tubuliferae*; those having nothing but ligulate flowers are assigned to the sub-family *Liguliflorae*.

WILD FLOWERS

It will be impossible to consider even the majority of wild representatives of this enormous family, yet it will be necessary to examine an exceptionally large number in order to get a general idea of the whole family. From this point of view, we are fortunate in that so many different genera and species grow wild in this country.

TUBULIFERAE

A common composite plant having nothing but tubular flowers is the **hemp agrimony** (*Eupatorium cannabinum*), seen flowering along river-banks and in damp woods during July and August (Fig. 99 and Plate 9). The plant is tall, and its upright stems do not branch until near the top. The leaves are compound, each composed of three or five leaflets, and each leaflet being toothed, lance-shaped, long and pointed. Both stems and leaves are covered with down.

The inflorescence of the hemp agrimony does not look like most of the composite inflorescences, and indeed it is not. It is more primitive, but obviously showing a tendency towards the capitulum of, say, the daisy. The mass of flower-heads is very conspicuous.

FIG. 99.—Hemp Agrimony.

Each flower-head or inflorescence looks like a single flower, but closer examination shows it to be composed of about five tubular flowers surrounded by about twice as many bracts (Plate 9).

The flowers are mauve in colour; in fact, there are no yellow members (the colour most common in composites) in this genus. The style of the flower is branched and hairy, and projects beyond the petal tube. The flower contains much nectar, and is frequently visited by butterflies. The fruit is beautifully plumed. (Plate 9.)

The **daisy** (*Bellis perennis*) is a good example of a composite flower, since it bears both tubular and ligulate flowers on its capitulum (Fig. 97 and Plate 9). This lovely plant grows almost everywhere, especially in meadows, and, alas, on lawns. It multiplies and hibernates by means of short underground stems. The leaves are inversely egg-shaped with rounded divisions on their margins. All of them grow from ground-level, and none from the flower-stalk. This is hairy and is never branched, therefore each one bears one flower-head. The leaves form a rosette flat against the soil surface, so that no other plant, not even grass, can grow beneath them. That is why this ' poet's darling ', as Wordsworth called it, is such a curse on lawns.

The disk flowers are tubular and yellow; the ray flowers are white tipped with pink. The former are hermaphrodite, having both stamens and carpels ; the latter are female only, having no stamens.

> Ah, drops of gold in whitening flame
> Burning, we know your lovely name—
> Daisies, that little children pull !
> *To Daisies* : FRANCIS THOMPSON

The common name of the daisy plant means ' day's eye ' because the flower-heads close at night and open out in the early morning— the ' eye of the day ' : so aptly put by Chaucer :

> That well by reason men it callë may
> That ' day's-eye ', or else the ' eye of day '.

This opening and closing is connected with pollination. The tubular flowers shed their pollen before the stigmas are ripe. Thus they ensure cross-pollination, for insects crawl over the pollen and so carry it to another flower where probably the stigmas are ripe. Towards evening, the ray flowers close over the disk flowers and thus bring their stigmas into contact with the shed pollen of the latter. The fruit is an achene and has no pappus.

The **blue fleabane** (*Erigeron acris*) grows on chalk downs and dry banks and exhibits its purple (not blue) flowers during July and August.

Its leaves are long and pointed and are not toothed (Plate 9). The tubular disk flowers are yellow, and the ligulate ray flowers purplish. The involucre of bracts is bristly. After fertilisation, the flowers die and the pappus then presents a head of down (Plate 9).

To the genus *Inula* belong several other fleabanes. One of the commonest and most attractive is the **common fleabane** (*Inula dysenterica*), whose handsome yellow flower-heads frequently assert themselves in marshy settings during summer (July to September).

In olden days, the floors of houses were strewn with rushes—a very unhygienic kind of floor-covering, for it attracted insects, especially fleas. The residents, therefore, used to burn fleabane in their houses, for the smoke from it was supposed to drive the insects away, and, indeed, this measure was probably quite successful, for no insect likes smoke. In any event it explains the common name of this plant.

The fleabane is sturdy but coarse-looking (Plate 9). The leaves are lance-shaped with wavy margins. They are arranged in opposite pairs, and the margins of each pair are joined so that the pair of leaves encircle the stem. The flowers are a beautiful golden yellow, with long ray flowers. Though the disk flowers are hermaphrodite, the ray flowers are all female only.

To the same genus, *Inula*, belongs the **ploughman's spikenard** (*I. conyza*) which in general resembles the blue fleabane, though its nearer relative is the common fleabane. It grows in copses and on dry

Henry Irving

FIG. 100.—Rosette leaves of Ploughman's Spikenard.

P

banks, and blooms at the same time as the common fleabane. It is not a very handsome plant (Plate 9). Its leaves are lance-shaped with fine-toothed margins. The flower-heads are borne in loose tufts. Each flower is long and thin. The styles of the outer flower are purple, and the pappus is reddish. The whole inflorescence is almost lost in a long involucre of brown bracts.

The ploughman's spikenard can be a nuisance as a weed on lawns, for its leaves growing at ground-level form a rosette like those of the daisy (Fig. 100).

Golden rod (*Solidago virgaurea*) is not very common, but it is some-times seen in woods and thickets, flowering during July to September. The stem is one to two feet high, and the golden-yellow heads of flowers are crowded together in dense panicles. All the flowers, both tubular and ligulate, are yellow. The ligulate ray flowers are few in num-ber, forming only a single row. The leaves are lance-shaped and hairy.

The **bur-marigold** (*Bidens tripartita*) is a rather interesting com-posite. It grows in marshy places, and flowers during July to Septem-ber. Its leaves are stalked and the blades are divided into three. The flower-heads droop slightly. To each one, there is an involucre of bracts in two series, the outer series being leafy and spreading. The flower-head is yellowish, and usually all the flowers are tubular. The fruit has no hairy pappus, but is compressed and has three to five longitudinal ribs, along each of which is a row of stiff bristles, and at the top the pappus, instead of being hairy, is represented by several bristles, one to each rib. All the bristles are hooked, and thus equip the fruit for distribution by animals.

The **yarrow** or **milfoil** (*Achillea millefolium*) is a very common plant, though none the less attractive. It is supposed to heal wounds ; in fact, its generic name comes from Achilles who was taught the virtues of plants by the centaur Chiron. The French for it is *herbe aux Charpentiers* because it was supposed to heal wounds made by carpenters' tools. It has a peculiar scent. It grows in fields and meadows, waysides and waste places. It sometimes gives trouble as a weed, because of its tough, underground spreading stems. The flower-heads appear during June to September.

The stem of this plant is very tough. The leaves are finely divided (Plate 9) so that each looks like a delicate fern. There are many leaves on the erect stems and many also tufted at the base, which explains the specific name of the plant, also its alternative common name.

The very large flower-masses—pure white and pale mauve—do

not look composite but rather umbelliferous. Actually each single small flower-head in the mass of flower-heads contains about half a dozen ray flowers surrounding a very small number of yellowish tubular disk flowers. Hundreds of these flower-heads are arranged in flat masses (Plate 9). There is no pappus to the fruit. The involucre surrounding each small flower-head is made up of insignificant chaffy scales.

The **scentless mayweed** (*Anthemis cotula*) is a rather attractive white composite, growing in fields (especially cultivated fields) and in waste places. It blooms during June to September. The plant grows from a foot to eighteen inches high. The leaves are inserted in alternating positions on the stems and in tufted masses at the base. Each leaf is spreading and finely divided (Plate 9). The whole plant is smooth.

Each flower-head is borne in a solitary terminal position, and has yellow, hermaphrodite, tubular disk flowers and large white ligulate ray flowers with no styles.

The **corn chamomile** (*A. arvensis*) is a member of the same genus. It is also a weed, though an attractive one, and is frequently seen flowering during June to August. It is somewhat similar in appearance to the scentless mayweed, except that the leaves, though very finely divided, are in outline not so spreading but lance-shaped, each one being divided into what appear to be deeply cut leaflets (Plate 9). The flower-heads are closely similar to those of scentless mayweed, though more robust, and the ray flowers sometimes hang reflexed, which is never seen in the scentless mayweed (Plate 9). The fruit is an achene with no pappus.

The **ox-eye, dog** or **moon daisy** (*Chrysanthemum leucanthemum*) is one of our loveliest wild white composites, growing in pastures and on banks, especially where the grass is long (Fig. 101). It is a summer flower (June to August), and frequently grows in masses of white. The leaves are not unlike those of the small daisy, though larger and more deeply cleft. The involucre of each flower-head is shaped like an inverted basin, having overlapping bracts, each green bract being edged with a brownish membrane. The ray flowers are large, long, and female only (Plate 9).

The **corn marigold** (*C. segetum*) is a generic relation, with yellow ray flowers. It sometimes, though not often, appears in cultivated fields.

Tansy (*Tanacetum vulgare*) is a very lovely plant growing in waste places and dry fields, displaying golden-yellow massed heads during

August and September (Plate 10). The leaves are divided into large blades each of which is very finely cut. Each capitulum is about half an inch in diameter, and there are many such in the massed heads (Plate 10). The golden-yellow, tubular, disk flowers are all male, since they have no carpels. The ray flowers are short and also golden. They contain the carpels. The fruit has no pappus.

The tansy is used as a medicinal herb, and was at one time employed as a flavouring in cooking.

The **wormwood** (*Artemisia absinthium*) is sometimes seen growing in waste places. Its leaves

Harold Bastin
FIG. 101.—Ox-eye Daisy.

are divided. The flower-heads droop. All the flowers are yellowish and tubular, and there are not many per head. The flavouring matter absinthe is derived from this and other species of wormwood.

Coltsfoot (*Tussilago farfara*) is a very common plant on moist soils. It is also interesting in that it flowers very early in the year (March to May), that is, before its leaves are open (Fig. 102). The leaves are unusual for a composite, being shield-shaped with several teeth (Plate 11). When very young, both sides of the leaf are covered with a white silky down; but after the leaf has opened this down falls off the upper surface. The plant reproduces itself by means of thick underground stems (Plate 11).

The flower-heads of coltsfoot are borne at the ends of thick, erect stalks which bear hairy bracts (Plate 11). Each flower-head is golden yellow, with a disk of yellow tubular flowers and an outer ring of yellow ligulate ray flowers. This plant has a very efficient means of preventing

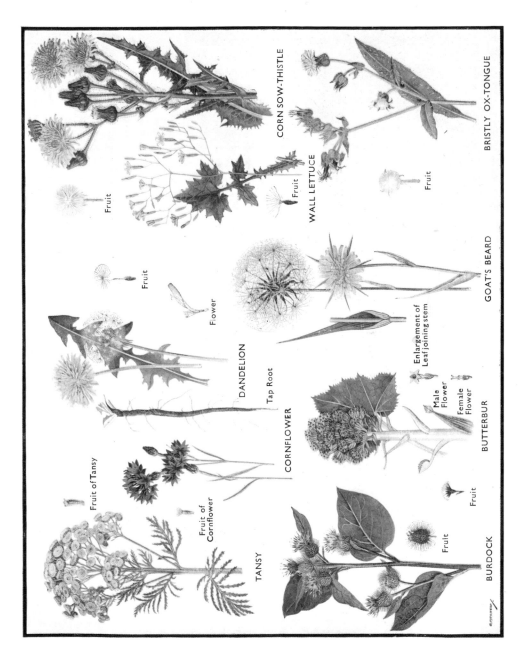

CORN SOW-THISTLE

Fruit

BRISTLY OX-TONGUE

WALL LETTUCE

Fruit

Fruit

Fruit

Flower

DANDELION

Tap Root

GOAT'S BEARD

Enlargement of
Leaf joining stem

Male
Flower

Female
Flower

CORNFLOWER

BUTTERBUR

Fruit of Tansy

Fruit of
Cornflower

TANSY

Fruit

Fruit

BURDOCK

PLATE 10

self-pollination. All the disk flowers are male only, though they have their styles, which are sterile. The ray flowers are female only. Only the male flowers secrete nectar. The male flowers ripen and shed their pollen within their own petal tubes. Then their sterile styles grow up and push the mass of pollen out of the tube and on to the stigmas of the ray flowers, which by this time are ripe. Each fruit has a pappus of hairs, which collectively give the head the appearance of a ball of fluff (Plate 11).

The **butterbur** (*Petasites vulgaris*) is in many respects similar to the coltsfoot, though not in general appearance (Plate 10). It is a moisture-loving plant, and grows in wet meadows and beside ponds and rivers. It spreads by means of underground stems. It also bears its flower-heads before the leaves are open. The leaves, when these open, are very large and conspicuous, sometimes attaining a diameter of three feet. Crowded together as they usually are, they form excellent cover for water-fowl. Each leaf is somewhat similar in design to that of the coltsfoot, except that it is more serrated and pointed. It also is downy beneath.

The flower-heads of butterbur are pink and are borne in dense spikes at the ends of thick stalks bearing bracts (also like coltsfoot). Towards the base of these stalks, the bracts merge into foliage leaves, and between the complete bract and the complete foliage leaf there are all possible gradations (Plate 10).

All butterbur flowers are tubular. In most cases the flower-heads are either all male or all female, one sex being usually confined to one plant. Sometimes, however, a flower-head may be preponderatingly male, but with a few female, and vice versa. Only the male flowers secrete nectar, and that in considerable amount.

FIG. 102.—Coltsfoot in Bloom.

Harold Bastin

The **groundsel** (*Senecio vulgaris*) is one of our most objectionable weeds, not only because it will grow almost anywhere, but also because it can produce several generations in one year, being such a hardy and quick-growing plant with flowers that are regularly self-pollinated, thus almost invariably ensuring fertilisation.

The leaf is very irregularly divided (Plate 11). The flower-heads are not conspicuous. All the flowers are tubular, and these, when in fruit, present a mass of white pappus hairs.

Altogether this plant is very unpopular, though its eradication is not difficult since it has no underground stems. Almost its only use is as food for birds, especially canaries.

Closely related to the groundsel is the **ragwort** (*Senecio jacobaea*), which, attractive though it is, is a weed on agricultural land. It has a short flowering season (July and August). The plant grows to a height of three to four feet. The flower-head has a rim of large ray flowers (Plate 11). The flower-heads grow in dense clusters, and since the plants themselves are thickly congregated, they often produce an impressive mass of gold on the landscape ; but the reactions of the artist and the farmer in this case are probably somewhat different.

We now come to somewhat different members of the Compositae, beginning with the thistles. There is a large number of these, so that we must be content with considering a very few.

The first, the **carline thistle** (*Carlina vulgaris*) has flower-heads very like a typical composite. These appear during June to October. The leaves, however, are lance-shaped, deeply toothed and bearing spines on their margins (Plate 11). Though the flower-head gives a shining yellow appearance, the actual flowers are purple and are all tubular. The yellow colour is due to extended prickly bracts of the involucre. These yellow bracts are on the inside and are surrounded by green, leafy, prickly bracts. Even after fertilization and the distribution of the fruit, these bracts persist because they are so tough, thus resembling the genera of 'everlasting' flowers belonging to this family (p. 226).

A more typical thistle is the **spear thistle** (*Carduus lanceolatus*) (Plate 11). This very common thistle grows in waste places, and is frequently a weed in fields and on arable land. Its conspicuous purple flower-heads are at their best during July to October. It is certainly prickly. Its stems are ridged, and down two opposite ridges are flanges bearing strong prickles. The leaves are very large, being anything from six inches to a foot in length, and these bear many prominent spines, very variable in size (Plate 11).

The flower-head is very familiar and is characteristic of thistles in general. All the purple flowers are tubular and are surrounded by a large tight involucre of green spiny bracts. Above this involucre, the purple flowers spread themselves into a handsome disk (Plate 11). Each fruit bears a large pappus of very long hairs, and while all the fruit remain in the flower-head, these hairs collectively give the appearance of a shaving brush.

There are several other common thistles belonging to the genus *Carduus*.

> Rank weeds, that every art and care defy,
> Reign o'er the land, and rob the blighted rye ;
> There thistles stretch their prickly arms afar,
> And to the ragged infant threaten war.
>
> *The Village* : G. CRABBE

The thistles bring us on to the **burdock** (*Arctium lappa*), a tall bushy plant seen growing in waste places and woodlands. The leaves are large and heart-shaped, but are not serrated (Plate 10). The flowers, which are all tubular, appear in purple flower-heads during a very long season (February to August) (Fig. 97). Each flower-head is surrounded by a close involucre of spiny bracts, which, after fertilisation, become brown, tough and hooked, collectively forming a bur (Plate 10). The flower-head itself becomes loose after fertilisation, so that it is easily removed. Thus the hooked bracts are able to cling tenaciously to browsing animals and the whole head is easily torn off the plant, and the fruit thus dispersed.

The last of the *Tubuliferae* to be considered here is the very attractive **black knapweed** or **hard-head** (*Centaurea nigra*). This plant may be found in varying habitats.

> By copse and hedgerow, waste and wall,
> He thrusts his cushion red ;
> O'er burdock rank, o'er thistles tall,
> He rears his hardy head ;
> Within, without, the strong leaves press,
> He screens the mossy stone,
> Lord of a narrow wilderness,
> Self-centred and alone.
>
> *Knapweed* : A. C. BENSON

The flowers appear during July to September.

The large leaves are very deeply divided (Plate 11). The inflorescence, even when in bud, can scarcely be mistaken. The very hard involucre is made up of overlapping green bracts each having a fringe of deep brown hairs.

Through the top of the ' hard-head ' the purple flowers grow. The disk flowers are tubular and hermaphrodite. The ray flowers are few, very large, and neuter (Fig. 98). The fruit is topped by a ring of bristly hairs.

The **great knapweed** (*C. scabiosa*) is of larger habit than the black knapweed. A less common plant is the **corn blue-bottle** or **cornflower** (*C. cyanus*) (Plate 10), whose disk flowers are purple and neuter ray flowers brilliant blue. (Fig. 98). It grows in cornfields, and blooms during June to August, but it is more familiar as a garden flower (p. 233).

> Then wait till June is over and the dogstar's burning ;
> Wait until the cornflower comes with harvest-tide ;
> Watch her in the barley blowing kisses in the morning,
> And tell me what is bluer in the whole world wide !
>
> *The Poor Man's Garden* : MADELEY

LIGULIFLORAE

To this sub-family of the Compositae belong all those members which produce nothing but ligulate flowers. There is also another general distinction between this sub-family and that of the *Tubuliferae*, and that is the former produces a milky juice or latex whereas the latter does not. This is seen especially well in the ligulate composite, the dandelion. Latex is sometimes of economic importance. In many cases, it contains a certain percentage of rubber; but in the British dandelion the content is not sufficiently high to pay for extraction, though experiments in this connection are being carried out to try and improve the content. In a species of dandelion native to the U.S.S.R., however, the content of rubber in the latex is sufficiently high to warrant commercial extraction, and these dandelions are now cultivated for the purpose in that country.

Doubtless the most common ligulate composite is the **dandelion** (*Taraxacum officinale*), which grows almost everywhere, and all too frequently where it is not wanted. It is a most troublesome weed, because it is able to change its habit according to its habitat. For example, if it is growing in long grass, then most of its leaves are large and erect. If it is growing as a weed on lawns, its leaves grow in a procumbent mosaic, making a perfect rosette, beneath which nothing else can grow. Furthermore, the plant is a perennial, and each year a bud is formed in the leafy axis, and this plunges into growing activity during the following year. Meanwhile the roots, as they reach maturity, contract and thus draw the leaf axis close to the soil-level. The root is also very difficult to remove, which is again a pity, for this adds to the gardener's troubles since any broken part of a root will form a callus across the wound from which eventually adventitious buds can arise, and out grows a new plant. It is useless to pull a dandelion from the soil unless the whole root is removed, and for this reason it is necessary to dig it up very carefully. So one can perhaps forgive the gardener, especially when he is trying to keep his lawns grassy and smooth, if he fails to appreciate the poet's description of the dandelion's appearance in his territory :

> The robe of Spring was incomplete at dawn ;
> The needles of the Sun had done their best.
> Gold buttons now are sewn upon the lawn—
> 'Final touch to a green vest.
>
> *Dandelions* : K. W. PORTER

The scape or stalk bearing the flower-head is cylindrical, smooth and hollow and contains much white latex. The involucre surrounding the head is composed of overlapping bracts, the outer ones being smaller and recurved. The receptacle bearing the flowers is bun-shaped.

All the flowers are golden-yellow and ligulate, and all bear stamens and carpels (Plate 10 and Fig. 98). After fertilisation, the pappus of sepals is pushed up on a long stalk, forming a perfect parachute for fruit distribution (Plate 10). Collectively they form an attractive white head, often called a ' clock '.

Altogether, weed or not, the dandelion with its golden flower-heads and its fascinating ' clocks ' is a striking plant.

The young leaves of the dandelion have been used as a green vegetable for centuries, though not so much in this country, except in green salads. In some parts of the United States they are boiled, buttered and covered with vinegar to mask their bitterness.

A particularly pleasing composite is the **goat's beard** (*Tragopogon pratensis*) found in meadows. So attractive is it that it has been introduced into the United States and there cultivated as an ornamental plant. Sometimes, also, its roots and leaves are eaten.

This plant has a short flowering season (June and July). It is also called ' **Jack-go-to-bed-at-noon** ' for no matter what the weather conditions are the flower-head closes up at noon (Fig. 103). The leaves are long and grass-like, with no stalks but sheathing bases which encircle the stem (Plate 10).

The involucral bracts are characteristic of the plant. They are very long, sometimes as much as an inch and a half, and thus extend

FIG. 103.—Goat's beard.

beyond the flower-head (Plate 10). All the flowers are ligulate and perfect, and the ' clock ' is a particularly large and handsome one.

The **corn sow-thistle** (*Sonchus arvensis*) is very commonly seen growing in cultivated fields. Its leaves are shaped like dandelion leaves, that is, with reflexed teeth if growing from ground-level, but the leaves growing on the stems are deeply notched with their teeth growing forwards. These leaves clasp the stem. The flowers, which appear during June to September, are borne in attractive yellow clusters (Plate 10).

The **bristly ox-tongue** (*Helminthia echioides*) is not attractive. It grows in fields and waste places, exhibiting its small clusters of yellow flower-heads during June to October. The plant grows about two feet high, and bears lance-shaped, rough, entire leaves, the upper ones embracing the stem. The involucre is composed of two whorls of bracts, an inner whorl of eight which are lance-shaped, and an outer whorl of five, heart-shaped and pointed (Plate 10).

The **wall lettuce** (*Lactuca muralis*) is the forerunner of the garden lettuce. It grows on old walls, and blooms during July. The leaf is particularly jagged, the lower part clasping the stem and the upper part forming a wide, triangular, deeply toothed lobe. The flower-heads are massed in loose panicles and each head contains five yellow ligulate flowers surrounded by an involucre of long green bracts (Plate 10). The young leaves make a good salad.

The flower-heads of the **nipplewort** (*Lapsana communis*) are very similar in appearance to those of the wall lettuce. The nipplewort grows in waste places, and flowers during July to September. Unlike the wall lettuce, however, the fruit has no pappus. The leaf is by no means so heavily toothed as that of the wall lettuce, yet in general construction it is similar, with a large triangular or oval lobe at the top and a few (usually two) smaller lobes near the base (Plate 11).

The **cat's ear** (*Hypochaeris radicata*) grows along waysides and displays its conspicuous golden flower-heads during July. All its leaves grow from ground-level and are somewhat like dandelion leaves but have blunted tips. The whole plant is smooth. On the flower-stalks, usually subtending branch flower-stalks, are small bracts, said to resemble cat's ears (Plate 11). The fruit has a feathery pappus.

Most wild members of the Compositae are either white, white and yellow, or yellow; a few are purple; but the only true blue ones are the cornflower (p. 222) and the chicory.

The **chicory** (*Cichorium intybus*) is a close relative of the garden endive. The lovely open blue flower-heads appear during July to October. The plant grows to a height of two to three feet, and the stem is tough. The lower leaves form a rosette; those growing on the stem are lance-shaped, strongly pointed and toothed. The large blue flower-heads are an inch across and lie flat against the stem which bears them (Plate 11). The involucre is composed of eight inner bracts united at their bases with five outer ones. The pappus is not hairy, but is composed of several tough teeth (Plate 11).

The root of the chicory is dried and roasted and then used either as a substitute for coffee or blended with it.

ORNAMENTAL FLOWERS

It is difficult to imagine any flower garden without some representatives of the Compositae in it. Most gardens naturally have a high percentage of members of this, the largest of all flowering plant families, though they are all herbs. Furthermore, nearly all garden flowers of this family belong to the sub-family *Tubuliferae*, though the majority have very pronounced ligulate flowers besides tubular flowers, and in certain cases, such as some varieties of *Dahlia*, though the genus belongs to the *Tubuliferae*, all the tubular flowers have become ligulate.

Only a very small number of cultivated composites can be considered here; but it is hoped they are representative.

Ageratum is one of the simplest composites, closely related to the hemp agrimony (*Eupatorium cannabinum*, p. 213). Most species are Asiatic, *A. conyzoides* being the most common weed in Ceylon. The cultivated species make splendid edging plants and are also useful in small beds, for they are of dwarf habit. There are blue and white varieties of flowers borne in small heads which are massed together more closely than those of the hemp agrimony.

Of the **small daisies,** which are varieties of the common wild daisy (*Bellis perennis*), there are many different shades of white, pink, red and zoned. Most cultivated varieties are so-called double in that the whorls

FIG. 104.—Perennial Aster
(*Aster subcoeruleus*).

of ray flowers are increased to such an extent as to hide almost completely the yellow disk flowers.

Related to the daisy within the composite family is the genus *Aster*, which contains some kinds of **perennial asters.** (The even more popular summer annual asters belong to another genus, *Callistephus*.) The perennial asters are of Asiatic origin and each large, mauve, single flower-head is borne on its own stalk from ground-level. Otherwise the perennial aster (Fig. 104) is very like the Michaelmas daisy.

Very popular varieties of the genus *Aster* are the many kinds of **Michaelmas daisy,** though the wild Michaelmas daisy, not often seen, but sometimes found growing in salt marshes, is not their forerunner. In habit the garden varieties range from a few inches to five feet tall, some of them attaining bushy proportions with flower-heads in enormous masses. Some flower-heads are single, others are double. In some cases the flower-heads are very small, whereas others may be an inch across. There are dozens of different shades of blue, mauve, crimson and purple, the masses of flower-heads making a brave show especially during the autumn months when many garden flowers are over. Most garden Michaelmas daisies are of American origin.

Summer **annual asters** are very popular. There are many different shades of colour, size and form, most of which are derived from the China aster (*Callistephus hortensis*).

Several varieties of **golden rod** (*Solidago virgaurea*, p. 216) are cultivated in the flower garden. All have masses of golden flower-heads, some in handsome arching sprays. These plants, also, are useful for autumn flowering.

The so-called '**everlasting**' **flowers** are sometimes valued for purposes of household decoration since their flower-heads retain their shape and colour almost permanently. The foliage withers, of course, and one does tend to get rather tired of the sight of them. There are

PLATE II

GROUNDSEL

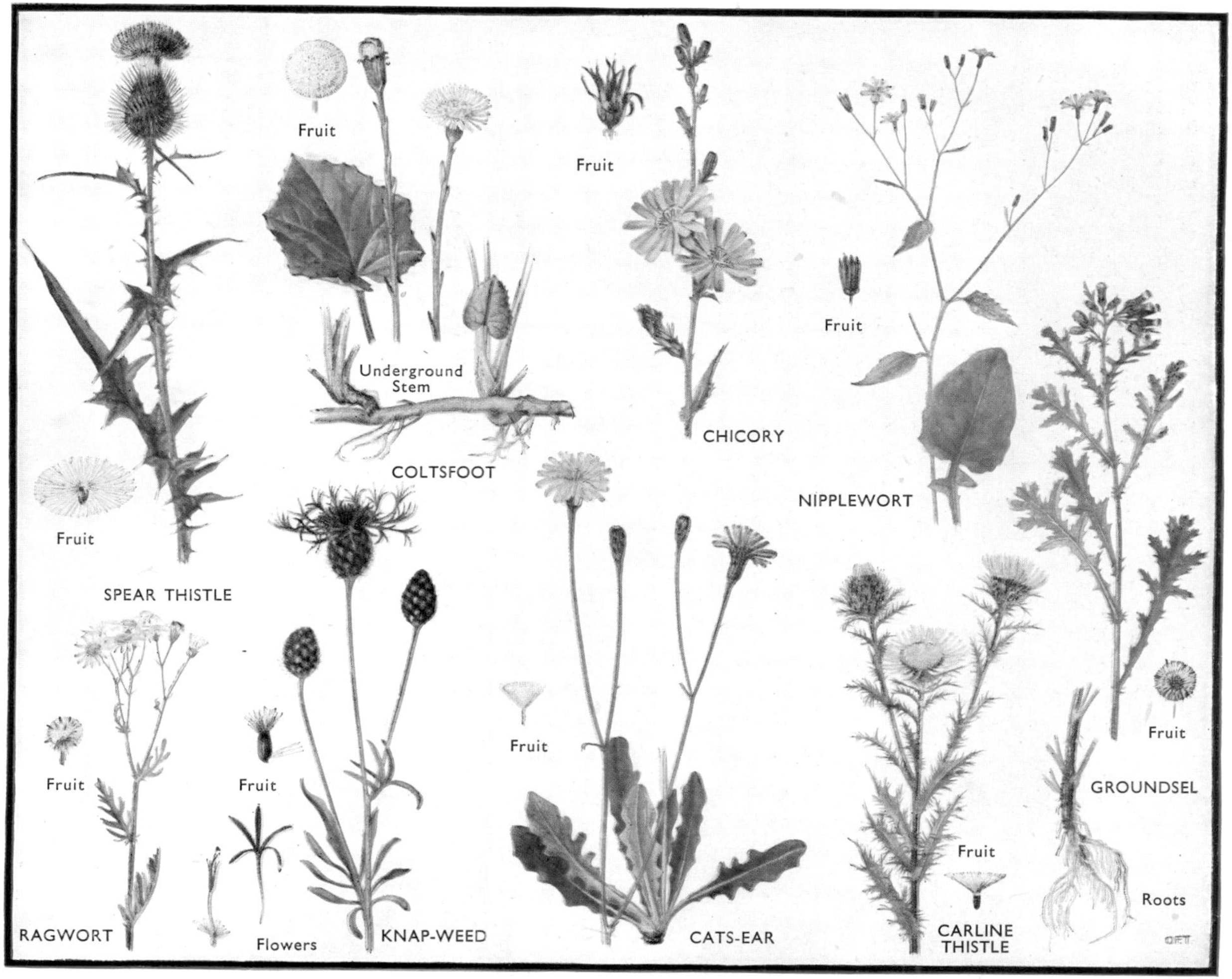

Fruit

Roots

CARLINE
THISTLE

Fruit

NIPPLEWORT

Fruit

CHICORY

Fruit

CATS-EAR

Fruit

COLTSFOOT

Underground
Stem

Fruit

Fruit

KNAP-WEED

Flowers

Fruit

SPEAR THISTLE

Fruit

Fruit

RAGWORT

several genera of these flowers. *Achyrachaena* is not well known to British gardeners, but it is familiar in the United States. The fruit (not the flowers) are saved as 'everlastings', for the pappus is made up of broad silvery scales which collectively are quite attractive. Of the genus *Ammobium*, a New South Wales native, the species *A. alatum* is sometimes cultivated in this country for its white everlasting flower-heads. The most popular genus, however, is *Helichrysum*. Most species and varieties of this are double, with several of the outer rows of flower-heads spreading, and

FIG. 105.—Vase of 'Everlasting' Flowers (containing *Acroclinium*, *Helichrysum*, *Rhodanthe* and *Xeranthemum*) and some ornamental grasses.

several inner ones closing over the central disk. The flowers are in shades of white, cream, silver, pink and red. *Rhodanthe* (or *Helipterum*) is another 'everlasting' genus; so also is *Xeranthemum* (Fig. 105).

Next we come to five genera all closely related to each other, and all extremely popular garden composites, very easily cultivated and therefore manageable by the most inexperienced gardener. They are, *Helianthus*, *Dahlia*, *Cosmos*, *Coreopsis* and *Zinnia*.

The very large **sunflower** (*Helianthus annuus*), with enormous leaves, thick stems growing to a height of ten feet, and flower-heads sometimes more than a foot across, is not a popular garden flower because it is ungainly, and never looks attractive except perhaps as a background to a tall, thick herbaceous border. The disk of tubular flowers is comparatively large, and the ray flowers comparatively small. This old-fashioned sunflower is often grown, however, for the oil its fruit contains. The fruit are fed to poultry, and in certain European and Asiatic countries, especially the U.S.S.R., people chew them (see also p. 233). There are some dwarf varieties of this plant.

There are also some handsome varieties of sunflower, most of which are perennial. Some have single flower-heads with large ray flowers. Others are semi-double with several rows of ray flowers. There is one drawback, however, in that most of them spread so persistently by means of underground stems.

The half-hardy annual sunflowers are most popular, giving flower-heads in lovely shades of lemon, bronze and red, and some show ray flowers with concentric zones of colour—for example, a dark centre surrounded by a zone of bright red formed by the lower halves of the ray flowers, this zone being again surrounded by an outer zone of yellow made up of the tips of the ray flowers.

There are many small-flowered varieties and hybrids of annual sunflower—all very popular, especially for household use.

The many species, varieties and hybrids of the genus *Dahlia* defy description. Most of the garden varieties are derived from the Mexican *Dahlia variabilis*. In many of the double flowers, the disk flowers have become ligulate (Fig. 106). Most kinds of *Dahlia* are half-hardy perennials, though many are treated as annuals. There are single and

FIG. 106.—Double *Dahlia*.

double varieties, in many shades—white, yellow, pink, scarlet and crimson. The plants vary in size from a few inches, useful for bedding, to six feet, useful for borders or special display. The flower-heads vary from a couple of inches to nearly a foot in diameter. Many of the larger kinds have almost spherical heads, and in some of the smaller kinds a pompom effect is achieved.

Cosmos is a very graceful plant, with the most attractive flower-heads, having small disk and large, long ray flowers. It hails from America and the West Indies. The plant is tall with slender stems bearing graceful, finely divided leaves. The flower-heads vary in shades of white, rose and crimson, and some are double. There is also a miniature yellow *Cosmos* with masses of star-like flower-heads. All are annual.

The genus *Coreopsis* shows a wide range of colour and of form in the flower-heads. It is a very popular genus, since the plants are very graceful like those of *Cosmos*, and the flower-heads are large-rayed. The ray flowers are particularly beautiful with indented tips and colours ranging from yellow, through brown to crimson. Some have different zones of colour (Fig. 107). The genus is native to tropical Africa and America.

Zinnia is a more recent introduction to this country, having been brought from its native North America. It has now achieved well-deserved popularity among British flower gardeners for its wide range of size and colour among its single and double flower-heads. The plant is particularly sturdy, and each flower-head lasts an unusually long time on the plant. There seems to be every variety imaginable, though the large double varieties are favourites. Some are enormous and present shades of white, yellow, orange, pink, scarlet and red. Others are smaller with an equally wide range of colour. Again, there are dwarf varieties, while some are quilled, with flowers showing

FIG. 107.—Hybrids of *Coreopsis*.

FIG. 108.—Hybrids of African or French Marigold (*Tagetes*).

one colour on the upper surface and a totally different colour on the lower. Some varieties have compact heads giving a pom-pom effect.

For brightness of colour it is difficult to beat the **English marigold** (*Calendula officinalis*). There are single and double varieties of this striking flower, varying in shade from lemon to deep orange. The disk flowers are male and the ray flowers female. Some gardeners dislike this genus, however, for its rough, bristly fruit are soon dispersed and easily grow, so that once the plant establishes itself in the garden it is constantly cropping up everywhere and sometimes becomes quite a nuisance.

The **African** or **French marigold** (*Tagetes* species) has not this disadvantage. In spite of its name, it is really a native of South America. The tall plant with its handsome, finely divided leaves is useful for bedding or for potting. The flower-head shows considerable variation (Fig. 108). There are single and double varieties, and the shades of colour are similar to those of the English marigold, whereas some are orange with stripes or blotches of brown, others are brown edged with orange, and so forth. The shape of the single flowers also shows great variation.

Gaillardia is a genus closely related to *Calendula* and *Tagetes*. For garden and household decoration these flowers are especially suitable, for they present some of the most gorgeous colours—bright yellow, orange, crimson and zoned. Most are single with very large ray flowers. Each flower-head is borne on a separate stalk and the leaves are simple and lance-shaped. This genus is also of American origin.

The various kinds of *Pyrethrum* are also popular.

The next on our list of cultivated composites is the genus *Chrysanthemum*, of which there are so many varieties that any attempt to describe them in a short space would end in certain failure. The several large white cultivated varieties of the wild *Chrysanthemum leucanthemum* (ox-eye daisy) are very familiar. They are often called **marguerites.**

The coloured single and double varieties and species of *Chrysanthemum* of gardens and greenhouses are mostly derived from the Chinese and Japanese *Chrysanthemum sinense* and *C. indicum*. The single varieties present different shades of white, sulphur-yellow and brown, some having zones of colour. But it is in the autumn-flowering double kinds of *Chrysanthemum* that the varieties seem endless, both in colour, size and form. The colours may be white, yellow, bronze, red or variegated, the form varying from flat to spherical flower-heads, and the size from pompoms and miniatures to heads six inches in diameter. In the double *Chrysanthemum*, as in the *Dahlia*, the disk flowers have become ligulate.

Chrysanthemum plants flower late in the autumn because they are what are called short-day plants. The flowering of any plant is conditioned by several factors, such as season, humidity, temperature, and light-intensity ; but what is frequently overlooked is the fact that length of time of presentation of light is also a conditioning factor. In the case of *Chrysanthemum*, flowering is favoured by short periods of light alternating with long periods of darkness.

FIG. 109.—*Cineraria.*

Several species of *Senecio* are cultivated, especially as greenhouse plants. One, *S. multibracteatus*, produces a large sheaf of long-stemmed flower-heads, with rose-coloured ray flowers and yellow disk flowers. *S. elegans* is the popular **Jacobea,** which produces dense heads of double flowers in various colours — white, rose, crimson, mauve and purple.

Related to *Senecio* is the very handsome greenhouse *Cineraria*. So closely related are these two genera that horticulturists often group certain species of *Senecio* under the genus *Cineraria*. All

Q

true species of *Cineraria* are natives of Madagascar and South Africa. These plants make a gorgeous show with their heart-shaped leaves and massed flower-heads with broad ray flowers of gay colours (Fig. 109). The disk flowers are subdued, and the ray flowers stand out in their wonderful variety of colour—white, blue, pink, ruby, scarlet and purple. Most of the colours are zoned with an inner circle of white.

Three other genera, not quite so popular, but nevertheless very lovely, are *Ursinia*, *Gazania* and *Dimorphotheca*. The genus *Ursinia* hails from South Africa and Abyssinia. The flower-heads are like large daisies borne in masses and presenting various shades of yellow. Several species of *Gazania* are now cultivated in the gardens of this country. The colours range from cream to orange and rich red, all the ray flowers being spotted at their bases with green or black. Each flower-head is large with particularly long ray flowers. The genus is native to Cape Colony. *Dimorphotheca* is another South African plant, often called **star of the veldt** and is very quick-flowering. The flower-heads are very like ox-eye daisies; though they are not only white but also lemon or orange (Fig. 110).

Fig. 110.—*Dimorphotheca aurantiaca.*

Echinops, the **blue globe thistle,** is an interesting cultivated genus in that the globular heads are really compound. Each globe is really a mass of flower-heads, and each flower-head contains only one sky-blue flower surrounded by its own involucre of bracts.

The last genus of cultivated composites to be considered here is *Centaurea,* the **cornflowers.** The flower-head is like that of the knap-weed in that it contains hermaphrodite tubular flowers and large outer flowers which are lobed and neuter. It is these large neuter flowers which give the whole flower-head its colour, which may be a vivid blue as in the wild cornflower (Plate 10 and p. 222), white or pink. Very frequently in the cultivated varieties there are so many neuter flowers that the flower-heads are said to be double.

ECONOMIC PLANTS

Though the COMPOSITAE is the largest of all flowering plant families, which has given a seemingly endless variety of ornamental cultivated forms, there are really very few of economic importance.

Perhaps most useful of all are the various cultivated **lettuces** (*Lactuca sativa*), which have been derived from the wild wall lettuce (*Lactuca muralis,* p. 224).

To the genus *Cichorium* belong two species of economic value, namely **chicory** (*C. intybus*), from the roots of which the coffee flavouring is prepared (p. 225), and whose blanched shoots provide a delicious vegetable, and the salad plant **endive** (*C. endivia*).

The **Jerusalem artichoke** is a species of *Helianthus* (*H. tuberosus*), and the artichoke used as a vegetable is a swollen stem tuber, botanically similar to a potato, though a rather shapeless organ. The true **artichoke** (*Cynara scolymus*) is also a composite, though it is not often grown in this country, but is popular in Mediterranean regions. In this case, the young flower-heads enclosed in their bracts are used.

In certain countries, especially in the U.S.S.R., India and Egypt, the large **sunflower** (*H. annuus*) is a valuable crop, for a sweet oil is extracted from the seeds, the leaves are used as fodder and the flowers yield a yellow dye. Oil from the seeds of this plant is useful for edible and culinary purposes, for making margarine, as food for cattle and poultry, for canning fish and making fine soap. Its gastronomic value is equal to the finest olive oil. Considerable research is now going on with the view of establishing the sunflower as an oil-yielding crop in Britain. The crop is widely tolerant of soil types, but removes large quantities of soil nutrient, most of which are retained in the stalk, and therefore can be returned to the ground after harvest. Sowing the seed at an even depth of $1\frac{1}{2}$-2 inches appears to be important, and $7\frac{1}{2}$ lb. of seed is needed to sow a crop by drill. Sunflower is a good cleaning crop, and in some countries appears to be little affected by disease, though it is susceptible to wire-worm attack and the depredations of birds at harvest time. Three semi-dwarf varieties—' Mars ', ' Pole Star ', and ' Southern Cross '—have so far been found to be most suitable for this country, for the giant varieties are here very susceptible to fungal attack. As the supply of fats and oils may be one of the most acute of our future problems, the crop appears worthy of extended trials, and the prospects seem good.

Many other genera and species of COMPOSITAE are used by herbalists for medicinal purposes. From the genus *Pyrethrum*, valuable insecticides are made.

50

GENTIANS
(*Gentianaceae*)

The gentian family (GENTIANACEAE) will be known to most people of this country by those species seen growing in rockeries rather than by the wild examples of the family. Perhaps the most familiar is the genus *Gentiana* itself—a genus of alpine plants usually of tufted growth with large blue flowers nestling close to the ground. Those who have visited alpine regions, such as Switzerland or the Tyrol, are bound to have been impressed by the conspicuous blue flowers growing in enormous masses and contributing in no small measure to the alpine scene. But people who have not had this unforgettable experience may be well acquainted with the exquisite shape and hue of the gentian, or can easily become so, for, like many alpine flowers, it is well adapted for cultivation here in rockeries.

> Then doth thy sweet and quiet eye
> Look through its fringes to the sky,
> Blue—blue—as if that sky let fall
> A flower from its cerulean wall.
> *To the Fringed Gentian* : W. C. BRYANT

Not all members of this family are alpine; in fact, the family is distributed throughout the world in a wide variety of habitats—alpine, arctic, salt marsh, marsh, aquatic, and some are even saprophytic (p. 193).

All its members are, however, herbaceous, and many are perennial. In most of the flowers there are usually five persistent sepals. The petals are usually five in number and are joined in bell or funnel form, though in some cases the petals spread out to form a salver shape. The stamens alternate with the petals, and there are two carpels joined to form a single- or two-chambered ovary, usually the former.

WILD PLANTS

There are several species of gentian growing wild in this country. The **field gentian** (*Gentiana campestris*) grows on chalk and limestone hills, and has pale blue flowers which appear during August and September. The whole plant is dwarf, and its leaves grow in opposite pairs. The sepals are joined to form a four-cleft tube, with the two outer segments larger than the two inner ones. The pale blue corolla funnel is fringed at the throat. It can therefore be pollinated only by long-tongued insects such as butterflies.

The **small-flowered gentian** (*G. amarella*) is found flowering at the same time on dry heaths. The flower is purple in colour. In this case, the sepal-tube is five-cleft with all segments equal in size. The petal-tube is again fringed. It also is pollinated by butterflies.

The **marsh gentian** (*G. pneumomanthe*) is not so common. It also flowers at the same time, but the flowers are large and blue, striped green on the outside, with the petals forming not a funnel but an open salver; that is, they are arranged in campanulate fashion. There is a long tube beneath the salver, so that only humble-bees with long tongues can get at the nectar. The petal-tube is naked—not fringed. This lovely flower was known to Pliny who called it the Calathian violet and referred to it as ' the gift of Autumn.'

There are several other British species of gentian.

The **buckbean** or **bogbean** is a British plant to be found growing in bogs. It is not common, but is frequently seen in the Lake District. It belongs to another genus, *Menyanthes* (*M. trifoliata*), displaying its attractive pink flowers during May to September. The plant, like many other marsh plants, has a creeping underground stem. As its specific name implies, its leaves are divided into three lobes which are lance-shaped and toothed. The flowers are easily identified. They grow in terminal inflorescences—about half a dozen flowers alternating on a large axis. The sepals are joined to form a five-cleft tube and the pinkish-white petals form a funnel the lobes of which spread out in campanulate fashion. They are very hairy. The five stamens alternate with the petals. There is a long style with a two-lobed stigma. The plant is bitter, and its dried leaves were sometimes brewed like tea or used for infusing wine.

The **common centaury** (*Erythraea centaurium*) is to be seen displaying its small bright pink flowers in tufts during June to September in dry pastures. The leaves are oval and narrow, and the erect stem grows to a height of three to twelve inches. The sepals form a five-cleft tube, and the five petals form a funnel with spreading lobes. The stamens project beyond the throat of the funnel (Plate 12).

The **yellow centaury** or **yellow-wort** is in a different genus, namely *Chlora* (*C. perfoliata*). It is an erect plant, growing six to twelve inches high in chalky pastures, and displaying its bright yellow flowers during June to September. The petal-tube has eight campanulate lobes, and there are eight alternating stamens. The ovary is single-chambered, the stigma three-lobed.

A water plant, rare, but sometimes seen in the south of England, is *Limnanthemum nymphaeoides*. It has long stems, with heart-shaped floating leaves which are attached to the inflorescence-stalks. The bright yellow flowers are borne in dense inflorescences. The five-lobed petal-tube spreads to a diameter of an inch.

ORNAMENTAL FLOWERS

One of the most beautiful of the alpine gentians is *Gentiana acaulis*, so it is no wonder that this species is a favourite in British rock gardens. Its blue flowers, lying close to the ground, are very conspicuous. Other species of *Gentiana*, usually cultivated in rockeries, have deep blue, pale blue or purple trumpets, and some are beautifully marked with green on the outside.

Varieties of *Menyanthes trifoliata*, with erect pink and white inflorescences, are sometimes cultivated near the edges of ornamental ponds or on marshy land. *Linanthemum nymphaeoides* is also used as an ornamental aquatic.

Erythraea massonii is a diminutive plant from the Azores, and displays many pink flowers.

Exacum is a campanulate genus, and the species *E. affina* makes a showy potted plant with masses of mauve, sweet-scented flowers.

51

THE PRIMROSE FAMILY
(Primulaceae)

The cottager when coming home from plough
Brings home a cowslip root in flower to set.
Thus ere the Christmas goes the spring is met
Setting up little texts about the fields
In sheltered spots.—Primroses when they get
Behind the wood's old roots, where ivy shields
Their crimpled, curdled leaves, will shine and hide.

Cowslips and Primroses : JOHN CLARE

The primrose family (PRIMULACEAE) comprises several genera native to this country, but without doubt the genus *Primula* is the most popular both among the wild and the cultivated forms. Among wild species of *Primula* are the primrose, cowslip and oxlip ; since the genus lends itself particularly easy to hybridisation, the cultivated species and varieties are legion.

Though the family is very popular in the flower garden, it produces nothing of value for the kitchen garden.

WILD PLANTS

The genus *Primula* is a particularly natural one in that all the species belonging to it are very similar in fundamental detail, not only floral but also vegetative.

All are herbs, having thick root-stocks with which they frequently reproduce themselves vegetatively. The leaves are very characteristic. Every leaf is borne at ground-level, and is egg-shaped with the lower part very elongated. The whole leaf-surface is very wrinkled, and the venation, especially on the lower surface, clearly marked (Plate 3).

All the flowers are borne in inflorescences, each flower being on a long stalk of its own ; but all the flower-stalks come off from the same point of a common stalk, thus forming an umbel. This applies even to the common primrose (*q.v.*), although in this case each flower seems to be on a separate stalk.

The primula flower is particularly well adapted for cross-pollination by bees, since there are two types of flower—one long-styled and the other short-styled (Plate 3). In each flower the five sepals are pale green and are joined to form a long tube with five pronounced teeth at its rim. The five petals also form a long tube which spreads out in salver fashion into five lobes (Fig. 16). There are five stamens inserted on the inside of the tubular part of the joined petals, and one carpel forming a single-chambered ovary with a style topped by a disk-shaped stigma. The ovules within the ovary are arranged around a vertical central axis.

The two types of primula flower are well seen in the common primrose. One type has a long style showing its stigma just above the throat of the petal-tube. In this case, the stamens are inserted about two-thirds of the way down the petal-tube. This flower is therefore said to be 'pin-eyed' because the stigma looks like a pin's head in the 'eye' of the flower. In the other type of flower the style is short, bringing its stigma about half-way up the petal-tube, and the stamens are inserted less than a quarter of the way down the petal-tube. This type of flower is said to be 'thrum-eyed' because in the 'eye' of the flower is seen a 'thrum' or tuft of stamens. Thus in the pin-eyed flower the stigma is above the stamens, and vice-versa in the thrum-eyed flower.

The advantage of having two types of flower like this is made manifest when long-tongued insects visit the flower in quest of the deeply seated nectar. The pin-eyed flower pollinates the thrum-eyed, and vice versa, as shown in Fig. 111, thus ensuring cross-pollination.

Fig. 111.—Cross-pollination of Thrum-eyed and Pin-eyed Primroses.

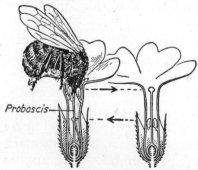

Proboscis—

The fruit is a round capsule which splits by opening into five valves at the top (Plate 3).

The **common primrose** (*Primula vulgaris*) marks the advent of spring, for it blooms chiefly during April and May, though some flowers appear much earlier under favourable weather conditions. In fact the name 'primrose' means 'first rose,' though this flower is not a rose at all. The generic name

Primula is a corruption of the French *primeverole* and Italian *primeverola*, which are compounds of the Latin *prima vera* which means ' first spring flower '.

> Primrose, first-born child of Ver,
> Merry spring-time's harbinger.
> *Two Noble Kinsmen* : BEAUMONT AND FLETCHER

Primrose flowers are pale yellow in colour with orange honey-guides at the base of the petal lobes near the throat.

Although each single flower appears to be borne on its own separate stalk, the flowers are really borne collectively in an umbel, for the stalks of several are united at the same point to a very short common stalk buried in the leaf-bases. One sometimes finds specimens in which the main stalk has grown out.

It is just as well that the primrose is able to reproduce itself vegetatively by means of the root-stock, for, in spite of its elaborate mechanism for ensuring cross-pollination by insects, this seldom occurs, because the bees are not yet about in any number so early in the year. So seeds are seldom set, except in the very late flowers. This is aptly alluded to by Milton :

> Bring the rathe primrose that forsaken dies
> *Lycidas* : MILTON

and more definitely by Shakespeare :

> pale primroses,
> That die unmarried, ere they can behold
> Bright Phoebus in his strength, a malady
> Most incident to maids.
> *Winter's Tale* : SHAKESPEARE

Primrose Day was inaugurated on April 19, 1882 and is associated with Disraeli, for they were his favourite flower. Queen Victoria often sent him gifts of primroses, and sent a wreath of primroses to his funeral.

The **cowslip** plant (*P. veris*) is very like that of the primrose, but it grows in more open meadows and presents its smaller flowers in pendulous simple umbels at the end of long flower-stalks (Plate 3). Also the cowslip blooms about a month later than the primrose—during May and June. The petals do not open out so widely as those of the primrose, and they are a deeper yellow in colour. It is worth noting that when the flowers are in bud they stand in almost erect umbels. When they are open and ready for fertilisation, they spread out and become pendulous. After they have become fertilised and the floral organs wither while the fruit ripens, the whole becomes erect again

(Plate 3). This ensures that the capsule which opens at the top into five valves cannot just drop its seeds near the parent plant, but has to to be shaken, thus ensuring a certain amount of wider dispersal.

> The sheep and cows are crowding for a share
> And snatch the blossoms in such eager haste
> That basket-bearing children running there
> Do think within their hearts they'll get them all
> And hoot and drive them from their graceless waste.
> —For they want some for tea and some for wine
> And some to maken up a cuckaball,
> To throw across the garland's silken line
> That reaches o'er the street from wall to wall.
>
> *Cowslips* : JOHN CLARE

A wine is sometimes made from the cowslip.

The **oxlip** (*P. elatior*) is not a very common wild flower. It is larger in general habit, especially of the flower, than the cowslip.

The **yellow loosestrife** is also a member of the primrose family, and therefore must not be confused with the purple loosestrife (p. 100). It belongs to another genus (*Lysimachia vulgaris*). Like the purple loose-strife, however, the yellow loosestrife grows along river banks, and has an erect stem of two to three feet, bearing opposite and whorled lance-shaped leaves, pointed at their tips and broad at their bases ; the blades are dotted with black.

The very attractive bright yellow flowers appear during June to August, borne on thin stalks either singly in the leaf-axils or in smaller axillary inflorescences near the top of the shoot (Plate 3).

Each flower has five sepals united and showing five teeth with red margins. The five petals are, of course, united, but their lobes open out fully, each lobe being broadly lance-shaped and dotted with orange (Plate 3). The fruit capsule opens out with five valves.

The origin of the word ' loosestrife ' is interesting, for even today some country-folk lay sprays of it under the yokes of horses to keep away flies. This was also done by the Romans, and by thus relieving horses and oxen of a source of irritation, prevented strife among the animals.

> Yellow Lysimachus, to give sweet rest
> To the faint shepherd, killing, where it comes
> All busy gnats and every fly that hums.
> *The Faithful Shepherdess* : BEAUMONT AND FLETCHER

Other members of the same genus (*Lysimachia*) are the money-wort or creeping Jenny and the yellow pimpernel, the latter not to be confused with the scarlet pimpernel, a plant belonging to the same family but a different genus. The **money-wort** or **creeping Jenny** (*L. nummularia*) grows in damp places and has a pronounced creeping main stem which gives off roots at its nodes, thus making spreading more effective (Fig. 112). The yellow flowers appear during June and July. The **yellow pimpernel** (*L. nemorum*) is not common but sometimes appears in shady places, displaying its flowers during May to August. The leaves are oval and are borne in opposite pairs. The flowers also appear to be borne in pairs, but this is because each is subtended by a leaf as in money-wort (Fig. 112).

The **scarlet pimpernel** (*Anagallis arvensis*) is sometimes called the **poor man's weather-glass** because its conspicuous scarlet flowers close up during dull weather, though they do so during the early afternoon no matter what the weather is like.

This pretty plant trails about in waste places, in gardens and on agricultural land, enjoying a long flowering season (May to November). The leaves are oval but broader towards the bottom, and they are borne in opposite pairs which alternate with each other. Since they have no stalks they almost encircle the stem. They are covered with darker spots.

The bright flowers are borne on long stalks from the leaf axils (Plate 3), and thus appear in pairs. Each flower has five united sepals and five united petals, the oval lobes of which form the bright red salver. On rare occasions one finds flowers with white petals. The fruit is particularly intriguing, for it is a spherical capsule, and when the seeds are ripe, the upper hemisphere opens up like a lid giving the whole the appearance of a small tureen (Plate 3).

A species of pimpernel sometimes found growing in marshes is the **bog pimpernel** (*A. tenella*). Its leaves are slightly stalked and are not dotted like those of the scarlet pimpernel. Its flowers are pink.

The **bastard pimpernel** belongs to another genus (*Centunculus minimus*). It also grows in wet places and has minute leaves. The

FIG. 112.—Money-wort or Creeping Jenny.

flowers are characteristic since the corolla tube is urn-shaped, that is, constricted both at top and bottom. Each flower is pink.

The **water violet** (*Hottonia palustris*)—rare in the wild state—is not a violet at all but a member of the primrose family. As its name implies, it grows in water. The submerged leaves are very finely divided ; the flowers are borne in terminal whorls above the water. They are pink in colour and are either pin-eyed or thrum-eyed.

The **sea milkwort** (*Glaux maritima*) grows on muddy seashores, and is decked with rose-coloured flowers during June and July. Here again, there are pin-eyed and thrum-eyed examples. Each flower grows in the axil of a leaf and has no stalk. The leaf, like those of many salt-water plants, is fleshy, since it has to conserve its fresh-water supply. The flower has no petals, so the rose colour is due to the five united petaloid sepals.

ORNAMENTAL PLANTS

Some gardeners take a particular interest in the genus *Primula*, for it is easily crossed and thus many different varieties and hybrids are produced, though they all fundamentally conform to the general primulaceous plant. The species which have given us the most showy cultivated plants are the **Chinese primula** (*P. sinensis*), the **Japanese primula** (*P. japonica*), and *P. obconica* (Fig. 113), *P. stellata,* and *P. malacoides* (Fig. 114).

FIG. 113.—*Primula obconica.*

In some species there are successive whorls of flowers on the same stalk. These are a particular feature of varieties of *P. japonica, P. malacoides,* and several other species.

Many of these primulas are greenhouse plants, but there are also many more hardy species, especially suitable for rockeries. *P. bulleyana* is a particularly showy plant with its several whorls of flowers in shades of orange and apricot. Many of the hardy species are apparently single-flowered like the common primrose, and present all shades of white, yellow, red blue and purple.

More sturdy and with very conspicuously coloured flowers are the many forms of auricula (*Primula auricula*). These plants are most useful, for they thrive in very exposed positions. The shades of colour of the large flowers range too widely to be profitably described here.

The equally colourful poly-anthuses are all hybrids of the oxlip (*P. elatior*). They are very hardy, and present shades of white, yellow, blue, pink and deep crimson. In many cases, the edge of the petals are laced with gold.

Fig. 114.—*Primula malacoides*.

The very popular **cyclamen** makes a handsome potted plant (Fig. 115). There is a wild species of this growing in Great Britain, namely, **sow-bread** (*Cyclamen europaeum*), though it is far from common. Some varieties of this species are cultivated, for they are hardy. But the most interesting and striking are the greenhouse forms. The cyclamen is interesting because after fertilisation the stalk coils spirally and thus brings the fruit down to earth. The cyclamen has a stout corm by means of which it hibernates. The flowers are pendulous and are borne on long, rose-coloured, fleshy stalks. The broad, wavy petals bend backwards (Fig. 115). The shades of colour vary from white through pink and mauve to crimson.

> Cyclamens, ruddy-muzzled cyclamens
> In little bunches like bunches of wild hares
> Muzzles together, ears aprick,
> Whispering witchcraft. . . .
>
> D. H. LAWRENCE

The very pretty alpine plant, *Soldanella alpina*, is sometimes seen in rockeries with its kidney-shaped foliage growing flat to the ground, and the fringed flowers, lilac in colour, borne in clusters on stems

FIG. 115.—*Cyclamen persicum.*

about four inches long. This plant is of particular interest to the botanist. It is actually a native of the European Alps and is able to flower at very low temperatures. Now plants, like all other living things, must respire, and in doing so they give off a certain amount of heat. The heat is produced during the 'combustion' of the foodstuffs within the respiring organism. Not much heat is given off by the average plant, though it is sometimes easily perceptible, as when the hand is placed in the middle of a pile of cut grass which has stood for some time. *Soldanella* is at home in the coldest surroundings even where there is much ice and snow. Its thick fleshy leaves act as a store-house for food, especially starch, and when respiration is going on apace, this food is used up and heat given off. During winter, the plant is covered with ice and snow, and respiration is at a low ebb. When spring comes, water begins to trickle down to the leaves and respiration increases, with the result that more heat is given off. Simultaneously the flower-stalk begins to grow, and by giving off this excessive heat, literally melts its way through any ice and snow that may be left.

Creeping Jenny (*Lysimachia nummularia*) is sometimes grown in rockeries, and is especially useful in hiding unsightly corners, for its deep green leaves lie close to the soil and its bright yellow flowers are very arresting. But the plant needs keeping in check, for it creeps everywhere.

The genus *Androsace* supplies useful tufted alpine dwarfs for rock gardens. There are species with white, pink and rose-coloured flowers.

Of the pimpernels, the yellow (*Lysimachia*, p. 240) appears sometimes in our gardens, but the scarlet (*Anagallis*, p. 241) supplies a large-flowered variety. There is also a blue variety of this plant.

Hottonia, the water violet (p. 242), is useful in water gardening.

So PRIMULACEAE, though not of economic importance, has contributed its share to our ornamental gardens.

52

THRIFT AND STATICE
(*Plumbaginaceae*)

The **thrift** or **sea pink** is one of the commonest plants on muddy seashores, and it is also found very frequently in the high mountainous regions of Scotland. It is the basis of the design on the twelve-sided threepenny-bits.

The thrift, and another plant, **sea lavender**, belong to the family PLUMBAGINACEAE, and are its only common British members. Most members of this family are herbs, though a few, especially some of the many examples seen growing in Mediterranean regions, are climbers. All are inhabitants of muddy seashores or of mountains. Though a few are of horticultural value and some are used in medicine, none is of any economic importance. All are perennial herbs, frequently having special adaptations to salt-marsh conditions.

In all cases the flower has five united sepals forming a five-cleft tube; five petals united only at their bases but otherwise free; five stamens; and five carpels which form a single-chambered ovary with five separate styles. The ovary only contains one ovule, so that the fruit, which is a nut, and therefore non-splitting, contains only one seed. This family therefore differs from the PRIMULACEAE chiefly in its ovary and styles.

WILD PLANTS

The thrift (*Armeria maritima*) bears its small rose-coloured flowers in dense heads each at the end of a long stalk (Plate 12). The flowering season is a long one (April to September). There is a thick woody root-stock from which grow tufts of grass-like leaves and the inflorescence-stalks. Each year most of the root-stock dies away, leaving a small axillary branch to carry on growth for the next year. The plant is therefore perennial.

Each flower-head is surrounded by an involucre of pinkish-brown bracts, the outer ones forming a sheath around the top of the stalk (Plate 12). Each flower produces a fruit in the form of a single-seeded nut to the top of which are attached the persistent five-toothed sepals which have now become membranous and act as a wing in wind distribution.

The thrift is sometimes called the 'sea gilliflower', while the water violet (p. 242) is frequently referred to as the 'water gilliflower.'

The leaves of the sea lavender (*Statice limonium*) are large and lance-shaped. Like those of the thrift, they all grow from ground-level. The sea lavender differs from the thrift chiefly in its form of inflorescence, for here it is by no means a dense head but a characteristically branched panicle bearing many small flowers along the upper surfaces of the branches only (Plate 12). This is specially well marked in the garden varieties of *Statice*. The purple flowers of the sea lavender are very small; but, as in the primrose, there are long-styled and short-styled kinds. The stamens of the thrum-eyed flowers are very conspicuous.

ORNAMENTAL PLANTS

The large number of species and varieties of cultivated sea lavender (*Statice*) have become very popular in recent years, especially for house decoration (Fig. 116). This no doubt is because most of the varieties are 'everlasting'. The inflorescence-stalks have pronounced green flanges. There are all sorts of colours of flowers—white, blue, mauve, pink, red and yellow. One very popular species, *S. suworowi*, is prominent because of its exceptionally long, arching inflorescences.

Fig. 116.—Bowl of *Statice*. The long spikes are *S. suworowi*.

Thrift (*Armeria*) is also prized as a border plant and for cutting. There are several large varieties with character-istic rose-coloured flowers, while others have deep red flowers.

Another genus belonging to this family (PLUMBAGINACEAE) is *Ceratostigma*, several species of which are cultivated in British gardens, though none is native. Most are dwarf and shrubby. They hail from Africa and China. The species *C. plum-baginoides*, for example, was dis-covered growing on the walls of Pekin.

53

THE PLANTAIN FAMILY
(*Plantaginaceae*)

The plantains (PLANTAGINACEAE) are not very attractive plants, though some bear handsome leaves. Their flowers, are insignificant, colourless and scentless. It is no wonder, therefore, that the family has been ignored by the horticulturist, nor is it of much use in any other way.

The chief genus is *Plantago*, about five species of which are native to this country. Another genus native to Great Britain is *Littorella*, and this differs from the genus *Plantago* chiefly in that while the flowers of the latter are hermaphrodite, those of *Littorella* are unisexual, though both sexes of flower grow on the same plant.

The **greater** or **lamb's tongue plantain** (*Plantago major*) is typical of the genus (Plate 12). It is a perennial plant with thick roots, and is found growing in pastures, showing its characteristically large, broad, oval, deeply ribbed leaves sometimes erect, sometimes in rosettes. For the latter reason, it and other species are pests on lawns. The leaves are cooked as greens in some parts of the country.

The inconspicuous flowers are borne in long dense spikes, each of which is produced at the end of a ribbed stalk arising from the axil of a leaf (Plate 12).

The flowers begin opening during June and continue to do so to the end of August. Each flower shows considerable reduction. The sepals are reduced to nothing but a four-cleft tube. The petals are well-nigh absent, being represented by a four-cleft disk. The four stamens, on the other hand, are very prominent; so also is the large style (Plate 12). As would be expected, the flowers are wind-pollinated, for there is little about them to attract insects. Nevertheless insects do visit them sometimes to collect pollen.

Cross-pollination is assured in that the stigmas and the stamens on the same spike ripen at different times. The styles of the lowest flowers push out first—in fact, they push themselves out while the rest of the flower is still in bud, and are thus pollinated from some other spike. Then as the styles further up are being pollinated, the stamens of the lower flowers show themselves. So it is possible to see a spike of this plant bearing stamens at the top, and having young fruit nearer the bottom (Plate 12).

The fruit-spikes are often fed to cage-birds, especially canaries.

The **hoary plantain** (*P. media*) is common in waste places, and sometimes too common on lawns, for its leaves are arranged in firmer rosettes than those of the greater plantain, and beneath them nothing can grow. It blooms during June to October. Its spikes of flowers are very much shorter than those of the greater plantain, being not much more than an inch in length and sometimes less, whereas those of the great plantain often reach a length of six inches. Each flower of this species is somewhat more prominent and is pleasantly scented.

The **rib-wort plantain** (*P. lanceolata*) has five very pronounced ribs on its leaves. It grows in pastures, and flowers during June and July. The inflorescence is almost globular.

The **buck's horn plantain** (*P. coronopus*) grows in sandy places and has hairy leaves in order to reduce water-loss. The inflorescence-stalk is not ribbed. The inflorescence is cylindrical and about an inch and a half long.

The **sea-side plantain** (*P. maritima*) grows in salt marshes, and, like other dwellers in such habitats, has succulent leaves.

The only other genus of the plantain family represented in this country is *Littorella*, to which belongs the **shore-weed** (*L. lacustris*) of the sandy margins of lakes. This plant is interesting because there are two forms of it. The land form produces its leaves in the form of rosettes pressed to the ground. It bears its unisexual flowers in groups of three, one flower being male and borne on a long stalk, the other two being stalkless females. Both stamens and styles are very long, which is to the plant's advantage, since the flowers are wind-pollinated. The other form of plant grows in the water and has erect cylindrical leaves. This form produces no flowers and therefore has to depend on a vegetative means of reproduction, namely, runners.

54

BELL-FLOWERS
(*Campanulaceae*)

It would be very difficult to mistake any member of this family (CAMPANULACEAE), for all of them have campanulate or bell-shaped flowers. All are herbs, and most are confined to temperate regions. In

Great Britain there are some wild representatives of the family, and there are some very lovely cultivated species and varieties.

WILD PLANTS

The most representative genus of this family is *Campanula* itself, and the most common wild member of the genus is the lovely **harebell** (*C. rotundifolia*) (Plate 12). This is the famous ' bluebell ' of Scotland. It thrives in pastures and on dry heaths, displaying its blue bell-shaped flowers during July to September. It is a very hardy plant.

> On the windy hills
> Lo, the little harebell leans
> On the spire-grass that it queens
> With bonnet blue.
>
> GEORGE MEREDITH

The stem of the harebell is very slender. There are three kinds of leaves merging into each other. The radical leaves (that is, those growing from ground-level) are oval, in fact, nearly heart-shaped and toothed ; the lower leaves on the stem are comparatively broad and lance-shaped ; the upper leaves are grass-like (Plate 12).

The flower is a beautiful blue bell, and there are several of them borne in a very open raceme.

> With drooping bells of clearest blue
> Thou didst attract my childish view,
> Almost resembling
> The azure butterflies that flew
> Where on the heath thy blossoms grew
> So lightly trembling.
>
> *The Harebell* : R. HEBER

There are five long, narrow sepals united at their bases ; five united petals with pointed recurved lobes ; and five stamens fused at their bases with the ovary wall. The style is long and hairy. The fruit is interesting. It is a capsule and at the top are the withered remains of the sepals and petals (Plate 12) ; also at the top rim are valves through which the seeds are dispersed as the capsule sways in the wind.

Another wild member of the genus *Campanula*, more closely related to the garden Canterbury bell, is the **nettle-leaved bluebell** or **bell-flower** (*C. trachelium*), which grows in woods and copses, throwing up its racemes of blue bells during a late season (September and October) (Plate 12). The stem grows to a height of one to three feet and is covered with reversed hairs. The leaves are long, very pointed and almost heart-shaped; their margins are notched and they have no stalks.

The flowers are large, bluish-purple, and are borne, sometimes one, sometimes a pair, in the leaf axils. Together they form a loose raceme at the top of the stem.

Each flower is similar to that of the harebell except that its sepals are covered with coarse hairs. Also the valves of the fruit capsule are at the base and not at the top (Plate 12). There is a reason for this. As the fruit ripens, it becomes pendulous, and thus brings the basal valves into an upper position and in this way guards against the seeds merely falling out near the parent plant. For purposes of satisfactory propagation, the seeds should be thrown out some distance by the swaying of the plant in the wind.

There are several other species of *Campanula* that grow wild in this country, but the harebell and the nettle-leaved bluebell are the most common. The **giant bluebell** (*C. latifolia*), of moist woods, is something like the nettle-leaved bluebell, but larger. Furthermore, its flowers are sometimes white.

The **ivy-leaved bell-flower** (*Wahlenbergia hederacea*) is rare. It grows in moist boggy places and creeps among the grass so that its blue bells are inconspicuous. The small leaves are like those of ivy.

To the campanulate genus *Jasione*, belongs the **sheep's-bit** (*J. montana*), sometimes called the **sheep's-bit scabious** because its inflorescence is very like that of the scabious (p. 209) in general appearance, though, of course, there is no fundamental relationship at all. The sheep's-bit grows on heaths, and is frequently found with the harebell and flowering at the same time (July to September).

The leaves are small, long and hairy.

The flowers are borne in terminal lilac heads, each head supported by an involucre of green bracts. Each flower is different from the flower of the genus *Campanula*. There are five small united sepals. The five lilac petals do not form a tube, but are oblong and free except at their bases where they are united (Plate 12). The five stamens are also interesting in that, although their filaments and heads are free, all five are united at their bases. The fruit is typical of CAMPANULACEAE.

A rather rare genus is *Phyteuma*, represented by the **rampion** (*P. orbiculare*). This plant presents globular heads of deep blue flowers

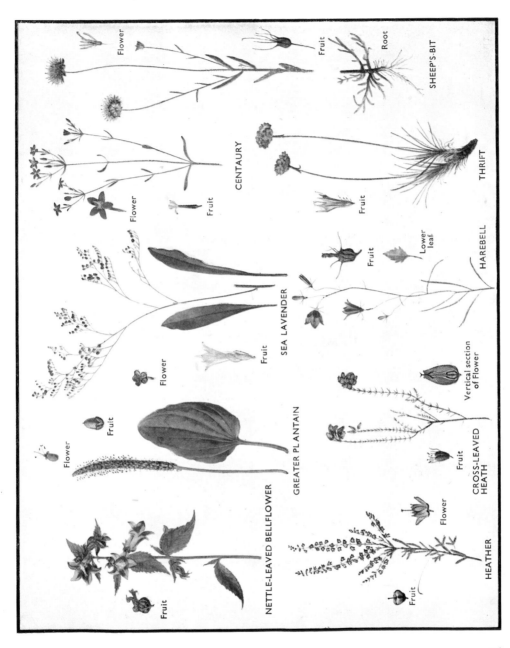

Flower

Fruit

Root

SHEEP'S-BIT

CENTAURY

Flower

Fruit

Fruit

THRIFT

HAREBELL

Flower

Fruit

Lower leaf

Fruit

Flower

Fruit

SEA LAVENDER

Vertical section of Flower

Flower

Fruit

Flower

Fruit

GREATER PLANTAIN

CROSS-LEAVED HEATH

Flower

NETTLE-LEAVED BELLFLOWER

Flower

Fruit

Fruit

HEATHER

PLATE 12

during July and August. The flower resembles that of the sheep's-bit in general structure.

ORNAMENTAL PLANTS

The genus *Campanula* has given us some of our oldest and most pleasing garden flowers. It is the most useful genus, for it supplies species and varieties which are not only prized as cut flowers but also thrive in almost any sunny position, from herbaceous border to rockery. Many are potted and grown in greenhouses.

The plants commonly called **campanulas** bear their flowers in long racemes (Fig. 117). Many species of the genus *Campanula* are very useful in borders and beds, presenting shades of white, royal blue, deep blue, mauve and purple.

A large number of species and varieties are dwarf, and since they are chiefly of alpine

FIG. 117.—*Campanula persicifolia.*

origin they thrive well in rockeries. They offer shades similar to those of herbaceous campanulas. Some campanulas are double.

Canterbury bells are most handsome plants, with enormous bells. The ordinary Canterbury bells are varieties of *Campanula medium*, some being annual and others biennial. The delicate shades of colour vary from white and blue, through mauve, to pink.

The very showy **cup-and-saucer Canterbury bells** are varieties of *Campanula calycanthema* (Fig. 118). The ' cup ' is a large bell made up of five united petals with recurved pointed lobes. The ' saucer ' is more open and results from the fusion of the five sepals, which have become petalloid. The shades of colour are similar to those of ordinary Canterbury bells.

FIG. 118.—Cup-and-saucer Canterbury Bell.

Another genus of this family, seldom seen in this country, but sometimes cultivated in greenhouses, is *Trachelium*. It is a native of Mediterranean regions. It is usually grown here in pots and produces clouds of flowers, either white or mauve in colour, superficially resembling *Gypsophila* (p. 83).

Lobelia, blue or white in colour, so widely used in edging, is frequently placed by botanists in the family CAMPANULACEAE; but as it differs from the other members of this family, especially in that its flowers are irregular, it would seem that this genus, together with others, should be regarded as a separate family—LOBELIACEAE.

The whole family is naturally tropical and sub-tropical, though there is a wild member of the genus *Lobelia*, namely, *L. dortmanna*, to be found growing wild in the Lake District of Britain.

The irregularity of the *Lobelia* flower is due to the petals. There are five of them, all united at their bases only, and with five differently shaped lobes. The two upper ones are small and upright. Then there are two broader ones forming side wings, and a lower petal not so large as those at the side. The stamens of *Lobelia* are united in an unusual way. Their filaments are free, but their anthers (heads) are joined to form a tube around the style.

There are three types of *Lobelia*, varying according to habit—the compact type, useful for edging and pot plants, the spreading type and the tall loose type.

The most common varieties of *Lobelia* are deep blue in colour, often with crimson foliage. Others are pale blue, white, blue with white 'eyes' and mauve.

The LOBELIACEAE is distributed in the warmer temperate and sub-tropical regions of the world, with some exceptions. In the higher elevations of Africa there are some remarkable tree-lobelias.

55

PHLOX AND PHACELIA

(Polemoniaceae and Hydrophyllaceae)

We now come to two families, neither of which is represented in the natural flora of this country, but which cannot be ignored altogether, for they contain some garden favourites, especially the first of them—POLEMONIACEAE.

POLEMONIACEAE is mainly a North American family which contains some very lovely flowers, notably *Phlox*. Most members of the family are herbs with alternate or opposite leaves, which may be simple, long, lance-shaped and with smooth margins, as in *Phlox*, or may be compound.

Phlox hails not only from North America but also from Siberia. The flower has five joined sepals ; five petals united to form a thin tube with five regular lobes opening out to form a plate ; five stamens alternating with the petals ; and three carpels united to form an ovary containing one ovule. The petals are very deciduous, which is unfortunate, as otherwise the flowers, which are borne in large terminal cymes, would make splendid household decorations.

Several species of *Phlox* are cultivated. The half-hardy annuals are usually varieties of *Phlox drummondii*. These are tall plants, useful in borders. The beautiful colours of this species are well known, presenting variations of white, pink, rose, crimson, yellow, blue and violet. Then there are annual dwarf varieties as well as some alpine varieties suitable for edging or rockeries—all in striking shades. Many varieties of the perennial *Phlox* (*P. paniculata*) are also cultivated. Most of these have large handsome flowers of varying colours.

Collomia, a western American genus, is sometimes represented in British gardens by *C. coccinea*, a hardy annual of compact growth producing large heads of orange-red, star-like flowers.

Gilia, a large American genus, is a half-hardy or hardy annual which produces finely divided foliage and long spikes of brilliant flowers in various shades of vermilion, through apricot, to yellow.

Polemonium is another temperate genus which is especially common in Chile. The well-known **Jacob's ladder** (*P. caeruleum*) is a border plant producing long sprays of sky-blue flowers with golden stamens that stand out conspicuously.

Cobaea is a genus native to tropical America. The genus *C. scandens* is a climber of very rapid growth, often cultivated in this country in greenhouses. It climbs by means of leaf-tendrils which have numerous branches, each ending in a hook. The flowers are first greenish with an unpleasant smell, and then turn bell-shaped and purple and emit a delightful smell of honey. Afterwards, the flower-stalks become contorted.

The family HYDROPHYLLACEAE contains some useful ornamental annuals.

The genus *Phacelia* is North American in origin. Several species and varieties of it are cultivated in this country. *P. viscida*, for example, has lovely rich-blue flowers and grows to the height of a foot. *P. campanularia* has bright blue bell-shaped flowers. *P. tanacetifolia* has large compact heads of pale mauve flowers.

Nemophila is another North American genus. It is a very old favourite as an annual and will grow almost anywhere. The flowers vary in colour—bright blue, mauve, purple, and white dotted with black.

56

THE FORGET-ME-NOT FAMILY
(Boraginaceae)

The forget-me-not family (BORAGINACEAE) is widely dispersed, especially in Mediterranean regions, and though all British members of the family, as well as those cultivated in our gardens, are herbs, some other members are shrubs and a few are trees. Only a few Mediterranean species produce useful substances, and even these are of minor importance.

A curious character of the several members of the family is the frequent tendency to change colour during the life of the individual plant. For example, the forget-me-not often changes from pink in the early stages of the flower to blue during the later stages ; and one of the scorpion grasses changes from yellow to dull blue. Several theories have been propounded to explain this colour change, but none has proved conclusive. Changes in acidity of the soil-water or of the plant sap do not give a full explanation of this strange phenomenon.

The flowers of most members of the family resemble each other fundamentally. Nearly all of them are regular. The sepals are five in number forming a tube with teeth. The five petals form a tube with five spreading lobes. The five stamens are inserted on the petal-tube, alternating with the lobes of the petals. The ovary is divided deeply into four parts, each part after fertilisation forming a small nut or nutlet.

WILD PLANTS

To the genus *Myosotis* belong the true forget-me-not and about half a dozen other species of scorpion grass. The other scorpion grasses in general resemble the forget-me-not though they are usually of coarser habit.

The true **forget-me-not, mouse-ear** or **scorpion grass** (*M. palustris*) grows in wet places such as marshes and beside ponds and rivers, where its sky-blue flowers bloom during June to August.

> I love its growth at large and free
> By untrod path and unlopped tree,
> Or nodding by the unpruned hedge,
> Or on the water's dangerous edge
> Where flags and meadowsweet blow rank
> With rushes on the quaking bank.
> *On a Bed of Forget-me-nots* : CHRISTINA ROSSETTI

The plant usually grows to a height of a foot, though when growing among taller plants it often reaches two feet. The leaves are lance-shaped and have no stalks ; they are arranged alternately on the stem (Plate 13). All the green parts of the plant, even the sepals, are covered with hairs.

The flowers are arranged in curious inflorescences, each resembling the coiled tail of a scorpion, and it is therefore said to be scorpioid. (This explains the common name of the scorpion grasses.) Thus the spike is curved backwards.

Each flower of the forget-me-not is usually blue, with very small, blunt, yellow scales at the throat of the tube. When very young, the flowers are often pink, and they sometimes, though not always, revert to pink as they get older. The small nuts are surrounded by a dry, persistent calyx (Plate 13).

There is no authoritative statement on the origin of the name 'forget-me-not'. There is an old legend that a knight was picking some of the flowers for his lady on the banks of a river. He fell in the river and was drowned, but while falling he exclaimed 'Forget-me-not'. There is no foundation for this legend, neither is there for other theories put forward to explain the name. In fact, the name has in the past been given to other flowers, especially the speedwells (p. 275).

Of the other scorpion grasses, the **creeping scorpion grass** (*M. repens*) is one of the most common. It grows in habitats similar to those of the forget-me-not. Its general structure, too, is similar, though the flowers are rather smaller and it spreads by means of branch stems in the form of runners which take root at their tips. The **tufted scorpion grass** (M. *caespitosa*) is also similar in most respects, but its leaves are bright green and shining. The petals form a sky-blue corolla with a yellow disk. The **field scorpion grass** (*M. arvensis*) grows in drier situations and can be distinguished by the fact that each flower-stalk in the inflorescence is much longer than in other species. The **yellow-and-blue scorpion grass** (*M. versicolor*) grows in damp meadows. Its flowers are yellow when young and then turn a dull blue as they open out.

The gromwells (*Lithospermum* species) are not very common flowers, though in spite of a different colour they are fundamentally similar to the forget-me-not. The throat of the flower is naked, having no scales. The sepals, too, are very deeply cleft and united only at their bases ; therefore they form no tube. The **common gromwell** (*L. officinale*) grows in copses and woods and has pale yellow flowers. The **corn gromwell** (*L. arvense*) grows in cornfields and displays its creamy-white flowers during May and June.

The **comfrey** (*Symphytum officinale*) is an attractive plant of large habit, growing along river banks and in other damp places. Its conspicuous purple flowers are seen during May and June. Here again, the flowers show the curious colour-change, being sometimes white, yellow or purple. Most frequently they are purple (Plate 13). The plant is of strong habit, growing two to four feet high. The large leaves are lance-shaped, the margins of each leaf continuing some distance down the stem. The stem and leaves are covered with coarse but rather brittle hairs.

The pendulous flowers are borne in dense clusters. Fundamentally each flower is typical of the family, though the five petal-lobes form a funnel rather than a salver. There are five awl-shaped scales at the throat. The fruit takes the form of small nuts (usually four) surrounded by a persistent calyx (Plate 13).

The comfrey plant is supposed to have medicinal properties. Sometimes the young leaves are cooked and eaten as greens ; sometimes ' comfrey tea ' is made from them. At one time it was considered that the plant would mend broken bones, and this explains the generic name, for in Greek it means ' to unite '.

A rarer species is the **tuberous comfrey** (*S. tuberosum*), having a slender stem and yellowish white flowers. It also bears stem-tubers like those of the potato.

The **borage** (*Borago officinalis*) grows in waste places, producing its bright blue flowers during June and July. It is a stout, leafy plant growing one to two feet high. The flowers are arranged in small terminal inflorescences. All green parts are hairy. The union of the sepals and of the petals is the least possible—at their extreme bases—so that at a casual glance they appear to be free, displaying lance-shaped lobes.

The borage is sometimes cultivated by bee-keepers, for it supplies plenty of nectar and pollen for bees. The nectar is secreted at the base of the ovary. The stamens form a hollow cone around the ovary and shed their pollen inside the cone. The pollen falls to the apex of the cone, since the flower is pendulous. Thus, as the bee gropes for the honey, it receives a shower of pollen. In older flowers, the stigma projects beyond the cone of stamens and is therefore touched first by the visiting bee. This ensures cross-pollination.

The old rhyme :

> I, borage,
> Bring courage

refers to its former use as a cordial. A few sprigs are still placed in claret cup and similar drinks.

Bugloss plants are very attractive, and there are two genera of them—the small bugloss and the viper's bugloss.

The **small bugloss** (*Lycopsis arvensis*) grows in waste places and around cultivated fields, displaying its bright blue flowers during June and July. The leaves growing from ground-level are oval ; those on the stems are lance-shaped with wavy toothed margins. All green parts are hairy. The flowers are borne in short racemes and each flower has a very short stalk. The petal-tube is curiously bent, and its throat is almost completely closed by five white scales. The long sepals persist after the petals have fallen, and they form a withered tube around the small nuts when they are ripe (Plate 13).

The **viper's bugloss** (*Echium vulgare*) is a very attractive plant, showing its floral colour-change—red, through purple, to blue—simultaneously on the same plant (Plate 13). It grows on waste ground and the flowers appear in their dense scorpioid inflorescences during June and July (Plate 13). The leaves are small and have no stalks. Both flower-stalks and leaves are covered with prickly hairs.

The flower of the viper's bugloss is irregular in that the five petal-lobes are uneven. There are no scales on the throat. The pollination mechanism is similar to that of the borage.

The **hound's tongue** (*Cynoglossum officinale*) is not a common plant, but it may sometimes be found growing in waste places and near sand-dunes, throwing up its loose inflorescences of purplish-red flowers during June and July (Plate 13). The leaves are lance-shaped and are covered with silky hairs. The petal throat is almost closed by prominent scales. The small nuts are covered with hooks which enable them to be dispersed by animals.

A rarer species, the **green hound's tongue** (*C. montanum*), grows in hilly districts. Its leaves are more or less round ; the flowers are blue and are borne in cymes.

There are several other genera of the forget-me-not family (BORAGINACEAE) ; but they are rather rare.

ORNAMENTAL PLANTS

The most popular members of this family grown in flower gardens are forget-me-not, heliotrope and *Anchusa*.

Forget-me-nots and other species of *Myosotis* are at their best when grown in large masses. Frequently they are used to form a massed ground-colour for taller bedded plants. The garden species must be treated as biennials, and are therefore usually bedded out in their second year.

The **cherry pie** (*Heliotropium peruvianum*) and the **heliotrope** (other *Heliotropium* species) do not give much of an impression when viewed singly, but a thick bed of them presents a rich mass of colour, usually dark lilac, and has a seductive perfume. The plants derive their generic name from the fact that the flowers always face the sun.

Anchusa gives some of the few really blue flowers of the garden. The species *A. officinalis* is sometimes found growing wild, but it is

PLATE 13

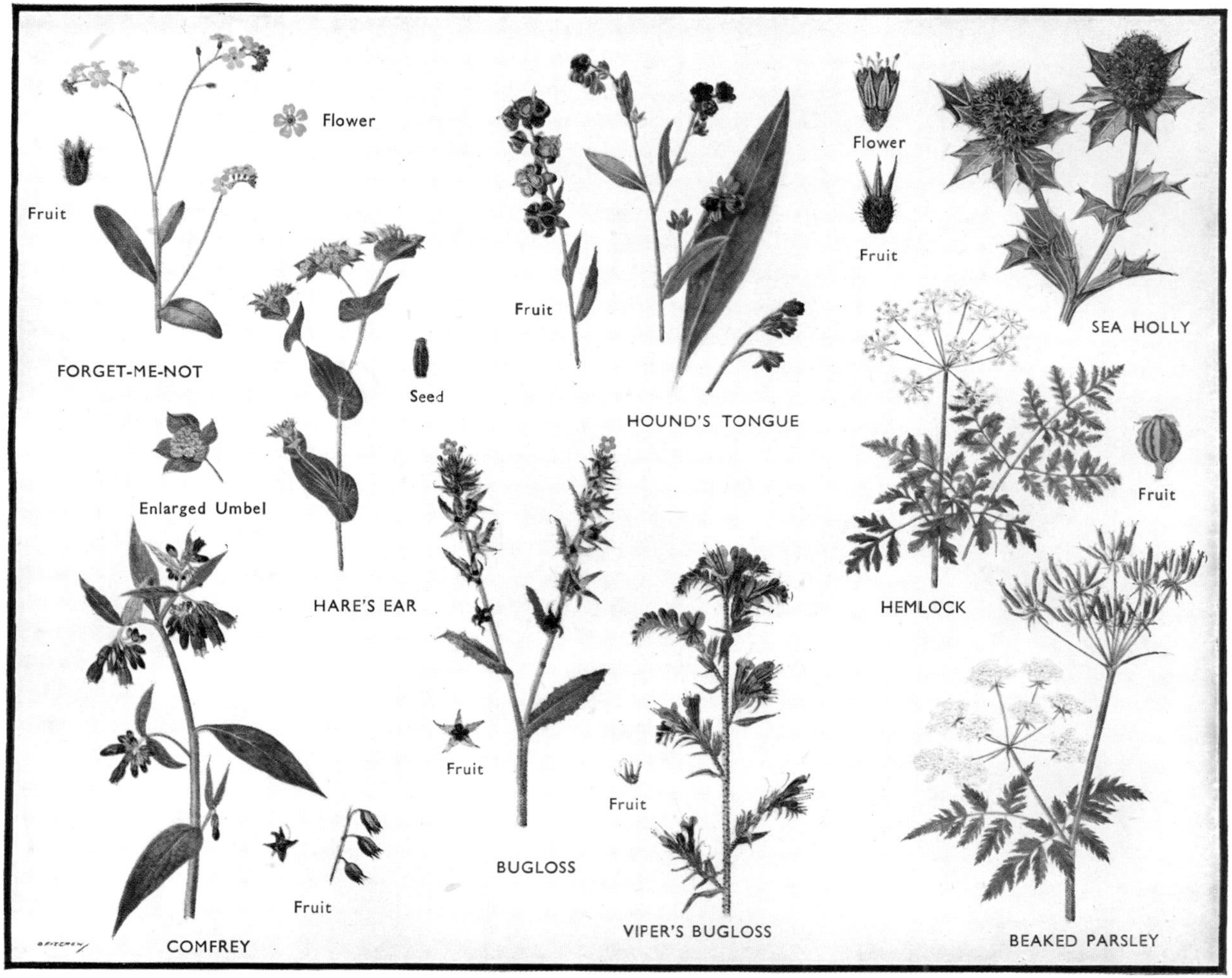

SEA HOLLY

Flower

Fruit

Fruit

HEMLOCK

BEAKED PARSLEY

HOUND'S TONGUE

Fruit

VIPER'S BUGLOSS

Fruit

BUGLOSS

Fruit

Seed

HARE'S EAR

Flower

Enlarged Umbel

Fruit

FORGET-ME-NOT

Fruit

COMFREY

fairly certain to have been originally a garden escape. The garden species and varieties may be annual, biennial or perennial. The flowers are like forget-me-nots borne in very dense terminal inflorescences, most kinds being of a rich or deep blue colour.

Several varieties of *Echium* closely related to the viper's bugloss are sometimes cultivated, and make a good show owing to their colour variations within the same plant.

The hound's tongue (*Cynoglossum* species) is represented in some gardens by several varieties with blue or white flowers.

57

THE POTATO FAMILY
(*Solanaceae*)

This is an extraordinary family, for it gives us the very valuable potato, tomato and tobacco, the beautiful flowering plants, *Nicotiana*, *Petunia*, *Salpiglossis* and *Schizanthus*—all from the Americas—yet the members native to this country, henbane and nightshades, are poisonous.

The family is distributed throughout temperate and tropical regions, though its chief centre is Central and South America. It contains herbs, shrubs and a few small trees; some are climbers. In most cases the leaves alternate on the stem, though they frequently pair up near the shoot tips where the flowers are borne.

WILD PLANTS

Three genera of the family SOLANACEAE are to be found growing wild in this country today, though it is more than likely that some were originally garden escapes. The floral structure of all of them is very similar.

The **henbane** (*Hyoscyamus niger*) is a shrubby herb growing about two feet high in waste places and areas surrounding villages. Its gay yellow flowers veined with purple are to be seen during June to September. The leaves are long, deeply toothed, and with bases encircling the stem. Both stems and leaves are covered with large hairs.

The flowers are borne in dense clusters fitting closely into the axils of the leaves. Each flower has five sepals, united into a tube with five prominent teeth. The five petals are united but have five large lobes arranged in a campanulate fashion about an inch in diameter. The five stamens are inserted on the petal-tube, each stamen alternating with a petal lobe. There are two carpels united to form a two-chambered ovary which contains many ovules. The fruit is a capsule enclosed in the remains of the sepals. It opens by means of a lid.

The henbane is narcotic, and from it a drug (hyoscyamine) is prepared. In fact, the plant is still cultivated for this purpose in some parts of the country. At one time, it was cultivated to a considerable extent, and most probably it was originally a garden escape. Some country-folk have been known to smoke the seeds and capsules as a cure for toothache, but this is a dangerous practice. Both seeds and leaves are used in *materia medica*. The tincture prepared from the henbane should be used only from a doctor's prescription, and then it is a useful and potent hypnotic or sedative.

> The prospect of finding anybody out in anything would have kept Miss Miggs awake under the influence of henbane.
>
> *Barnaby Rudge* : DICKENS

The symptoms of henbane poisoning are loss of speech and paralysis. It has been suggested that henbane was the 'juice of cursed hebenon' with which Hamlet's father was murdered, though this is doubtful. It might have been the 'insane root that takes the reason prisoner' in *Macbeth*.

Two of the four wild nightshades—black nightshade and woody nightshade (or bittersweet)—belong to the solanaceous genus *Solanum* ; the third—deadly nightshade—belongs to the genus *Atropa*, also of this family ; the fourth—enchanter's nightshade—is not a member of this family at all, but belongs to the ONAGRACEAE (p. 104), and, unlike the other three, it is not poisonous.

The **black nightshade** (*S. nigrum*) is a small herbaceous plant, growing six inches to two feet in height, and is frequently seen in waste places. It is also a common weed. The flowers appear during August to October and are white, the lobes of the petals being lance-shaped, and the heads of the stamens presenting a very prominent erect cone. The fruit is a black berry. This is poisonous, though the leaves are not, for in Mauritius they are eaten like spinach.

The **woody nightshade** or **bittersweet** (*S. dulcamara*) is a very lovely plant commonly seen climbing over hedges and presenting its drooping purple flowers during July to September (Plate 16). The leaves are heart-shaped and pointed, often with smaller lobes at their bases or on their stalks. Each flower is similar to that of the black nightshade, but larger and with large purple petals, each having a green spot at the base of the lobe. (Sometimes white flowers may be seen.) The cone of stamens is very conspicuous (Plate 16). The berries are red when ripe (Plate 16) and are rather poisonous. The alternative common name (bittersweet) and the specific name (*dulcamara*) are derived from the fact that the berries are first bitter and then sweet.

The **deadly nightshade** or **belladonna** belongs to another genus (*Atropa belladonna*). It is not very common in this country. It is a sturdy plant, growing about three feet high and having broad oval leaves (Plate 16). The flowers are solitary and each is borne on a short stalk in the axil of a leaf. Each flower has a five-toothed calyx. The five petals are joined and have five purplish blue lobes about an inch long (Plate 16). These lobes do not spread as they do in the genus *Solanum*. The fruit is a large, globular black berry.

The deadly nightshade is very poisonous. The drug atropine is prepared from this and related plants. This drug is a sedative when used in correct doses; it is also used for several other therapeutical purposes, such as controlling sweating and the relief of pain, and of bronchial irritation in such complaints as whooping cough. It is valuable in the treatment of eye troubles. The word *belladonna* in Italian means beautiful lady and was applied to the deadly nightshade because it was once the practice of ladies to touch their eyes with it in order to make the pupils larger and more lustrous. Weak extracts are still used for this purpose, especially among theatrical people.

To the genus *Mandragora* belongs that strange plant, the **mandrake** (*M. officinarum*) which is not grown in this country, but is native to regions stretching from the Mediterranean to the Himalayas. Around this plant all sorts of superstitions have developed, often because its root is fleshy and forked and often grows in the form of the lower limbs of a man. For example, it was believed to shriek when pulled from the soil :

> And shrieks like mandrakes torn out of the earth, that living mortals, hearing them, run mad.
>
> *Romeo and Juliet* : SHAKESPEARE

In the East, the plant was often used in love potions, and its fruit was supposed to make child-birth easier.

The whole plant is poisonous and is used as an emetic, purgative and narcotic. The stem is short with purple flowers. The fruit is an orange-coloured berry.

(The name ' mandrake ' is also given to the American may apple (*Podophyllum peltatum*) which, however, belongs to the family BERBERIDACEAE, p. 51.)

ECONOMIC PLANTS

Some of the members of this family (SOLANACEAE) are so very important from the economic point of view that they will be dealt with before the ornamental plants are considered.

Perhaps the most important culinary vegetable in this and other countries is the **potato**. This belongs to the genus *Solanum* (*S. tuberosum*). There can be no doubt about this fact, for its flowers are very like those of the wild species of *Solanum* already described.

The plant is a somewhat woody herb, with large compound leaves. The flowers are borne in umbels at the ends of long stalks carried on the shoots. They are of varying shades of purple or may be white or cream with large cones of stamens. The fruit is seldom seen in gardens, but it is a large berry, first green, then yellow or orange and finally deep purple (Fig. 119). All these characteristics conform to the general form of the genus *Solanum*. Even the fruit is poisonous.

FIG. 119.—Flowers and Fruit of Potato.

Everyone knows what the edible portion of a potato looks like, and that it usually grows below the soil surface. Yet it is not a root, for it bears shoots, which roots never do. These shoots grow out into branches if the potato is stored in a dark place. The shoots develop from the ' eyes ' of the potato, which are really young buds in the axils of very small, insignificant scale-leaves. The edible portion of the potato is therefore an underground stem. It is called a stem-tuber. The underground stems of the potato actually grow along beneath the soil, and it is towards their tips that they swell and form the familiar tubers. The food stored in these is chiefly starch with a certain amount of protein.

But the tuber is not only used as the plant's food store. It is also a means of vegetative reproduction. The ordinary gardener never uses the real seeds of the potato for the production of new crops ; he uses the tubers, saved from the plants of the previous season's growth. They are usually called ' seed ' potatoes, though they are not really seeds. Whereas a true seed usually begins growth by the production of roots, the potato tuber, once it has been placed in the soil and growth conditions are favourable, begins by the production of new shoots. These grow out from the buds of the eyes. Each eye sends out at least one shoot, and that is why, for the sake of economy, seed potatoes are often cut, for so long as there is an eye and a certain amount of the flesh on each portion it will grow. Nowadays, sometimes only a single eye is used, together with the minimum amount of fleshy tissue. This saves considerable space, especially in transport, and the Canadian Government is now encouraging this method of transporting seed potatoes. On the other hand, the Government of the U.S.S.R. is experimenting with potato peelings.

When planted, the shoot goes on growing, getting the food that is necessary for its growth from the tuber, until it emerges from the soil, then it unfolds new foliage leaves, which, since they are green, can manufacture a new supply of food. But these leaves must have water and mineral salts from the soil, and so, to prepare for this, those parts of the stems of the new shoots growing below the soil give off adventitious roots. Thus the new plant becomes established in the soil.

The origin of the potato has been the subject of much controversy. Wild potato plants have been found in both Chile and Peru. It was supposed to have been brought to Spain by a monk during the sixteenth century, and thence it passed east to Italy and north to France and Belgium. It is also supposed that the navigators Drake and Hawkins

s

introduced the potato into England from South America during 1563, but the botanist Sir Joseph Banks claimed that what they brought was the sweet potato (p. 272). Recent research, however, suggests that Banks was wrong. (The sweet potato, the tubers of which are much favoured in the United States and certain tropical regions, is not a member of the SOLANACEAE, but it is closely related to the potato, for it comes in the next family, CONVOLVULACEAE. Its tubers, however, are root- and not stem-tubers.)

It is certain that Sir Walter Raleigh brought the potato from North Carolina to Ireland and planted it on his estate near Cork in 1586, though by that time the plant had already arrived in Continental Europe.

More recent research into the early history of the potato shows that it was actually under cultivation in South America so early as A.D. 200 ; it was often used as the motif for the Indian pottery of those regions at that time. It now seems clear that there were two original areas of cultivation, namely, Chile and Peru together with Bolivia.

The **tomato** also belongs to the genus *Solanum* (*S. lycopersicum*). In fact, it looks very like an enlarged nightshade plant with trusses of yellow flowers. The fruit is a large berry, with persistent sepals, green when first formed and turning usually red but sometimes yellow when ripe (Fig. 120).

FIG. 120.—Tomatoes under Cultivation.

This berry is a source of food and vitamins. For ripening it requires plenty of warmth and sunshine, therefore the plant may or may not succeed when planted outdoors in this country, for so much depends upon the weather; in greenhouses, of course, it succeeds under controlled conditions.

The tomato is another native of the centre of this family, namely, South America. It was brought to Europe first by the Spaniards, when for a long time it was called the 'love-apple'. As a vegetable, it has been popular in this country for only about eighty years. Now, as a result of intensive cultivation, there are about a hundred and fifty varieties in Great Britain alone. The canning of tomatoes is gradually becoming a thriving industry, especially in the United States and Great Britain. Here, the most extensive areas of cultivation are the Lea Valley, Sussex and the Channel Islands.

The **egg-fruit** (*S. melongena*) is a popular fruit in the tropics.

The spice, **capsicum** or **chilli**, is the fruit of another genus belonging to the same family (*Capsicum annuum* and *C. frutescens*), yet another native of Central and South America. The fruit is an elongated red berry which, when dried, produces the spice used in pickles, and when ground and powdered makes red or Cayenne pepper.

The genus *Nicotiana* gives us not only some very popular ornamental flowers (p. 266), but also the plant of the widest economic importance, namely **tobacco** (*Nicotiana tabacum*).

The product of this plant may be smoked or chewed; some of the inhabitants of Africa and certain American indians eat it; and during the eighteenth and nineteenth centuries it was popular in many parts of the world, including Great Britain, in the powdered and perfumed form—snuff.

The history of tobacco is also very interesting though it has not yet been clearly elucidated. Columbus noticed the American Indians using it when he visited that continent in the latter part of the fifteenth century. They also used to smoke powdered willow bark.

It is certain, however, that the tobacco plant is yet another native of Central America. It was brought to Europe in 1558 by a Spaniard named Francisco Fernandez, and was later popularised in this country by Sir Walter Raleigh, who is said to have smoked a pipe of it when on the way to the scaffold.

The main source of the world's supply of tobacco is *Nicotiana tabacum*, though other species are sometimes used. This is an annual plant which attains a height of five feet or more. It terminates in a large inflorescence of pink flowers. The leaves are long, broad and lance-shaped. Sometimes they reach a length of two feet. It is from the leaves that the product is prepared.

The main source of tobacco is the United States, chiefly the State of Virginia, but the plant is also cultivated to varying degrees in many other places, such as Brazil, China, Japan, Dutch East Indies, Canada, Cuba, Africa, Turkey, the U.S.S.R., Germany, and even in certain parts of the south of England. The bulk of tobacco now smoked is American, usually called Virginian. Egyptian, Turkish and Russian cigarettes are stronger and are usually treated with perfume.

As the leaves of the plant begin to mature, they turn a brighter green and frequently become covered with yellow spots. They are then gathered and hung on long sticks in sheds to dry. Then they have to be 'cured'. In favourable districts this is done merely by exposing them to the sun ; if the weather is unfavourable, however, fires have to be used. Then the leaves are piled in heaps where they are allowed to ferment. After fermentation they are tied up in bales and graded. These bales are stored until the tobacco is mature.

Well over four thousand million pounds of tobacco are produced in the world each year (see also p. 5).

ORNAMENTAL PLANTS

Among the members of the SOLANACEAE cultivated in this country for ornamental purposes are some beautiful outdoor plants and some lovely greenhouse exotics.

Perhaps the most popular outdoor plant is the **flowering tobacco** (*Nicotiana* species). This sweet scented plant will grow outdoors quite happily, though some kinds need greenhouse shelter. The flower varies in size and colour according to species or variety, the chief shades being white, yellow or red (Fig. 121).

FIG. 121.—Flowering Tobacco (*Nicotiana affinis*)

To the genus *Physalis* belong several species useful for Christmas decoration because of their bright berries. The **winter cherry** (*P. alkekengi*) is a popular pot plant. This small shrub has masses of small, simple, lance-shaped leaves and during the summer months it becomes covered with small white flowers very similar to those of *Solanum*. Many of these flowers drop before fertilisation, but a large number are fertilised and produce berries first green, then yellow and finally bright red towards the end of the year. The equally popular **Cape gooseberry** (*P. peruviana*) is a large plant with arching sprays bearing big heart-shaped leaves. It will grow outdoors in this country, given a dry sunny position. It owes its distinctiveness to the large, bladder-like persistent calyx which looks like a Chinese lantern. This calyx is first green, then turns to varying shades of yellow, orange and red. Within the lantern, as one would expect, is the fruit—a small berry.

Certain species of *Solanum* and *Capsicum* are also cultivated on account of their red berries which come in useful for household decoration during the sparse winter months.

The **thorn apple** (*Datura stramonium*) is also sometimes cultivated. In its native tropics it is used for medicinal purposes. The fruit is a four-valved capsule covered with spines. Certain of the cultivated species bear attractive, sweet-scented, trumpet-shaped flowers, white or yellow in colour.

For compelling beauty, the laurels of the family SOLANACEAE must go to the genera *Salpiglossis*, *Petunia* and *Schizanthus*.

Salpiglossis is a South American genus which has given this country some very lovely plants which produce most striking effects in borders. Others look best in pots. The large flower

FIG. 122.—Hybrids of *Salpiglossis*.

FIG. 123.—Giant Hybrid *Schizanthus*.

trumpets (Fig. 122) offer all kinds of colours, such as white with gold throat, dark blue and gold, light blue, rose, yellow, crimson, red, deep blue, and so forth.

Petunia hails from both the Americas. In this country the species are half-hardy annuals with very large flowers, useful in borders, pots and window-boxes. The plant is more compact than *Salpiglossis*. There are both single and double varieties. Sometimes the petals are fringed, and there are many shades of colour—white, pink, rose, crimson, blue, violet, together with variegated kinds, striped or blotched.

Perhaps the most exquisite of the lot is *Schizanthus* which has come to us from Chile. The flower of this plant is very irregular. Two of the petals form a lower lip which is three- or four-lobed. Then there are two lateral or side petals, each usually four-lobed. The upper petal is usually small and simple, though it might sometimes be slightly bi-lobed. Thus the flower is somewhat papilionaceous like most of the LEGUMINOSAE : in fact, *Schizanthus* is frequently called the **butterfly flower**. The different species and varieties of this plant look very fine in pots (Fig. 123). Alas, when bordered out they are not very successful except in particularly warm positions. The flowers vary in size and form, and the infinity of colours defies description.

58
THE CONVOLVULUS FAMILY
(Convolvulaceae)

The convolvulus family is one of woody twiners. Its members have characteristic habits and most of the flowers are unmistakable. Included in the family is a well-known parasite, the dodder. There are a few ornamental plants and some which yield useful products though these are not cultivated in Great Britain.

WILD PLANTS

A plant very characteristic of the family is the **great bindweed** (*Convolvulus sepium* or more correctly *Calystegia sepium*) which twines over hedges displaying its handsome almost arrow-shaped leaves and large flower trumpets during June to August. Although the flowers are sometimes pink, they are most often white and of such a dazzling whiteness as to stand out very conspicuously in any hedge where they grow.

> There is an herb named in Latin Convolvulus (*i.e.* with wind), growing among shrubs and bushes, which carrieth a flower not unlike to this Lilly, save that it yieldeth no smell nor hath those chives within ; for whiteness they resemble one another very much, as if Nature in making this flower were a learning and trying her skill how to frame the Lilly indeed.
>
> *Historia Naturalis*, Bk. **21** : PLINY

Pliny was right not only about the flower's dazzling whiteness but also its lack of scent. It is nevertheless visited by insects and usually depends on hawkmoths for pollination. This is unlike the small bindweed, which has sweet-scented flowers and is therefore visited by a variety of insects.

FIG. 124.—Bindweed twining around oat stalks (anti-clockwise).

The great bindweed climbs surrounding plants, and eventually the hedges, by twining its own long woody stem around the support in an anti-clockwise direction as also does the small bindweed (see p. 270) (Fig. 124).

The flower has five overlapping sepals which are very distinct but are enclosed by two green bracts. The five very large petals, usually white, are united to form a five-angled tube which closes up at night. The five stamens are fixed to the base of this petal-tube and alternate with its segments. There are two carpels fused to

Henry Irving

form a two-chambered ovary having a long hair-like style with a cleft stigma.

The **seaside bindweed** (*Convolvulus* or *Calystegia soldanella*) grows on shady seashores. It is more closely related to the great bindweed than to the small bindweed. Its stem is prostrate and, as in most seashore plants, it has fleshy leaves. These are kidney-shaped.

The **small bindweed** (*Convolvulus arvensis*) is all too familiar to the countryman, for it grows not only in fields but also on agricultural land and in gardens, where it proves to be a very troublesome weed because the roots are prolific in the production of adventitious buds from which long yellowish underground stems grow. Thus the plant spreads vegetatively and is very difficult to eradicate, for almost any part left will develop into a new plant.

In spite of this, the small bindweed is an attractive plant with pretty pink flowers appearing during June to August (Plate 16). It is smaller in habit than the great bindweed, though fundamentally similar, except that its stem is frequently prostrate, though it often climbs any plant growing nearby. The flowers also have a delicate scent. Further-more, the bracts, instead of surrounding the sepals, are inserted well down the flower-stalk (Plate 16). Sometimes the flowers are white.

The troublesome nature of the small bindweed as a garden weed is well described by Wordsworth writing of a deserted garden:

> The cumbrous bind-weed, with its wreaths and bells,
> Had twined about her two small rows of peas,
> And dragged them to the earth.
>
> *The Excursion* : WORDSWORTH

The bindweeds have had a whole series of local names, such as 'woodbine' (see also p. 205), 'hedge-bell' and 'withwind'.

We now come to the second genus of wild plants in this family, and it is of particular interest, for its members not only twist round the supporting plants but are also parasitic on them. This genus is *Cuscuta* and comprises the **lesser dodder** (*C. epithymum*), parasitic on gorse, thyme and ling, and the **greater dodder** (*C. europaea*), parasitic on stinging nettles and vetches (Fig. 125).

The dodder has a yellowish thread-like stem which twines round the stalk of its host. At intervals up the stem the parasite sends off suckers which penetrate the stem of the host and thus extract food from it. This being the case, one would not expect to find leaves growing on the dodder itself. Yet they are there, though they are reduced to colourless scales. The plant has no roots. When its seed germinates it develops a short root for the purpose of anchorage, but once the shoot has twined round the stem of its host and pierced it with a sucker then this root withers away.

The small flowers of the dodder are produced during July to August in rosettes and are pink in colour. The sepal-tube is four-cleft, as is also the petal-tube. It is therefore more salver-shaped than funnel-shaped. Otherwise, the flower is similar to the rest of the CONVOLVULACEAE.

Henry Irving

FIG. 125.—Dodder parasitic on Stinging Nettle.

ORNAMENTAL PLANTS

The well-known **morning glory,** usually called convolvulus, does not belong to the genus *Convolvulus* but to the genus *Ipomoea* to which the sweet potato belongs.

Morning glory (mainly the species *I. purpurea*) makes a good twining plant for trellis-work, arbours, and so forth, presenting a variety of shades—deep blue, pale blue, blue striped with white, etc.

Other species of *Ipomaea* are cultivated for their showy flowers, though most of them need greenhouse care.

The true species of *Convolvulus* (*C. althaeoides*) is a creeper with pink flowers and silver foliage. It is useful in rock gardens; but like its wild relative (*C. arvensis*) it soon gets out of hand if not carefully watched, for it is a notorious ' invader '.

The genus *Nolana* comes from Chile and Peru where there are several fleshy seashore species. One of them (*N. grandiflora*) is sometimes utilised in this country for covering bare patches in sunny positions, since it spreads quickly. The convolvulus-like flowers are large and lavender blue with white throats.

ECONOMIC PLANTS

The family CONVOLVULACEAE does not offer much of economic value apart from the sweet potato.

From the thick underground stem of *Convolvulus scammonia*, a plant cultivated in eastern Mediterranean regions, a resinous juice is obtained from which the purgative scammony is extracted. Some species also yield rosewood oil.

The genus *Ipomoea* gives the sweet potato and jalap.

The **sweet potato** (*I. batatas*) is a tropical species and is cultivated for its club-shaped root-tubers, containing much starch, which are cooked and used like the stem tubers of the ordinary potato. In this respect, it is an important food crop in the United States, ranking second to the ordinary potato. It is a climber with pink flowers very like those of *Convolvulus*.

The **jalap** (*I. purga*) is a Mexican climber, very typical of the family, with purplish-pink flowers. Its thick underground stems give off roots which swell and resemble turnips. When these are worm-eaten they are even more useful, for the worms devour only the non-resinous parts and the resinous portions are thus available for the extraction of the drug, which is a strong purgative, often used in the treatment of dropsy.

59

THE SNAPDRAGON FAMILY

(*Scrophulariaceae*)

The family SCROPHULARIACEAE and the rest of the dicotyledonous families which follow, especially the last (LABIATAE), show a consistent and usually high degree of floral irregularity. The highest degree of all is reached in the LABIATAE. In the SCROPHULARIACEAE some plants have only a suggestion of irregularity in their flowers.

The family SCROPHULARIACEAE is very generally distributed, and most of its members are herbs or shrubs, though there are a few exotic trees. Large though the family is, it has few members of any economic importance except for some medicinal plants. Many are cultivated for ornamental purposes.

WILD PLANTS

Most British members of the family will thrive on infertile soils, and in spite of this often present very showy flowers. This is because a large percentage of them are semi-parasitic, chiefly on the grass-roots around them.

One of the genera which show the least floral irregularity is *Veronica*, the speedwells, of which there are about seventeen species in this country. This genus is confined to temperate regions, and a number of them are of alpine habit. The commonest British species is the **germander speedwell** (*V. chamaedrys*), a plant which grows in several different habitats such as banks or hedgerows, and in gardens as a weed. In certain localities it is called ' bird's-eye '. It grows nine inches to two feet in height and flowers early in the year (May and June) (Plate 14).

Hairs grow on the stem in two longitudinal opposite fringes. The leaves are borne in pairs, each pair being in a plane at right angles to the adjacent pair. The leaf is stalkless, heart-shaped and serrated.

The bright blue flowers are borne in small, loose racemes, each of which is produced on a long stalk in the axil of an upper leaf. The racemes therefore come off in opposite pairs (Plate 14). Each flower is about a third of an inch in diameter.

Though most members of the SCROPHULARIACEAE have five sepals and five petals, the numbers in the speedwells have been reduced to four during evolution ; that is, there is reason for believing that the speedwell flower is derived from an original flower with whorls of five. Herein lies the slight irregularity of the flower. In the case of the sepals, one has just disappeared. In the case of the petals, the two upper ones have become fused into one large petal, the two side petals are slightly smaller but equal in size to each other, and the lower petal is the smallest and is frequently of a lighter shade of colour. The four petals are united only slightly to form a small tube. The lobes are therefore very pronounced. The number of stamens has become reduced to two. The two carpels are joined to form a two-chambered ovary with a single style. The fruit is a dry capsule surrounded by a persistent **calyx**.

The **brooklime** (*Veronica beccabunga*) is frequently seen growing in ditches, displaying its typical blue flowers during May to September. Like most water-loving plants it is quite free of hairs, and the stem is somewhat succulent with a tendency to be procumbent. Though of somewhat larger habit, it resembles in general the germander speedwell.

The **small speedwell** (*V. buxbaumii*) has the brightest blue flowers among all speedwells. It is not common, but may sometimes be found in fields. Its stem is procumbent.

Among other species of speedwell may be mentioned the **wall speedwell** (*V. arvensis*), a smaller plant with crowded inflorescences, growing in dry places and flowering during April to July; the **field speedwell** (*V. agrestis*), also a small plant with pale blue or white flowers, growing in fields and waste places and flowering during April to September; the **marsh speedwell** (*V. scutellata*), with large white and pink flowers, appearing during July and August; the **water speedwell** (*V. anagallis*), having pale mauve or white flowers which appear during July and August; and the **common speedwell** (*V. officinalis*), with very small pale blue flowers borne in dense racemes, which appear during May to July.

Veronica is named after St. Veronica, who, according to legend, gave her handkerchief to Christ to wipe the sweat off his face when on the way to Calvary. When He returned it to her, there was an image of His face on the handkerchief.

None of the British species of *Veronica* has any economic value, though in the United States some closely related species are eaten in green salads. Some exotic species of *Veronica* are shrubby and produce attractive spikes of flowers. Others, though not many, attain the height of small trees.

The genus *Verbascum* comprises the mulleins, which are very tall and conspicuous plants with showy flowers. The most common species is the **great mullein** (*V. thapsus*). This tall, very handsome plant grows in dry chalky places and displays its dense inflorescence of large yellow flowers during June to August (Plate 14). The whole plant looks woolly because its stems, leaves, and even inflorescences are covered with thick white hairs. The leaves are particularly large and lance-shaped, the largest being at the base of the tall, erect and sturdy stem.

The flowers are borne in dense woolly spikes, each flower being subtended by a pronounced green bract (Plate 14). The Old English name for this plant is 'hedge-taper' or 'torch'. Since the lower flowers open first, this name is appropriate.

Each flower has five united sepals; five petals joined to form a short tube and opening out into five large lobes nearly equal in size; five stamens; and the carpels are united as usual to form a two-chambered ovary with a single style.

The other species of mullein are rare. At one time, some of them were used for medicinal purposes.

It will have been noted that, so far, one genus (*Veronica*) has two stamens, and the second (*Verbascum*) has five. Others will be seen to have four. This suggests that the family originally had five stamens and that during evolutionary progress there has been a tendency towards reduction in the number.

The genus *Pedicularis* contains the louseworts, which are semi-parasitic on the roots of grasses and other hosts. The **marsh lousewort** (*P. palustris*) displays its pink, two-lipped flowers during May to September. The **field lousewort** (*P. sylvatica*) is similar, though its stem branches at the base whereas that of the marsh lousewort does not. Furthermore, it blooms earlier (April to July).

The **yellow rattle** represents another genus, *Rhinanthus* (*R. crista-galli*). It also is semi-parasitic on grasses. It grows in poor dry pastures and sends out suckers which penetrate the grass-roots, thus supplementing its own food supply (Plate 14). The plant is tall and stiff and blooms during May to July.

The leaves grow in opposite pairs. Each is lance-shaped, though the lower part is very broad and the tip very pointed. The margins are conspicuously toothed (Plate 14).

The sepals of the flower form a pale green, four-toothed inflated tube. The petals are responsible for a very irregular flower. There are five forming a gaping tube which spreads upwards into a two-lobed lip which is compressed vertically, and obliquely downwards into a three-lobed lip. The lower lip acts as a landing-stage for visiting insects. The upper lip protects the four stamens and the style, the latter projecting forward so as to touch the visiting insect's body first and receive pollen from another flower, thus ensuring cross-pollination. As the insect probes deeply for the nectar, pollen is showered on its back from the stamens which are above it. The flattened capsule is large and enclosed in the inflated persistent calyx.

The **cow-wheat** (*Melampyrum pratense*) is also a semi-parasite, growing in copses and producing yellow flowers in axillary pairs during

May to July. In fundamental structure its flower is similar to that of the yellow rattle. The stalks of the stamens bear many sharp teeth.

The **red bartsia** (*Bartsia odontites*) is another plant which grows semi-parasitically on grass-roots in waste places and in dry fields. The plant is very conspicuous because its bright red flowers are borne in long unilateral racemes (Plate 14). They appear during June to August. The stem is erect, six to eleven inches high, and smooth. The leaves are borne in opposite pairs and are narrow, though lance-shaped, with toothed margins.

The red flower is similar in structure to that of the yellow rattle, having an open petal-tube. The upper lip is arched, and the lower lip has three lobes which are curved backwards. The four stamens are of unequal length—two long and two short. Cross-pollination is ensured by the stamens ripening before the stigma of the same flower. The fruit is surrounded by a persistent calyx (Plate 14).

The **eyebright** or **euphrasy** (*Euphrasia officinalis*) is a pretty little plant growing only a few inches in height and thriving on heaths, where it is semi-parasitic on grass-roots. The stem is strong and branched, the branches coming off in opposite pairs (Plate 14). The leaves, borne in pairs, are stalkless and deeply serrated. The small flowers are white or lilac with purple veins, and are borne in dense terminal spikes during May to September (Plate 14).

The structure of the flower is again similar to that of the yellow rattle, with the mid-lobe of the lower lip yellow in colour. Cross-pollination is ensured by a similar means, in that the style projects beyond the stamens, thus touching the body of the insect visitor before they do.

The eyebright was once upon a time recommended for treating bad eyesight, hence its common name.

> Michael from Adam's eyes the Filme remov'd
> Which that false Fruit that promis'd clearer sight
> Had bred ; then purg'd with Euphrasie and Rue
> The visual Nerve, for he had much to see.
> *Paradise Lost* : MILTON

The genus *Linaria* comprises several species, but the two most common are the interesting ivy-leaved toadflax and the yellow toadflax.

The **ivy-leaved toadflax** or **mother of thousands** (*Linaria cymbalaria*) is a very pretty plant frequently seen growing on old walls and flowering during May to September. The long straggling stems are quite hairless. The leaves are shaped somewhat like ivy leaves though the lobes are blunt. Each of the bluish-purple flowers is borne on a separate stalk (Plate 14).

The five sepals form the usual tube. Unlike the yellow rattle, the two lips of the petal-tube are pressed firmly together like those of the snapdragon. At the back of the petal-tube is a spur containing nectar, and the mid-lobe of the lower lip has a yellow honey-guide. Only strong insects, like bees, are able to force the two lips apart to get at the honey, which is just as well, as otherwise smaller insects might get at it without pollinating the plant.

The ivy-leaved toadflax is particularly interesting because it sows its own seeds in suitable media. The unfertilised flowers stand erect on their long stems. After they have been fertilised the stems bend over and gradually curve towards any crack in the wall where there is a certain amount of soil and moisture. Then the fruit capsule bursts and the seeds are sown.

The **yellow toadflax** (*L. vulgaris*) grows in fields and on banks, and closely resembles a yellow snapdragon. It is a perennial and reproduces itself vegetatively by means of adventitious buds which grow on the summits of the roots. The stem is erect, and towards its base the lance-shaped leaves are very crowded. Further up the stem they are more widely spaced in alternate positions.

The large yellow flowers are, like those of the snapdragon, borne in long dense inflorescences which appear during July to October (Plate 14). The yellow petals form a long tube with a pointed spur at the back. Here lies the nectar. The two lips are compressed, so that only bees can get at it. The honey-guide is orange in colour. Reference to Fig. 19 shows how cross-pollination is ensured, by the style meeting the head of the on-coming insect before the stamens. The flower of the yellow toadflax is curious in that it often suddenly grows into a regular shape.

The figworts belong to the genus *Scrophularia*. The **knotted figwort** (*S. nodosa*) is a tall plant which grows in moist places, producing its rather insignificant flowers during July to September. This plant has very large leaves (Plate 14), shaped like elongated hearts, blunt at the end and slightly toothed. The root-stock produces tubers.

The flowers are arranged in very loose racemes (Plate 14). The sepals form a five-toothed tube. The petals form a two-lipped tube. They are dull purple or even brown in colour, with the tube itself shading into orange. The upper petal-lip is two-lobed with a single scale on its inner surface, and the lower lip is three-lobed.

The plant is usually pollinated by wasps, which seem to be attracted by its unpleasant smell. The stigma ripens before the stamens, thus ensuring cross-pollination.

The **water figwort** (*S. aquatica*) grows along river banks and in marshes.

The most conspicuous of all the wild members of this family is the stately **foxglove** (*Digitalis purpurea*). It is sometimes seen growing in hedgerows, woods and on banks by the roadside.

The plant grows to a height of two to four feet bearing its large handsome flowers in long racemes during June to August. These racemes are one-sided, an effect produced by the twisting of each single flower-stalk. (Plate 14.) Meredith noticed how the foxglove hangs ' an ever lessening bell ', the flowers growing smaller and smaller up the stem. Unfortunately the petals are very deciduous, and most often one finds racemes with their lower flowers fallen while the upper ones are sometimes even still in bud (Fig. 126).

> Through quaint obliquities I might pursue
> These cravings ; when the foxglove, one by one,
> Upwards through every stage of the tall stem,
> Had shed beside the public way its bells,
> And stood of all dismantled, save the last
> Left at the tapering ladder's top, that seemed
> To bend as doth a slender blade of grass
> Tipped with a rain-drop . . .
>
> *The Prelude* : WORDSWORTH

The leaves are very large and lance-shaped, wrinkled and covered with light down. Like those of the mullein and many other genera of the family, the larger ones are at the base.

The flower is large and particularly attractive. The sepals form a tube with five distinct but unequal teeth. The petals are irregular, forming a purple bell with four or five shallow lobes. At the mouth of the bell are dark spots and white hairs which act as honey-guides. The stamens ripen before the stigma. As in other genera, there are two long and two short stamens (Plate 14).

The fruit is a large capsule which is surrounded by the persistent calyx.

This plant is very useful for the drugs collectively called digitalis

Eric Hosking

FIG. 126.—Foxgloves.

which is extracted from its leaves. Several drugs are prepared from the digitalis extract, all having a physiological influence on the heart, therefore to be used only under medical authority.

ORNAMENTAL PLANTS

The family SCROPHULARIACEAE gives a very large number of ornamental genera, several of which are very popular.

T

Perhaps the most familiar of them all is the **snapdragon** or **chatter-box** (*Antirrhinum*), which is sometimes found growing wild on walls, though it is really a garden escape. The most frequently cultivated species is *A. majus*, the flowers of which have petal-tubes swollen at their bases but without spurs. The mouth of the tube is closed by the two lips, thus preserving the nectar for bees, which are almost the only insects strong enough to force an entrance and thus pollinate the flower.

The snapdragon has been known by other names in the past, none of them very complimentary, such as 'lion's mouth' and 'calf's snout'. It was once believed to afford protection against evil spirits.

> Antirrhinum, more modest, takes the style
> Of Lion's-mouth, sometimes of Calf's-snout vile,
> By us Snapdragon called, to make amends,
> But say what this chimera name intends ?
> Thou well deserv'st it, as old wives say,
> Thou driv'st nocturnal ghosts and sprights away.
>
> *Plantarum* : A. COWLEY

In the flower garden, the *Antirrhinum* is usually treated as a perennial. The flowers are borne in long, very conspicuous racemes (Fig. 127) of varying hues—yellow, white, cream, salmon, crimson, mauve and many of two shades. There are very small varieties used for bedding and larger ones suitable for borders. All species of *Antirrhinum* are herbs with the exception of *A. speciosum*, which is a shrub bearing scarlet flowers and about five feet high. It is found on Catalina Island off the Californian coast.

The **foxglove** (*Digitalis purpurea*) is also a favourite garden plant, useful in herbaceous borders owing to its height, and often broadcast in ornamental woods. Unfortunately the petals

FIG. 127.—*Antirrhinum*.

R. A. Malby & Co.

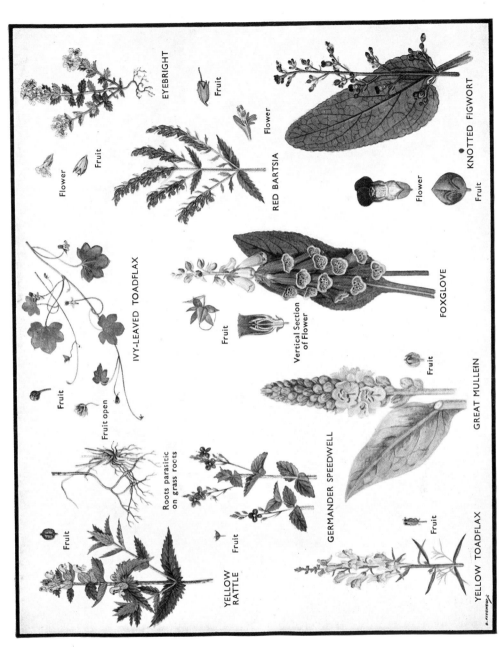

EYEBRIGHT

Fruit

Flower

Fruit

Flower

RED BARTSIA

Fruit

Flower

KNOTTED FIGWORT

Flower

Fruit

IVY-LEAVED TOADFLAX

Fruit

Fruit open

Fruit

Vertical Section
of Flower

FOXGLOVE

GREAT MULLEIN

Fruit

Roots parasitic
on grass roots

Fruit

GERMANDER SPEEDWELL

Fruit

Fruit

YELLOW
RATTLE

Fruit

YELLOW TOADFLAX

PLATE 14

are very deciduous so the handsome racemes are not much use for household decoration. The colours of the garden varieties of this plant vary—white, cream, apricot, purple, purple and white spotted, and so forth. It has been suggested that the white variety does not attract insects.

> White foxglove, by an angle in the wall,
> Secluded, tall,
> No vulgar bees
> Consult you, wondering
> If such a dainty thing
> Can give them ease.
>
> *White Foxglove* : T. E. BROWN

Several species and varieties of the conspicuous **mullein** (*Verbascum*) are cultivated, often making a bright show in borders (Fig. 128). Again there are many different colours such as white, pink, yellow, blue, mauve and purple. These plants are particularly useful in permanent borders because they are perennials.

A very lovely genus of this family is *Pentstemon* which hails from North America and eastern Asia. Like the flowers of the foxglove these have wide open throats. There are many species of this delightful flower growing wild in America, but the British cultivated varieties originated chiefly from the American *P. hartwegii* and *P. cobaea*. The plants are frequently reproduced by cuttings taken from the lower branches of the stems. The flowers are borne in large handsome racemes. Though the plant resembles the foxglove very closely, it is more graceful and in general smaller, but the flowers are just as large, in fact, more conspicuous. The shades of flower colour are various, but perhaps the reds and pinks are

FIG. 128.—*Verbascum phoenicium.*

R. A. Malby & Co.

FIG. 129.—*Rehmannia henryi.*

the most popular, with white, pink and white, purple, blue and white, following as good seconds.

The **monkey flower** (*Mimulus luteus*) is another garden and greenhouse favourite. It is sometimes found growing wild along river-sides (being actually a garden escape from North America), showing its lovely yellow flowers with purple spots during July to September. But it is more often cultivated in warm gardens and in greenhouses.

The **musk plant** (*Mimulus moschatus*) is another favourite in old-fashioned gardens and in cottage windows. This plant is a native of many parts of the world, especially in mountainous parts, with the exception of Europe. Other species and varieties are cultivated; but they do best in warm, moist situations, and present various shades of yellow, red, and scarlet. Many are blotched. The musk plant was at one time very popular because of its musk scent, then during 1919-20, the plant almost suddenly lost its perfume throughout most parts of the world. The reason for this strange loss of scent was never discovered beyond doubt.

The genus *Calceolaria* has given us numbers of very showy plants, some for herbaceous borders and beds, but many more for indoor and greenhouse cultivation in pots. The genus is native to South America, where its members are frequently called the **slipperworts** owing to the shape of the flowers. The shades of colour and the size of the flowers, which grow in large dense heads, vary over very wide ranges.

The genus *Linaria* (**toadflax**), as one would expect, has presented some useful varieties to the garden. They are usually treated as annuals, though some perennials are grown. Most of them look like small, graceful snapdragons. There are several colours—white, golden, pink, mauve and variegated (usually crimson and gold).

Some species and varieties of *Veronica* (**speedwell**) are also grown in beds and borders. Most are blue. There are also some useful evergreen shrubs, all of which are very free-flowering.

Torenia is a tropical genus which is frequently cultivated as a greenhouse annual. It blooms profusely, bearing flowers of blue, mauve or yellow.

The genus *Rehmannia* is a native of Japan and China; but it is so handsome that certain species and varieties are cultivated here in flower borders, though they need very careful attention. They look somewhat like tall stately *Pentstemons* (Fig. 129). The flowers are usually a rich violet with golden stamens, though there are other colours.

The only true tree belonging to the SCROPHULARIACEAE, is *Paulownia*, a native of Japan and China. The species *Paulownia imperialis* is sometimes cultivated in parks in this country. There is a very fine specimen in the Royal Botanic Gardens at Kew. The tree is tall and deciduous with handsome foliage. The flowers are purplish-violet and resemble foxgloves hanging in pendulous panicles.

60

MORE PARASITES
(Orobanchaceae)

This very exceptional family (OROBANCHACEAE) is of scattered distribution, chiefly in north temperate regions. All its members are parasitic on the roots of selected plant hosts ; therefore, since the plant parasite does not need its own food factories, namely, the leaves, these are reduced to whitish-yellow scales. The parasite taps its host for food by sending suckers into the roots, somewhat as the stem of the dodder pierces the stem of its host with suckers.

There are about half a dozen genera in this family, all of which are entirely parasitic ; but only two genera are native to this country : they contain the broomrapes and the toothworts.

There are five species of broomrape (*Orobanche*), but only two of these are comparatively common.

Though all the broomrapes have colourless stems bearing whitish-yellow scale leaves, their flowers are conspicuous. The petals are arranged irregularly to form a two-lipped corolla. There are four stamens, two long and two short, and all four are attached to the petals. The two carpels are joined to form an ovary bearing a single style with a two-lobed stigma. The sepals persist after fertilisation.

The **greater broomrape** (*Orobanche major*) is parasitic on broom (hence the common name of the parasite, though this suggests that it has more vicious intentions than it really exhibits) and other shrubby members of the LEGUMINOSAE.

It has a stout stem swollen at the base and growing one to two feet high. The sepals are reduced in number to one, two or three. The petals take the form of two lips, the upper one being simple and the lower three-lobed and spreading. They expand to a diameter of an inch and are yellowish and purplish. The fruit is a capsule.

The **tall broomrape** (*O. elatior*) is very similar to the great broomrape, but its flowers are always yellow. It is parasitic on knapweeds.

The other species of broomrape are not common. They are : the **red broomrape** (*O. rubra*) with dull red flowers, parasitic on thyme ; **least broomrape** (*O. minor*) with yellow or purplish flowers, parasitic on clover ; **clove-scented broomrape** (*O. caryophyllacea*) with reddish-brown or purplish flowers, parasitic on species of *Galium*. Some of the species of broomrape are able to live on other plant hosts ; but there are still other species which are always confined to one host, for example, *O. hederae*, whose sole host is the ivy.

The other British genus of this unusual family is *Lathraea*, and it contains several species, the most common of which is the **great tooth-wort** (*L. squamaria*), which is parasitic on the roots of hazel, beech and other trees. The stem is four to ten inches high. The flowers are purplish and are borne in one-sided racemes. It has been suggested that the leaves of this parasite are capable of trapping and absorbing insects, but this is doubtful. The fruit is a capsule.

L. clandestina is a rare tooth-wort parasitic on the roots of willows.

61

PLANTS WHICH PREY ON INSECTS

Although animals consume plants, either whole or in part, very few plants are so organised that they can consume animals. Normally they only absorb the very much changed products of animals.

Yet there are examples of plants that can prey on living animals. They actually catch the animals, kill them and then digest certain parts of them. It is no wonder, then, that animal-catching plants have fixed the imagination of many people, especially those who have never seen one. Travellers have often fed these imaginations with startling stories which have not always stood the test of investigation. There was a widespread belief, for example, in the existence of a 'man-eating tree' in certain tropical regions which was supposed to trap a man with its long tendrils, then engulf him and digest him.

All the same, there are some animal-trapping plants, though these are all content with very small prey—usually insects, for which reason they are called insectivorous plants. Although not very common, they are naturally of peculiar interest, and have developed most wonderful mechanisms for catching their insect prey. A few of these are British.

It is quite true that these plants consume insects, but not one of them depends completely on insects for its food. In fact one can go still further and say that insects form a very small part of their diet. All such plants have green leaves and are accordingly able to make their own food. Then why do these plants catch insects ? The explanation is that most insectivorous plants inhabit swampy or boggy localities. The plant and animal populations of such habitats are usually sparse, so the water-logged soil is practically devoid of natural manure or humus. Consequently its nitrogen content is low, and what nitrates are present are constantly being leached out by the ever-present water. Now insects have a high protein content, and proteins contain nitrogen. Therefore they are caught by insectivorous plants to supplement the meagre nitrogen supply.

Though insectivorous plants could actually do without such animal food, there is little doubt that the nitrogen obtained from them is valuable. This was aptly phrased by Julius von Sachs, the eminent German botanist, when he remarked : ' In Poland and Ireland a great many people live only on potatoes, but it does not follow that a beef-steak wouldn't be a good deal better.'

British insectivorous plants belong to two families : LENTIBU-LARIACEAE, which comes in at this stage of our classification, and DROSERACEAE, which comes much nearer the tropical insectivorous families, all of which have their place much earlier in the scheme, that is near the SAXIFRAGACEAE (p. 74). Since the insectivorous habit of all these plants is of paramount interest, all the families have been left for consideration at this point.

BUTTERWORT AND BLADDERWORT

The family LENTIBULARIACEAE is represented by two genera in this country, namely, *Pinguicula*, a terrestrial plant, and *Utricularia*, an aquatic genus with floating leaves.

The **butterwort** (*Pinguicula vulgaris*) is a herb with leaves one to three inches long which are arranged in rosette fashion (Plate 16). The upper surface of the leaf is covered with a pale yellow sticky substance which looks like butter, hence the name. An unwary insect alighting on this sticky surface is caught like a fly on a fly paper. The margins of the leaf are slightly incurved, and once the insect is caught they curve over still further, thus trapping and holding the prey firmly.

On the surface of the leaf are certain microscopic glands which secrete a digestive juice. This juice acts on the body of the insect and makes its nitrogen-containing parts soluble. These are then absorbed by the leaf.

The purple flower is borne on a long stalk. Its petals are united to form a spurred, two-lipped tube (Plate 16). There are two stamens joined to the petals. The ovary is single-chambered.

The butterwort is comparatively common in certain parts of Great Britain, especially on the Somersetshire Plain, and on the Yorkshire and Scottish moors. It is widely distributed throughout north temperate lands, and is particularly common in North America. The rarer species, *P. lusitanica*, is found on the western shores of Britain.

An even more ingenious method of trapping insects is seen in the other genus of this family, which is represented in this country by the **common bladderwort** (*Utricularia vulgaris*), a water plant.

The leaves of the bladderwort are finely divided, as would be expected since they are usually submerged in the water or floating loosely on the surface. Certain of the leaf segments become modified into bladder-like structures (Fig. 130). Each bladder has one opening protected by a valve which will open inwards but not outwards (Fig. 130). Some books tell us that small aquatic animals, such as certain Crustacea, (probably seeking sanctuary from their enemies) force their way past this valve into the bladder. This is not true. The insect prey is actually captured by the bladder. The animal enters the vestibule of the bladder quite unawares, and when it touches the hairs there the valve is stimulated to open. The walls of the bladder, hitherto compressed, now expand and draw water into the bladder, thus sucking in the prey. The bladder on such occasions has been calculated to expand as much as 88 per cent. Within about twenty minutes it is back to normal and ready for more prey. The inner surface of the bladder has glands like the upper surface of the butterwort leaf (Fig. 130), and these secrete digestive juices, which do the rest of the work in the digestion and absorption of the trapped insect.

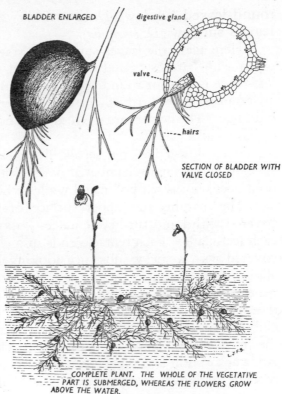

SECTION OF BLADDER WITH VALVE CLOSED

COMPLETE PLANT. THE WHOLE OF THE VEGETATIVE PART IS SUBMERGED, WHEREAS THE FLOWERS GROW ABOVE THE WATER.

FIG. 130.—Bladderwort.

The bladderwort is rather common in Great Britain, especially in brackish waters. It is also to be found in many other north temperate regions.

It has rich yellow flowers borne singly on stalks well above the surface of the water (Fig. 130). Each flower has a long spur, and is fundamentally similar to that of the butterwort.

The **lesser bladderwort** (*U. minor*) has smaller leaves with fewer forked lobes. The flower is paler yellow with only the suggestion of a spur.

SUNDEWS AND VENUS'S FLY-TRAP

As mentioned above, the family DROSERACEAE has its true place much earlier in our scheme of classification, that is, following the SAXIFRAGACEAE (p. 74).

It comprises several genera, but we have only one in this country, namely *Drosera*. This genus contains two common members—the round-leaved sundew (*D. rotundifolia*) and the less common long-leaved sundew (*D. longifolia*).

Here again the leaves supply the trapping mechanism. They are green with patches of red on them and they have long stalks. The leaf-blade is long or round according to the species. Again the leaves are arranged in the form of a rosette. They are green with a pronounced red tinge. The flowers are white and are borne in long inflorescences on upright stalks.

Each flower has five sepals, five petals, joined and regular, five stamens and a single-chambered ovary with six to eight styles. It seldom opens but is self-pollinated while in bud.

The margins and upper surface of the leaf of the sundew are covered with long hair-like tentacles—about two hundred tentacles to each leaf-blade. Each tentacle ends in a club-shaped swelling which is covered with a sticky substance looking like dew. When the insect alights on the leaf it is caught by the sticky tentacles. Then there is a general bending of the tentacles towards the mid-rib, with the result that the insect is caught and pressed firmly against the leaf surface. The club-shaped ends of the tentacles then secrete the digestive juices, and the nitrogen-containing parts of the insect are digested and absorbed. After absorption is complete, the leaf opens out again, and the insect's remains are blown away by the wind. The movement of the tentacles can be stimulated by touching the leaf with a pencil (Fig. 131).

The two species of sundew mentioned are common in the swampy regions of Great Britain as well as in North America and Australia.

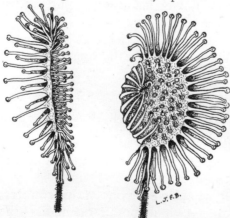

FIG. 131.—Leaf of Sundew.
Left, side view ; right, front view after having been touched by a pencil.

A very interesting sub-tropical member of this family is **Venus's fly-trap** (*Dionaea muscipula*). This plant is very common in the peat-bogs of North and South California. The first full description of its insectivorous habit was given by Charles Darwin, though it had been noticed before.

The mechanism is again produced by the leaf. The leaves are arranged in rosette fashion like those of British terrestrial insectivorous plants. Each leaf has two lobes on either side of the mid-rib. On the margins of each lobe are long firm spikes (Fig. 132). The surface is covered with glands, and each lobe has three bristles which are sensitive to touch. When an insect alights on the surface of the leaf it cannot help but touch at least one of these sensitive bristles. The result is that in less than a second the two lobes of the leaf move quickly towards each other, using the midrib as a hinge (Fig. 132). Then the margins of the lobes meet and their spines interlock. Thus

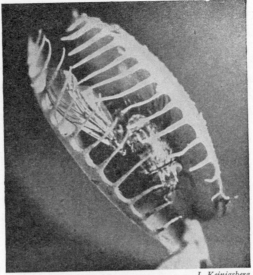

L. Keinigsberg

FIG. 132.—Venus's Fly-trap closing on a Fly.

the insect is trapped as if in a gin. Then the leaf-surface exudes its digestive juices and the victim is absorbed. After absorption, the leaf opens again and the remains of the insect are blown away by the wind.

PITCHER PLANTS

Perhaps the most interesting type of insectivorous plant is represented by the so-called **pitcher plants,** belonging to the family NEPENTHACEAE, which comes near DROSERACEAE in classification. They are all sub-tropical and tropical in distribution, being native to tropical Asia, North Australia and Madagascar. North Borneo is particularly rich in them (Fig. 133).

Some pitcher plants belong to the genus *Nepenthes* and there are about sixty species of these. The majority are shrubby plants climbing by means of tendrils, each of which is really an extension of the mid-rib of the leaf-blade. Other species grow as epiphytes on trees. Certain leaves appear to develop pitchers at the ends of their blades, but this is not really the case. The lid of the pitcher is the modified leaf-blade, and the pitcher itself is part of the leaf-stalk modified. Therefore, since something else must carry on the function of the leaf-blade proper, the rest of the leaf-stalk has become flattened and expanded to carry on normal food manufacture. Thus what appears to be the lance-shaped leaf-blade is really part of the leaf-stalk.

Royal Botanic Gardens, Kew

FIG. 133.—A Pitcher Plant (*Nepenthes*).

The pitcher itself is a tubular structure, often bearing two wing-like flanges running down its sides. The rim of the mouth has an incurved margin, which has a firm, shining surface. The mouth has a definite lid, just like that of a coffee pot or hot-water jug. When the pitcher is very young, the lid covers the opening; but as the pitcher grows, the lid opens and is then stationary. It takes up an oblique position, and is probably used for keeping rain-water out of the pitcher.

The size of the pitcher varies with the species, from that of a thimble to that of a quart mug. The outside of the pitcher is often brightly coloured. The colours vary from shades of red to yellow. These bright colours, like the bright colours of flowers, serve to attract the insect. A sweet substance is also secreted by the stems of the plant and right up to the lid of the pitcher. Still more sweet material is given off inside the pitcher, just below the margin.

The insect is first attracted by the bright colours. Then in its attempt to get the sweet food material it crawls up to the margin of the pitcher, and tries to get at that just inside. In doing so, it often slips on the shining surface of the rim and tumbles into the pitcher. Once inside it is trapped, for two reasons. The inner surface of the pitcher is covered with glands. These glands secrete a watery substance which collects in the bottom of the pitcher. Into this liquid the insect tumbles and is thus disabled. Also, on the inner surface, near the top of the pitcher, is a ring of hairs which point downwards. It is easy to see, therefore, how the insect can fall over these hairs; but, even if it can attempt to climb out, the downward pointing hairs prevent it. Thus the insect gets fatigued, falls into the liquid, and is finally drowned. Then the same glands secrete a protein-digesting enzyme, and the insect body is thus digested and finally absorbed.

This is a fascinating mechanism and seems to be very efficient as a means of trapping insects. But, in Nature, the pitcher plant is not so efficient as one would imagine. Although insects are trapped in this fashion, botanists who have studied pitcher plants in their native localities tell us that they are sometimes so inefficient that they do not work at all. This happens to such an extent that mosquitoes have been known to enter the pitchers, lay their eggs, and the young have been hatched out and escape.

Other types of pitcher plant belong to another family, SARRA-CENIACEAE, which contain several genera, chiefly *Sarracenia*. These are all native to the eastern regions of the United States, and there are about seven species of them. They are all herbs. The leaves grow direct from the soil, and some of them form pitchers. In this case, the leaf is different from that of *Nepenthes* in that, except for a broad sheathing base, the whole leaf forms a long, tubular, often brightly coloured pitcher, with a lid at the mouth. These pitchers are similar to those of *Nepenthes* in their mechanism for trapping insects. They are, how-ever, probably more efficient. Sometimes, in fact, the pitcher is almost full of insects. Thus, when the *Sarracenia* plant dies, it supplies a consider-able amount of manure to the soil in the form of dead insect humus.

Sarracenia is also known to act as a means of catching insect prey for other animals. The pitcher is often so efficient that it catches many more insects than it can possibly absorb, and as it becomes nearly full of them insect-eating animals, such as larger insects and even birds, come along and help themselves to the prey. Insects have been known to enter the pitchers of *Sarracenia* and lay their eggs. The eggs hatch, and then birds have been seen to slit open the pitchers with their beaks and feast on the insect larvae inside.

Pitcher plants are sometimes cultivated in greenhouses in this country for the bright colours of their pitchers. They may be seen too in the greenhouses of many public botanic gardens. Those in the Royal Botanic Gardens, Kew, are excellent specimens, and well repay a visit.

62

SOME CULTIVATED FAVOURITES

At this point come a number of families, four of which contain a large number of cultivated genera and species, though all of them with one exception are derived from plants native to other countries.

GESNERIACEAE

This is a tropical and sub-tropical family of herbs and shrubs having large and showy flowers. To it belong several genera which have found favour with greenhouse gardeners. Perhaps the greatest favourite is **gloxinia,** which hails from Brazil. Although there is a genus *Gloxinia* in this family, the cultivated 'gloxinias' in this country are derived mostly from another genus, *Sinningia,* chiefly from the species *S. speciosa.*

The plants produce very large upright bell-shaped flowers borne in crowded inflorescences (Fig. 134). There are white varieties and many others of brilliant colours, such as iridescent scarlet, bright scarlet with white throat, crimson, purple, pink, and many with a ground of one colour gaily striped with other hues.

Fig. 134.—*Gloxinia* (Sutton's ' Triumph ' strain).

The genus *Gesneria*, and also the related genus *Naegelia*, hail from tropical America. They produce spikes of pendulous flowers in varying shades of white, yellow, pink, orange, carmine, crimson and so forth.

Achimenes is another tropical American genus sometimes grown in greenhouses for its profusion of flowers of varying shades.

Streptocarpus is the African **Cape primrose**, which grows wild, especially in Madagascar. Its leaves are very like those of *Primula*. The flowers are very large and showy. Each petal-tube opens into five lobes which betray a certain irregularity in that the two upper petals are somewhat smaller than the rest. The flowers are borne in crowded inflorescences and present various shades of white, pink, and blue, and mixed colours. Often the throat of the flower is one colour, and the petal-lobes are another.

The genus *Ramondia* comes from the mountains and alps of southern Europe, and therefore some of its species do well outdoors and in rockeries. The flowers are nearly regular and are usually deep purple with orange stamens.

BIGNONIACEAE

This is a family of trees and shrubs, rarely herbs, most of which are native to tropical and sub-tropical regions. One genus—*Catalpa*—is represented in this country by several species of trees grown in some parks and gardens. There is a handsome group in the forecourt of the Houses of Parliament.

The most commonly cultivated species in this country is *C. bignonioides* or **Indian bean,** which has long white tubular bell-shaped flowers streaked with yellow and purple. This species comes from the United States. There are other cultivated species with flowers of varying colours.

Another genus sometimes cultivated in this country is *Campsis*, often erroneously called *Bignonia*. *C. grandiflora* is a handsome climber with rich orange-scarlet flowers. It hails from China and Japan and will thrive only in warm parts near the sea. *C. radicans* is a climber from North America having handsome scarlet flowers.

ACANTHACEAE

This family is composed chiefly of herbaceous climbers, some of which have been brought here from warmer regions of the Mediterranean, United States, Australia, India, Malaya, and so forth. Most are adapted for living in dry conditions and have thorny leaves. *Acanthus spinosus*, of the eastern Mediterranean, is supposed to have inspired the original motif of the capitals of the Corinthian columns. *A. lusitanicus* is sometimes cultivated in the sunny parts of this country.

The genus *Thunbergia* has given many greenhouse climbers and plants suitable for hanging baskets. The flowers of the different varieties present many shades of colour.

VERBENACEAE

The VERBENACEAE provides the only wild member of this miscellany of families. It is the **vervein** (*Verbena officinalis*). There are no other wild species of the genus ; in fact, vervein itself is not very common, though it might be found in dry waste places, growing to a height of one to two feet and displaying its long dense spikes of lilac flowers during July to September. The five sepals are united ; the five petals are joined to form a two-lipped tube ; the four stamens are unequal in length—two long and two short ; the two carpels are joined as usual in this family.

The leaves of this plant are either deeply divided into several opposite lobes or into three lobes.

The vervein was once held in great esteem as a cure for eye trouble. It's bright-eyed petals, like those of the eyebright or euphrasy (p. 276) were believed to indicate the plant's curative properties. It was also believed to have other medicinal values, and to be a shield against witchcraft. In medieval times it was supposed to provoke merriment.

> And thou, light vervain, too, thou must go after,
> Provoking easy souls to mirth and laughter ;
> *The Faithful Shepherdess* : BEAUMONT AND FLETCHER

The cultivated species of *Verbena* are very popular, presenting large, dense, almost spherical inflorescences of various colours, and having a delightful scent.

Lantana is a tropical and sub-tropical genus, most of its members being shrubs which are sometimes used as hedges. Some produce edible fruits. This genus is not often cultivated in this country, though one hybrid is sometimes grown as a half-hardy bedding shrub with large heads of flowers of varying hues.

Other genera are cultivated in this country ; all of them are greenhouse plants.

63

THE MINT FAMILY
(*Labiatae*)

Here's flowers for you ;
Hot lavender, mints, savory, marjoram.
Winter's Tale, Act 4, Sc. 4 : SHAKESPEARE

This is the last family of dicotyledons to be considered. It is a highly organised family with very irregular flowers, most of which have particularly efficient mechanisms for ensuring cross-pollination. There is, however, a tendency to exaggerate the importance of these mechanisms. That of the sage flower (p. 300) is almost unique.

The family contains about two hundred genera of cosmopolitan distribution, though the chief centre is the Mediterranean regions. Some genera are very localised. There are no real trees. Most members of the family grow on dry land, though a few genera, such as that of the mint itself, are marsh plants, and a few are climbers. Many are adapted for growth in very dry conditions.

The floral structure of the family is a very natural one in that most genera conform to it, and this also applies to the general plant habit. For example, most members of the family have stems which are square in cross-section. The leaves are usually arranged in opposite pairs, though in a few cases they are in whorls, and the majority are simple without stipules. The leaf-blades are usually hairy, and many of them have oil-glands secreting volatile oils which give the plants their various characteristic smells.

The LABIATAE family is well represented in the British wild flora by about twenty genera. Apart from these, considering its size, the family offers little else. Only about half a dozen are cultivated for ornamental purposes, and most of those are not grown very frequently, for they are neither conspicuous nor showy. About a dozen genera are of certain economic value for their volatile oils, such as rosemary and lavender, which yield perfumes, and others such as sage and thyme, which are useful as pot-herbs. No member of the family is cultivated for food in this country, and very few elsewhere.

WILD PLANTS

One of the most common and characteristic of labiate plants is the genus *Lamium* to which belong the deadnettles.

The **white deadnettle** (*Lamium album*) is very common and grows in a number of habitats, especially in hedgerows and on the edges of woods, standing out conspicuously from May to September owing to its whorls of comparatively large white flowers (Fig. 135). The plant is usually found growing in large groups because it spreads by means of long, straggling, tough, underground stems.

The erect stem is characteristically square in cross-section. The leaves are heart-shaped, pointed at their tips and deeply notched. They are arranged in opposite pairs and are hairy.

The flowers are arranged in whorls in the axils of the upper pairs of leaves. Six to a dozen flowers are borne in each whorl, forming a circle, each flower with its back to the stem.

There are five sepals forming a campanulate tube with five teeth and ten ribs (Fig. 136). The five petals are united to produce a very irregular corolla well constructed for aiding pollination by bees and characteristic of the family in general. The petals form an inflated curved tube, pointed at the base, where much nectar is stored. This is surrounded by a ring of hairs. The upper lip of the corolla forms a perfect hood for the protection of the style and the stamens; the lower lip projects as a platform on which the insect alights, and then it spreads downwards to form a sort of flag to attract the insects. The lower lip is divided into three parts, a central wide lobe and two side teeth. In this corolla there is no definite indication of separate petals. The four stamens are of unequal length—two long and two short. The two carpels are fused to form a

FIG. 135.—White Deadnettle.

Harold Bastin

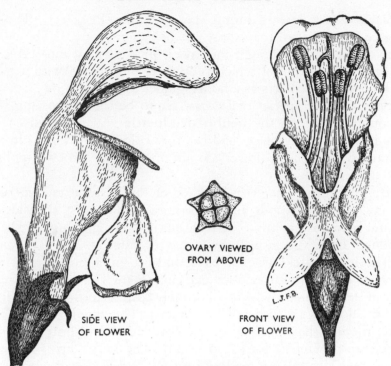

OVARY VIEWED
FROM ABOVE

SIDE VIEW
OF FLOWER

FRONT VIEW
OF FLOWER

FIG. 136.—Flower of White Deadnettle.

four-chambered ovary with a long common style bearing a two-cleft stigma. The fruit takes the form of four small nuts or nutlets, each of which contains one seed, and these are surrounded by a persistent withered calyx (Fig. 136).

The **red deadnettle** (*L. purpureum*) is equally common in fields and waste places, blooming during the same season as the white. It also prefers to grow among other tall plants, such as grasses—another characteristic shared with its close relative. Again, the red deadnettle is very like the white deadnettle in general habit, though the former is somewhat smaller and its stems and leaves are tinged with red, and the lower leaves are borne on long stalks (Plate 15).

The flower of the red deadnettle is purple, and the petal-tube is not curved as it is in the white deadnettle, neither is there a ring of hairs. The lower lip has a central lobe shaped like an inverted heart and this is surrounded by two tooth-shaped lobes. The fruit takes the form of four nutlets surrounded by a persistent calyx.

The **archangel** or **yellow deadnettle** (*L. galeobdolon*) is a particularly attractive labiate which grows in woods and thickets, displaying its golden yellow flowers during May and June (Plate 15). The leaves are more lance-shaped than those of the other species. The flower is typical of the genus, though the lower lip is divided into three equal lobes, the middle one of which is spotted and veined with a reddish-brown colour which acts as a honey-guide.

Several other species of *Lamium* are to be found growing wild in this country. One is the **henbit deadnettle** (*L. amplexicaule*) which grows in waste sandy places and has rose-coloured flowers. In spring and autumn some of the flowers do not open but become self-pollinated while still in bud.

Bugle (*Ajuga reptans*) is another of the more attractive labiates. It grows in damp woods and sometimes along moist roadsides. Its beautiful blue flowers are to be seen during May and June. The plant reproduces itself vegetatively by means of runners.

The leaves are borne in pairs and are of a nondescript shape, somewhat oblong with smooth margins (Plate 15). The flowers are borne in dense whorls which collectively form a loose spike. In each whorl the flowers are suspended by bracts. The blue flower is a typical labiate, though the upper lip of the corolla is very short and slightly notched, and therefore forms no hood. The lower lip is three-cleft.

There is also the rare **yellow bugle** (*A. chamaepitys*) whose yellow flowers are borne in axillary pairs and whose leaves are each divided into three lobes. Whereas the blue bugle is smooth, the yellow is hairy.

A very common plant of moist pastures is the **self-heal** (*Prunella vulgaris*), which is easily identified because its purplish-blue flowers are borne about six to a whorl which is surrounded by leafy bracts. Several whorls are closely packed in dense terminal inflorescences (Plate 15).

The flowers appear rather late in the season (July to August). The leaves are stalked, lance-shaped and borne in pairs. The upper lip of the corolla is erect, and the lower three-lobed and spreading. The common name of this plant dates back to the time when it was supposed to be a cure for all ills.

To the genus *Nepeta* belong two well-known plants, namely, ground-ivy and cat-mint.

The **ground-ivy** (*N. glechoma*) is an attractive plant which grows in all sorts of places, spreading by means of procumbent creeping stems (Plate 15). The leaves are borne on long stalks and are kidney-shaped with deeply waved margins. The plant is a very early-flowering specimen, blossoming during March to June. The purplish-blue flowers closely resemble those of bugle, but are arranged in whorls spaced further apart and each flower is stalked. The general floral effect is therefore less dense. For a long time this plant was used as a medicinal herb; a tea was brewed from it.

The **cat-mint** (*N. cataria*) is a tall plant, sending up erect leafy shoots to a height of two to three feet. The leaves are heart-shaped and serrated, and the flowers are white, though the cultivated varieties are of various shades of mauve and lilac, and borne several in a whorl, with a large number of whorls forming a terminal spike. The plant grows on banks and in waste places.

The **skull-cap** (*Scutellaria galericulata*) is a comparatively rare plant which grows in marshy places and along river banks. The plant is of slender habit, bearing very pointed, lance-shaped leaves in opposite pairs. The flowers are also borne in pairs in the axils of the leaves (Plate 15). Each flower of a pair faces in the same direction. The flower is blue, sometimes shading down to a white tube which is exceptionally long. The two lips are very short. The flowers appear during July and August.

There is also a **lesser skull-cap** (*S. minor*) to be found growing in similar habitats but flowering over a longer season (July to October). It is of smaller habit and its flowers are pink or purple.

To the genus *Stachys* belong several common species, of which the most common is the **hedge woundwort** (*S. sylvatica*) of woods and roadsides. It is a tall erect plant which displays attractive crimson flowers in terminal spikes during July to September (Plate 15). The spikes are usually four and may be as much as eight inches long. The whole plant is hairy and has a disagreeable smell. The leaves are stalked and heart-shaped with extended and pointed tips and serrated margins. As usual they are borne in pairs. The flowers are borne in whorls of about six, and a large number of whorls are spread into the form of a spike. Each flower is crimson with its lower tip ringed with white. There are the usual five sepals. The upper lip of the corolla is arched, and the lower lip is three-lobed, the two lateral lobes being reflexed.

The **wood betony** (*S. betonica*) presents its purple flowers in much denser spikes. It grows in copses and along roadsides, and blooms during June to August.

The **corn woundwort** (*S. arvensis*) grows in cornfields and in waste places and has a weak, procumbent stem. Its leaves are long and oval. The flowers appear for a very long season—April to November

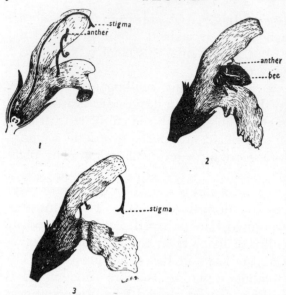

FIG. 137.—Insect-Pollination of Sage Flower.

—and each flower has a long petal tube of white shading into pink at the lobes.

The **marsh woundwort** (*S. palustris*) has a hollow stem bearing very long lance-shaped leaves. The flowers are borne in purple whorls on an elongated interrupted spike. The plant grows in moist places and blooms during July to August.

The **sage** or **clary** (*Salvia verbenaca*) sometimes grows in dry pastures, but it is not very common in the wild state. A related species is frequently cultivated (p. 302). The stem is erect and leafy, the leaves being long and irregularly notched. The flowers are purplish-blue, borne six to a whorl. They appear during July to September. They are arranged in long, terminal, hairy spikes.

The flower of the sage has an unusual but very efficient means of ensuring cross-pollination (Fig. 137). There are two stamens which ripen before the stigma. Each filament is T-shaped. There is only one anther-head, and that is at the end of the upper branch of the T. The style is long and reaches out over the stamens, so that it is not in the way of the visiting insect. When the bee alights on the lower lip of the corolla and forces its head into the tube to get at the nectar at the base, it pushes itself against the lower branch of the T-shaped anther, which then acts as a lever, with the result that the upper branch (by now bearing exposed pollen) is forced over on to the back of the bee. There the pollen is shed. All this time, the style is well above the bee and is therefore not touched by the insect. This does not matter for the time being, for in any event the stigma is not yet ripe ; but once the pollen has been shed the stamens wither and the stigma ripens. Then the style bends downwards and in so doing brings the stigma into a direct line with the back of the next bee that comes along. It thus brushes the back of the bee and picks up any pollen that may be present on it.

A cordial, known as clary water was once made with sage flowers mixed with brandy and cinnamon.

The various mints belong to the genus *Mentha*, and some of them are cultivated for economic purposes (p. 304). The flowers of this genus are nearly regular. The sepals form a five-toothed tube, and the petals a five-lobed tube (Plate 15).

One of the most common wild species of mint is the **water-mint** (*M. aquatica*) which grows in marshes, ditches and along river banks, blooming during August and September. The plant is tall and is covered with soft hairs. The leaves are oval and serrated, and become so small towards the top of the stem that they resemble bracts. The flowers are lilac and are borne in axillary whorls towards the top of the shoot and also in dense terminal heads. The long style with a cleft stigma frequently persists in the fruit (Plate 15). Other species of mint can be found growing wild but they are not particularly common. They are: **horse-mint** (*M. sylvestris*), of moist waste places, growing two to three feet high; **marsh whorled-mint** (*M. sativa*), of a similar habit, bearing its lilac flowers in dense whorls spaced at some distance from each other; **corn mint** (*M. arvensis*), of cornfields, with lilac flowers in axillary whorls; the **round-leaved mint** (*M. rotundifolia*), of moist places, with its whorls of pink flowers in terminal interrupted spikes; **spearmint** (*M. viridis*), of wet places, with lilac flowers growing in slender interrupted spikes (p. 304), and **peppermint** (*M. piperita*), also of wet places, with lilac flowers growing in dense whorls arranged in interrupted spikes (p. 304).

The **thyme** (*Thymus serpyllum*) grows on dry heaths and displays its rosy-purple flowers during July and August. The stem is prostrate and covered with small oval leaves; the flowering stems are erect. The flowers are borne in terminal whorls arranged in the form of a large pin's head. The calyx of the flower is irregular, with an upper lip divided into two teeth and a lower lip divided into three. The upper lip of the corolla is notched, and the lower is three-lobed. The throat of the petal-tube is hairy. The cultivated garden thyme is *Thymus vulgaris* (p. 305).

The **marjoram** (*Origanum vulgare*) grows in dry hilly districts. It and related species are used as pot-herbs (p. 304). It is a strong woody herb which grows to a height of about two feet, displaying its purplish-crimson flowers during late summer (July to September). The plant spreads by means of a root-stock (Plate 15). The stem is thin, but being woody it is very tough. The leaves are borne in pairs, each leaf having a particularly long stalk (Plate 15). The flowers form crowded terminal inflorescences, with others at the ends of branch stems. Each flower is subtended by a coloured bract and has a five-toothed calyx. The petal-tube is nearly regular, though the upper lip is definitely formed from two petals and the lower lip is three-lobed.

There are several other wild genera of LABIATAE, but none is of particular importance.

Calamintha contains several species, namely : the **basil thyme** (*C. acinos*), of dry banks and fields, bearing purple flowers spotted with white and darker purple ; the **calamint** (*C. officinalis*), of dry situations, with purple flowers ; and the **wild basil** (*C. clinopodium*), of copses and dry rocky situations, also bearing purple flowers in crowded whorls.

The **wood sage** or **germander** (*Teucrium scorodonia*) grows in woods and on heaths. Its yellowish-white flowers are borne in one-sided terminal and lateral racemes.

The **white horehound** (*Marrubium vulgare*) has white flowers which are borne in dense whorls. The calyx of the flower has ten teeth. A remedy for coughs is prepared from it.

The **black** or **foetid horehound** (*Ballota nigra*) presents reddish-purple flowers, also in dense whorls. It grows in hedge banks, and blooms during June to September.

The genus *Galeopsis* contains the hempnettles. The **red hemp-nettle** (*G. ladanum*) has rose-coloured flowers and grows in cornfields and waste places ; the **common hempnettle** (*G. tetrahit*) is found in similar places bearing yellow and purple or white flowers ; the **large-flowered hempnettle** (*G. versicolor*), again of similar habitats, has large flowers with petal-tubes more than an inch long, yellow with a purple blotch on the lower lip.

ORNAMENTAL PLANTS

We must admit that in general the family LABIATAE is not a very attractive one so far as the flowers are concerned, and this explains why, large though the family is, few of its members are cultivated in our gardens.

Lavender (*Lavandula* species) is sometimes grown in borders and occasionally used as hedges in small gardens. The plant is usually cultivated for its sweet-scented spikes of flowers (p. 304).

The **wild thyme** (*Thymus serpyllum*) is sometimes grown on paved

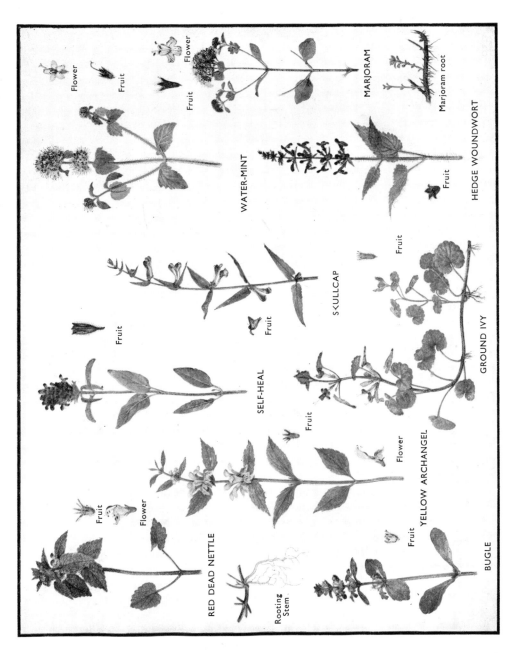

Flower   Fruit   Fruit   Flower

MARJORAM

Marjoram root

Fruit

HEDGE WOUNDWORT

WATER-MINT

SKULLCAP

Fruit

Fruit

GROUND IVY

Fruit

SELF-HEAL

Fruit

YELLOW ARCHANGEL

Flower

Fruit

Fruit   Flower

RED DEAD NETTLE

Rooting Stem

BUGLE

PLATE 15

walks because it emits an agreeable odour when trodden on. This was noted by Bacon :

> Wild thyme and water mints . . . those flowers which perfume the air most delightfully, not passed by, as the rest, but being trodden upon and crushed.

The genus *Salvia* has given the flower garden the most lovely flowering varieties of the whole family. In general habit, they resemble the ordinary *Salvia verbenaca* (p. 300) ; but the flowers are unusually large and of bright colours—scarlet, rose, blue and mauve. The variegated foliage of some adds to their general attractiveness.

Nepeta has given some useful border plants, with flowers of pale mauve or blue. Some species of *Stachys*, too, are cultivated in the flower garden. Cat-mint (p. 299) is also popular.

The most conspicuous cultivated genus is *Coleus*, and the beauty of this plant is due to its large, gaily coloured leaves, and not its flowers. The genus is native to the tropics, but it is often cultivated in greenhouses here. There are many forms with variegated and coloured leaves, which are very large but shaped somewhat like those of the deadnettle.

ECONOMIC PLANTS

Most labiate plants of economic value are cultivated as pot-herbs for the essential oils which they contain.

The **rosemary** (*Rosmarinus officinalis*) is a Mediterranean shrub adapted to living in arid conditions. The main seat of water-loss in the normal plant is the under-surface of the leaf, where there are many microscopic pores through which water evaporates from the plant. In the case of the rosemary, these pores are sunk into deep groves which are covered with hairs, and the margins of the leaves are curled over almost to cover their under-surfaces. Thus evaporation, and therefore water-loss, are very much reduced. The flowers of rosemary are blue. The plant was highly esteemed in ancient times for its aromatic qualities and also for its medicinal properties. Today, the essential oil is distilled and used in perfumery. Rosemary has played a considerable part in folk-lore and is the emblem of remembrance.

> There's rosemary, that's for remembrance ; pray, love, remember : and there is pansies, that's for thoughts . . . There's fennel for you, and columbines : there's rue for you ; and here's some for me :

we may call it herb-grace o' Sundays ; O, you must wear your rue
with a difference. There's a daisy : I would give you some violets,
but they withered all when my father died. . . .

Hamlet, Act 4, Sc. 5 : SHAKESPEARE

Lavender is native to Mediterranean regions and thence to Japan.
It belongs to the genus *Lavandula*, and the most common species is *L.
vera*. In many places this shrub is cultivated for its essential oil, which
is extracted chiefly from the flowers. In this country the plant has been
cultivated (chiefly in Surrey and Hertfordshire) for this purpose since
1568, though the cultivation was not on a commercial basis before 1823.
The dried flowers have also been used for perfuming linen and so forth
for centuries, though not so much today, and, alas, the old London
cry, almost a song, ' Won't you buy my sweet-scented lavender ? ' is
fast dying out. Another means of perfuming a room, especially during
Victorian days, was to burn the flowers or the spikes.

The smaller species, *L. spica*, also yields an essential oil which is
utilised in the painting of porcelain and also in veterinary medicine.
Lavender water is also prepared from it. *L. stoechas*, also a Mediterranean species, has very dark purple flowers which yield an essential
oil.

The genus *Mentha* contains several useful species, which have
been known for centuries.

Woe unto you, . . . for ye pay tithe of mint and anise and cummin . . .

ST. MATTHEW, Ch. 23, v. 23

The **peppermint** (*M. piperita*) is distinguished from other species
in having stalked heads with long spikes of flowers. There are two
varieties of the species, black and white. It is cultivated in many parts
of the world for the sake of the essential oil that it yields. The medicinal
value of this oil, which contains menthol and menthene, has been known
since 1721. It is used as a local anaesthetic and is a powerful antiseptic.
It is also useful in relieving toothache and certain types of dyspepsia
and colic.

The **pennyroyal** (*M. pulegium*) is sometimes used for its properties
as a stimulant.

Spearmint (*M. viridis*) is very commonly cultivated in this country
and elsewhere as a pot-herb, and the essential oil is extracted for
flavouring sweetmeats and also in medicine.

The **wild marjoram** (*Origanum vulgare*) is sometimes used as a
pot-herb, as also is the **sweet marjoram** (*O. majorana*) and the **pot**

marjoram (*O. onites*).   The tops of the plants are cut and dried just as they are beginning to flower.   From *O. majorana* the essential oil, oil of marjoram, is obtained by distillation.

Salvia officinalis is the **garden sage** used for culinary seasoning. The supposed healing properties of this plant are reflected in its name from the Latin *salvo*.

The **thyme,** which is also used in seasoning, is the species *Thymus vulgaris*.   This plant also yields an essential oil from which thymol, a palliative for catarrh, is produced.

Satureia hortensis and *S. montana* are the **summer** and **winter savories,** cultivated condiments grown more often in warmer regions.

PART IV

MONOCOTYLEDONS

The monocotyledons comprise those families of flowering plants which have only one seed-leaf or cotyledon. The foliage leaves are usually parallel-veined and almost invariably have smooth margins. The number of floral parts is usually three or multiples of three. Seldom do mono-cotyledons exhibit secondary thickening (p. 13), for most of them are herbs ; but there are a few exceptions (Chap. 72).

There are also other striking tendencies among the monocoty-ledons. For example, in many of the more advanced families the sep-arate identity of sepals and petals is gone, so that frequently the two whorls or sets of whorls have coalesced, or even more often they are of the same form and colour. At any rate, the sepals have usually become petalloid. In such cases it is not possible to separate the petals and sepals with certainty, so the two whorls are grouped together and called the perianth.

There can be no doubt that the percentage of monocotyledons used for ornamental purposes, and above all for food, is much higher than that for the dicotyledons. All cereals, for example, are monocoty-ledons ; in fact, they all belong to the same family, GRAMINEAE.

64

SOME AQUATIC MONOCOTYLEDONS

Before we come to the very important lily family (LILIACEAE) there are about twenty-five different families of monocotyledons. Many of these are small, and quite a number of them are not represented in this country at all. A very few have given us some garden flowers, whereas certain others are quite important food plants, such as banana and arrowroot. A brief survey of this miscellany is therefore desirable before going on to the lilies.

This miscellaneous lot of families will be considered in two sections, for there is an artificial line of demarcation. The first section is composed of aquatic or semi-aquatic families. The second section has few such

families, but contains certain food plants. The water plants admit of
some clear distinctions. There are those that inhabit fresh water, and
those that prefer salt water. Some are partially submerged; others
totally. In certain of the families, it will be seen that the plants, which
have clearly been derived from terrestrial plants have, during their
evolutionary progress, become adapted to life in water, especially in
their leaf-forms and frequently in the reduction of those parts of the
flower which cannot function under water.

FLOWERING RUSH

In some very wet ditches and more often alongside rivers, often
frequently growing some distance out into the water, may on occasion
be seen the lovely **flowering rush**, which is really not a rush at all.

This plant belongs to the BUTOMACEAE, which is probably the
most primitive of all monocotyledonous families. The family is small,
but is spread over temperate and tropical zones. There are about five
genera, but the only one native to Britain is *Butomus*, to which the
flowering rush (*B. umbellatus*) belongs.

This very attractive plant grows in the mud of rivers and ditches,
through which it spreads by means of a creeping root-stock. This
sends off long slender leaves which grow erect and, at a casual glance,
look like those of the rush. The flowers are borne in umbels at the
ends of thick, upright, reddish-green stalks which sometimes attain a
height of five feet, though the normal height is two to three feet.
(Plate 17.) The flower-stalk bears no leaves.

Each umbel is surrounded by about three membranous bracts. There
are about a dozen flowers in each umbel and these open at varying times.

Each flower is borne on a comparatively long stalk (Plate 17).
There are six perianth leaves of a rosy tint, spreading to a diameter of
about an inch. The perianth encloses nine stamens and six carpels.
These latter, after fertilisation, form a collection of follicles which
eventually split to release their seeds (Plate 17).

The flowering rush is so handsome that it is frequently cultivated
in water-gardening.

ELODEA, FROG-BIT AND WATER-SOLDIER

The family HYDROCHARITACEAE contains both fresh- and salt-
water herbs, some of which grow with their roots fixed in the mud

whereas others are free-floating. The family is a large one and is distributed chiefly over the warmer parts of the world, though a few interesting genera are to be found in this country.

The genus *Elodea* is not native to Great Britain, but one species introduced here, *Elodea canadensis*, the **Canadian water weed** is now unfortunately very much in evidence owing to its prolific means of vegetative reproduction. It grows almost everywhere where fresh water is to be found.

Any small part of this plant, if broken off, will develop into a new plant. So prolific is it that once *Elodea* establishes itself in a suitable pond or lake it will choke it unless there is a periodic clearing-out. That is why this plant is such a nuisance in water-works. The great rate at which the plant is able to reproduce itself by this vegetative means can be judged from the fact that before 1841 it was quite unknown in this country. Now it is one of the most common water plants in England, Wales and Scotland. It is actually a native of North America. It was introduced mysteriously into Co. Down, Ireland, in 1836, and into England in 1841, and today it is common in lakes, ponds, streams and ditches throughout the islands.

The plant floats on the water and has much-branched stems covered with small lance-shaped leaves borne in opposite pairs or in whorls. The flowers are unisexual, but in this country the plant depends solely on its all too effective means of vegetative reproduction, for here male flowers are unknown. The female flowers have a perianth of six greenish-purple segments which float on the surface of the water.

The **frog-bit** (*Hydrocharis morsus-ranae*) is a rather rare member of this family, though it is sometimes found floating on ponds. It is not fixed to the bottom. The floating leaves are round and are about one and a half inches in diameter. The plant reproduces itself vegetatively by means of winter buds. During the summer it spreads by means of horizontal branches which form new plants at their tips. In the autumn large buds are formed on these branches, and they finally fall off and spend the winter at the bottom. In spring they float to the surface and develop into new plants.

The flowers are borne on erect stems above the surface of the water. Each flower has three narrow green sepals, three oval white petals, three to twelve stamens, and six styles with cleft stigmas.

The **water-soldier** (*Stratiotes aloides*) is another rare representative of this family. This plant bears sword-like leaves with serrated edges— the latter being a rather unusual characteristic in monocotyledons. In the summer the whole plant floats to the surface and bears its flowers, which are white and about an inch and a half in diameter. It sinks again in the autumn.

ARROW-HEAD AND WATER-PLANTAIN

The ALISMATACEAE is another family of marsh and aquatic herbs distributed throughout temperate and tropical regions. It is represented in this country by two genera, *Sagittaria* and *Alisma*.

The **arrow-head** (*Sagittaria sagittifolia*) is fairly common in shallow water and blooms during July and September. The plant spreads by means of thick stems in the mud and reproduces itself vegetatively by means of winter buds. Its leaves and flowers are rather striking. There are two types of leaves. Those submerged are ribbon-shaped, and those which stand erect have long stalks with a leaf-blade the shape of an arrow (Plate 17). Sometimes there is a third type of leaf, namely, that which floats on the surface of the water. This style is not common, but when it appears it produces an oval leaf-blade.

The flowers are large and white and are borne in whorls of three at the end of an erect flower-stalk (Plate 17). They are unisexual, but both male and female flowers grow on the same plant. Each flower has three sepals surrounding three white petals having purple blotches at their bases. The male flower has numerous stamens, and the female numerous carpels. The fruit is a collection of small nuts (Plate 17).

The **water-plantain** (*Alisma plantago*) is not a plantain at all, of course, but it is so named because its erect leaves are very like those of the plantain (p. 247). It grows in ditches. The flowers are pale purplish pink and are borne in branched racemes at the ends of long stalks. There are three sepals, three petals, six stamens and six or more free carpels.

ARROW-GRASS

JUNCAGINACEAE is represented in Great Britain by the **arrow-grass** (*Triglochin palustre*), which is another inhabitant of marshes and wet meadows. The leaves are erect and thread-like. The inconspicuous flowers appear during June to August. They are purple, with six perianth segments, six stamens and two carpels.

In salt marshes another species of this genus may be found, namely *T. maritimum*, the flowers of which are borne in denser racemes. Both species are of tufted habit.

EEL-GRASS

The **eel-grass** or **grass-wrack** (*Zostera marina*), which grows on our more gently sloping seashores is the only representative of an entirely salt-water family—ZOSTERACEAE, which, though composed of only two genera, is spread throughout the world.

The eel-grass has nothing striking about it, and it is not particularly useful except as packing and for stuffing cushions. Yet it is of particular interest because it is one of the most perfect examples of a land plant which has become totally adapted to aquatic conditions; for the whole plant, including the flowers, is entirely submerged below the surface of the sea.

It spreads by means of a creeping stem and has long ribbon-shaped leaves which are sheathed at their bases.

Since even the flowers are submerged, they are, as one would expect, reduced in structure, yet so well-adapted have they become to their unusual environment that they do not suffer from it even as regards pollination. The inflorescence is a succulent spike bearing male and female flower and is called a spadix (see also ARACEAE, Chap. 67); the entire spadix is enclosed in a large sheath called the spathe. The flowers form two vertical rows, and are so much reduced that the male flower is composed of only one stamen and the female of one carpel with two flattened stigmas. So complete is the plant's adaptation that even the pollen grains are of the same specific gravity as the sea-water in which they are shed, so that they may float at any level. The stigmas are so large that they are very capable of catching some of the pollen floating around. The whole mechanism is therefore very similar to that of wind-pollination. The fruit is an achene.

POND-WEEDS

The entirely fresh-water family POTAMOGETONACEAE comprises one genus only, namely, *Potamogeton*, and that is well represented in this country by about a dozen different pond-weeds.

The leaves of the different species indicate a gradual transition from land-forms to water-forms. The **broad-leaved pond-weed** (*P. natans*) shows the least modification to suit aquatic life. The upper leaves are leathery and oval and float on the surface. The lower leaves are somewhat ribbon-shaped. In the **various-leaved pond-weed** (*P. heterophyllus*) all submerged leaves are linear and narrow; but the floating leaves, if present, are oblong. Then there are the **shining** pond-weed (*P. lucens*) and the **curly pond-weed** (*P. crispus*) with completely submerged leaves which are lance-shaped ; and finally such species as the **small pond-weed** (*P. pusillus*) the leaves of which are all submerged and ribbon-shaped.

The leaves of all the pond-weeds are typically monocotyledonous and are therefore parallel-veined. In most species the flowers are borne in axillary or terminal spikes which project above the water. Each flower has a much-reduced perianth represented by leafy outgrowths from the four stamens. The flower is wind-pollinated. The fruit is an achene, the outer wall of which contains air-spaces which make it buoyant, and so ensure its distribution by water. Later the air escapes and the fruit sinks to the bottom where the seed eventually germinates.

NAJAS

The Najadaceae comprises one genus only, namely *Najas*, represented in Britain by some inconspicuous, totally submerged fresh-water annuals. The stem is slender, and the leaves ribbon-shaped and toothed. The flowers are unisexual, the male being represented by one stamen, and the female by one carpel sometimes surrounded by a rudimentary perianth. Pollination takes place under water as in the case of *Zostera*.

65

SOME ORNAMENTAL AND EDIBLE MONOCOTYLEDONS

We now come to the second group of miscellaneous families before the great lily family. This contains several families of plants from which various foodstuffs are obtained, and some handsome garden plants.

SPIDER-WORTS

Commelinaceae is a family of tropical and sub-tropical herbs with jointed stems and alternating leaves with sheathing bases. No members of the family are native to this country, but some are cultivated for their rather attractive flowers.

The structure of the flower is that of a typical monocotyledon,

x

though the sepals and the petals are quite distinct. There are three sepals and three petals, six stamens, and three joined carpels. Frequently some of the stamens are absent or sterile.

Commelina coelestis is an attractive perennial sometimes cultivated for its glossy foliage and bright sky-blue flowers. *C. benghalensis* is curious in that it bears some flowers underground. These never open, of course, and are therefore self-pollinated.

Several species of the **spider-wort** (*Tradescantia*) are garden favourites. The leaves are long and pointed with large sheathing bases. The whole plant is hairy. The six stamens are covered with unusually large hairs. *T. virginiana*, with its deep blue flowers, grows wild in North America and is often cultivated in Great Britain. Other cultivated species have pale blue, azure blue or deep rose-coloured flowers. Some of these are double.

PINEAPPLE

The family BROMELIACEAE is not seen in this country, except in the greenhouses of some botanic gardens. It is native entirely to

FIG. 138.—Pineapple 'Fruit'.
From 'Pineapple Culture' by Hearne and Miller, Florida Agricultural Experiment Station

tropical America, though some genera are now cultivated in other tropical and sub-tropical regions. The family is worthy of mention, however, for some of its genera supply valuable fibres, and the genus *Ananas* contains the delectable **pineapple** (*A. sativus*), which, strictly speaking, is not a fruit.

The Spaniards who explored America gave the pineapple its name because it looked like a pine cone. Actually the so-called 'fruit' is a swollen stem or really an inflorescence-stalk, combined with the real fruits. The stringy nature of the 'fruit' is due to large masses of conducting woody tissue embedded in this swollen inflorescence stalk. Before it is ripe, the stalk bears many flowers, and the diamond-shaped areas on the surface of the ripe 'fruit' mark the remains of the fertilised flowers. After fertilisation the fruit themselves swell simultaneously with the stalk, and the resulting mass forms the barrel-shaped 'fruit'. Thus the 'fruit' is a mixture of swollen inflorescence stem and swollen fruit all merged into one mass. At the top is a tuft of green foliage leaves (Fig. 138).

The pineapple plant is a native of tropical America, but it is now cultivated elsewhere, especially in the Hawaiian group of islands, as well as in certain parts of the Old World. The complete plant is a low shrub and bears the fruiting inflorescence as a terminal spike. Below this is a large number of long, sword-shaped green foliage leaves.

Royal Botanic Gardens, Kew

FIG. 139.—Banana in Fruit.

BANANA AND MANILA HEMP

The tropical family MUSACEAE contains one genus only, namely, *Musa*, and to this the banana belongs.

The **banana** plant, large though it is (Fig. 139), is really a herb. The stem is thick and grows underground. What looks like the aerial stem is nothing but the stalks of the gigantic leaves sheathing around each other. The leaves are some of the largest in Nature, often attaining a length of three yards. They are broad and lance-shaped and are simple, though as they get older they frequently become shredded by the wind. The flowers are borne in long pendulous inflorescences. They are unisexual, but both male and female are borne on the same inflorescence, the female in a group at the top, that is really the base of the inflorescence nearest the 'stem', and the male at the bottom or actually the tip of the inflorescence. After fertilisation, the female flowers develop into the well-known long fruit, which are in reality long berries, and the male flowers wither (Fig. 139). Each fruit is the result of the fertilisation of three joined carpels, as may be seen when a banana is cut in cross-section. On the tree the berries grow upright.

More than two hundred different varieties of bananas are cultivated. The centre of the industry is the West Indies. There the commercial banana is a variety of the ' plantain ' (*Musa paradisica*) ; it is therefore named *M. paradisica* var. *sapientum*. The smaller Canary banana of the Canary Islands is *M. cavendishii*. The main food stored in the banana is starch ; much of this becomes converted into sugar during ripening. The cultivated forms of banana produce no seeds, so new plants are propagated vegetatively from the underground stems.

Manila hemp or **abaca** is obtained from another species of the same genus, *M. textilis*. The large leaves of several other of the forty-five species of *Musa* are used in thatching, packing and in plaiting mats.

GINGER, TURMERIC AND E. INDIAN ARROWROOT

The ZINGIBERACEAE is another family of tropical and sub-tropical herbs, usually aromatic, and many having horizontal, thick, tuberous underground stems. A large number are cultivated for the foodstuffs they yield.

Zingiber officinale yields ginger. Like the banana, this plant is propagated entirely by vegetative means. The tuberous underground stems are dug up and killed by plunging in boiling water. Scraped or coated ginger is produced according to whether the tubers are peeled or not.

The genus *Curcuma* contains several species of economic value. The tuberous stems of *C. angustifolia* furnish East Indian arrowroot ; the dried and powdered underground stems of *C. longa* produce the yellow dye turmeric ; and the tuberous stems of *C. zedoaria* yield zedoary, which is used in Eastern countries as a tonic and a perfume.

CANNA

The family CANNACEAE has only one genus—*Canna*. It is a native of tropical and sub-tropical America, but is often seen cultivated in this country, especially in greenhouses, though the **Indian shot** (*C. indica*) is sometimes bedded out in the warmer regions of the south.

The plant is tall and leafy. The leaves are large, lance-shaped and broad with a pronounced mid-rib, resembling those of *Aspidistra*, though not so thick nor of such a deep green. Among cultivated varieties, the leaves are sometimes particularly attractive, for they are of various colours, especially bronze. The general habit of the plant is very like that of the members of the family ZINGIBERACEAE.

The large flowers are borne in dense spikes and are irregular. They present a wide variety of shades, chiefly yellow, pink, red and maroon. At a casual glance the flower looks like a large *Gladiolus*. There are three sepals and three showy petals. The six stamens are petaloid, that is they resemble the petals in form. The three stamens in the outer whorl are sterile. The three carpels are joined.

W. INDIAN ARROWROOT

The MARANTACEAE is a family of perennial herbs native to the primary forests of tropical and sub-tropical countries, chiefly America.

Several of the genera have tuberous underground stems from which certain foodstuffs are prepared. From *Maranta arundinacea* the West Indian arrowroot is obtained by grinding the stem and washing it free of starch. The stem tubers of *Calathea allouia* (known as topee tampo) are eaten like potatoes in the West Indies.

66

LILIES AND THEIR RELATIVES
(*Liliaceae*)

'Thou wert not, Solomon ! in all thy glory
   Array'd ', the lilies cry, ' in robes like ours ;
How vain your grandeur ! Ah, how transitory
   Are human flowers ! '
                    Hymn to the Flowers : HORACE SMITH

The term ' lily ' is very loosely handled in literature and elsewhere, and even among commonly applied botanical names there are some misleading conceptions. For example, the water-lily (p. 47) certainly does not belong to the lily family : it is not even a monocotyledon. Neither is the arum-lily (p. 332), though it is very near the lily family in flowering plant classification. Even among the family itself, the term is somewhat confusing. Most of the true lilies belong to the genus *Lilium*, yet not one member of this extremely popular garden genus is found growing wild in this country. The wild lily of the valley

Harold Bastin

FIG. 140.—Bluebells.

belongs to another genus (*Convallaria*). In fact, the whole family LILIACEAE is represented in Great Britain by a very miscellaneous collection of wild plants, such as bluebell, bog asphodel (rare), lily of the valley (rare), autumn crocus (rare) and Solomon's seal (rare). It is to our flower gardens and greenhouses that we must go in order to see the most typical members of the family, such as the Madonna lily, tiger lily, Turk's cap, tulip, hyacinth, and so forth.

The LILIACEAE are distributed throughout temperate and sub-tropical regions. It is a very large family and comprises chiefly perennial herbs, most of which produce thick underground stems, corms or bulbs and sometimes tubers.

There are very few of economic importance.

WILD PLANTS

Perhaps the most typical wild member of this family is the lovely **bluebell** (*Scilla nutans*, formerly known as *Hyacinthus nonscriptus*) which so often covers the floor of open woods with a misty blue carpet during May and June (Fig. 140).

Tonight from deeps of loneliness I wake in wistful wonder
　　To a sudden sense of brightness, an immanence of blue—
O are there bluebells swaying in the shadowy coppice yonder,
　　Shriven with the dawning and the dew ?

Bluebells : LUCIA C. MARKHAM

Sweet bluebells we,
Mid flowers of the lea,
The likest in hue to heaven,
Our bonnets so blue
Are tinged with the dew
That drops from the sky at even.

Our bloom more sweet
Than dark violet,
Or tulip's purple stain,
At every return
Of the dew-breathing morn,
Grows brighter and brighter again.
Song of the Bluebells : GEORGE DARLEY

The 'bluebell of Scotland' is the harebell (*Campanula rotundifolia*, p. 249), not *Scilla*.

The bluebell (or wild hyacinth as it is sometimes erroneously called) produces a typical bulb. This takes the form of a large bud just beneath the surface of the soil. It is composed of a bun-shaped stem giving off roots below and bearing above thick, fleshy, white leaves forming the mass of the bulb (Plate 17) surrounded by a few brown membranous scale leaves. In the axils of some of the fleshy leaves new bulbs are formed from buds, and by this means the plant spreads. The flowers also set seed ; but once these have germinated it takes three years before the bulbs produced from them are sufficiently large to develop flowering shoots. In the centre of the bulb, that is, at the top of the bun-shaped stem, a terminal bud grows out early in the year and produces the flowering stalks and foliage leaves.

The leaves are typically monocotyledonous. They are long and linear, attaining a length of ten to eighteen inches, pointed at the tips and with parallel veins.

The blue flowers are borne in lovely pendulous racemes, so that all the flowers seem to be coming off from only one side of the inflorescence axis. There are six to twelve flowers in each inflorescence (Plate 17).

FIG. 141.—Section through Bluebell Flower.

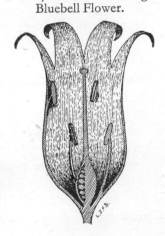

Each flower is subtended on the stalk by a long, narrow, deep greenish-blue bract. Again, the flower is very typical of monocotyledons, having all its floral organs in whorls of three or its multiples. There is no distinction between sepals and petals, and the six blue perianth segments are joined to form a bell with six small spreading lobes which curve backwards. There are six stamens, one attached to the inside of each of the perianth segments. The three carpels fuse to form a three-chambered ovary bearing a long style at the top of which is a stigma shaped like a pin's head (Fig. 141). As in many members of this family, the flower droops and thus protects the pollen from the rain, but after fertilisation the fruit-capsule stands upright so that the seeds must be shaken out and thus assured of a reasonably wide distribution (Plate 17).

The **lily of the valley** (*Convallaria majalis*) is a wild plant, though it is far from common. Its shy beauty and exquisite scent are so irresistible, however, that it is no wonder that the plant is extensively cultivated.

The lily of the valley grows in woods, for it is a shade-loving plant. There it spreads by means of a thick underground stem, each branch of which produces a few new scales and one pair of foliage leaves each year. Thus a well-established plant which has been spreading for some years produces a mass of broad, lance-shaped leaves which are themselves very beautiful with their delicate green and wavy margins.

The white flowers appear in the wild state during May and June. They are borne about six to twelve in a drooping raceme which frequently hides beneath the canopy of leaves.

> And the Naiad-like lily of the vale,
> Whom youth makes so fair and passion so pale,
> That the light of its tremulous bells is seen,
> Through their pavilions of tender green.
> *The Sensitive Plant* : SHELLEY

The flower has a campanulate perianth which is almost globular with the six free tips recurved. Otherwise it is fundamentally similar to the bluebell. Both stamens and stigma ripen at the same time so that in the absence of insects the flower is self-pollinated. This is a useful precaution, for the racemes are so often out of sight among the leaves. The fruit is a spherical red berry.

In bogs and other wet places grows the **bog asphodel** (*Narthecium ossifragum*) which spreads through the water-logged soil by means of thick underground stems. The leaves are rigid and strong, conspicuously ribbed and ending in an extended point. The flowers are conspicuous, since they are golden-yellow in colour and are borne in racemes. They appear during July and August. The perianth segments are very spreading. Although the flowers are very conspicuous, they contain no nectar and are therefore frequently self-pollinated. The fruit is a long red capsule.

Solomon's seal (*Polygonatum multiflorum*), a plant sometimes found growing wild in woods, but more often seen cultivated, derives its common name from the fact that the annual shoots, when they die away, leave curious seal-like markings on the thick, fleshy, underground stem. The specific name indicates that it bears many flowers.

The oblong and pointed leaves are borne alternately on arched stems, two to three feet long. Hanging from the stem at close intervals of about a foot and a half are the inflorescences of from two to five inconspicuous greenish-white flowers. The flower is not subtended by a bract. The perianth is narrower in the middle, and the six free tips are not very pronounced. The stamens and the stigmas ripen at the same time, but the flower is usually pollinated by bees.

The **autumn crocus** or **meadow saffron** (*Colchicum autumnale*) is a member of the lily family, and must therefore not be confused with the ordinary cultivated crocus, which is a member of the iris family (Chap. 70).

The autumn crocus produces a large corm (which differs from a bulb in that the mass of the corm is swollen stem, whereas the mass of the bulb is swollen leaves, p. 317). The corm grows below the surface of the soil. In the autumn, a large solitary purple flower projects out from the soil, but it is inserted direct on to the corm, without an intervening stalk (Fig. 142). Sometimes the flowers form a purple mass, which is not often seen in this country except in parks, though it is a common enough sight in the mountainous regions of continental Europe. The perianth-tube is several inches long, and the ovary which is at its base is therefore almost on the corm itself and thus below ground where it is protected from the autumnal weather. The perianth-tube opens out into six large free segments very like those of the true crocus (Fig. 142). The six stamens are inserted at the mouth of the

FIG. 142.—Autumn Crocus in Bloom.

Harold Bastin

perianth-tube, one each at the base of a free segment. The ovary is formed by the fusion of three carpels and has three chambers. It bears three very long styles which stretch right up the perianth-tube and then spread out among the stamens within the cup formed by the free perianth segments. The flower is pollinated by bees. The fruit is a capsule which is brought above the surface of the soil by the elongation of the floral receptacle after fertilisation has taken place. While this is going on, the long lance-shaped leaves grow.

It is sometimes said that the autumn crocus has an effect on other plants growing in close proximity to it. So far, this has not been confirmed, but from its seeds is now extracted a chemical substance called colchicine about which scientific investigators are making some rather astounding discoveries, for it certainly does affect other plants in their growth and development—frequently making them larger and more robust.

Another rather rare liliaceous plant native to this country is the **star of Bethlehem** (*Ornithogalum umbellatum*) which presents its flowers in dense white racemes in which the flower-stalks are of unequal length (longest at the base) so that all the flowers in one head are brought up level with each other. The perianth of the flower is spreading, with six separate segments. There are six stamens, and the ovary and the style are three-angled. All the leaves grow from ground-level and are long and linear. The white inflorescences appear during May and June.

The **yellow star of Bethlehem** is even rarer and belongs to a different genus (*Gagea lutea*). All its leaves also grow from ground-level, and the flowers appear early in the year (March and April). They are borne four to eight in an umbel which is subtended by one to three bracts. The flowers close during the afternoon. In some of the leaf-axils the axillary buds develop into bulbils (p. 38), which, if the flowers have not been fertilised, drop off and eventually develop into new plants.

The **snake's-head** or **fritillary** (*Fritillaria meleagris*) is an inhabitant of hedgerows in the south of England ; but this beautiful wild flower is all too rare. Matthew Arnold knew

> What white, what purple fritillaries
> The grassy harvest of the river-fields,
> Above by Ensham, down by Sandford, yields.

and the flower remains faithful to its old haunts.

The genus is more familiar to us through the **crown imperial** (*F. imperialis*) of flower gardens (p. 322). The large, dull red or purple flowers are beautifully tesselated and appear during May. On occasions, white specimens may be found.

The stem is about eighteen inches high, and bears many long, linear leaves. There is usually only one solitary flower to each stem. At the bases of the perianth segments are large nectaries. The flower-bud stands erect, so does the fruit-capsule, but the open flower droops pensively.

ORNAMENTAL FLOWERS

So particularly lovely are the flowers of the lily family that nearly every wild member is also given a place in our gardens—bluebell, lily of the valley, Solomon's seal, autumn crocus, star of Bethlehem and snake's-head or fritillary.

The **bluebell** (*Scilla nutans*) has many varities of form in the garden. Some are white, others are blue, and most of them are larger and more sturdy than the original wild plant.

Closely related to *Scilla* is the genus *Hyacinthus*, which contains the popular forms of **hyacinth,** most of which are derived from the species *H. orientalis*. This plant presents very large, robust, conspicuous and many-flowered inflorescences arranged in a symmetrical spike—not pendulous and one-sided like that of *Scilla*. The range of colour is considerable, but the most popular are varying shades of white, cream, blue, yellow, pink and mauve. The seductive perfume of the flowers, which are sometimes brought on in greenhouses and later bedded out, is an additional attraction.

It is better when referring to the ' hyacinth ' to adhere to the genus *Hyacinthus* and even to avoid the term ' hyacinth ' in describing the bluebell as the ' wild hyacinth ', for this has lead to considerable confusion. It is certain that many writers of the past, especially poets, are referring to the bluebell when they use the word ' hyacinth '.

The **grape hyacinth** is another garden favourite, especially in rock gardens, but this again belongs to another genus (*Muscari racemosum*). The plant derives its common name from the fact that the flowers are borne in very dense symmetrical spikes, and each flower is almost globular. In most varieties the flowers are an intensely deep blue in colour. Frequently, the upper flowers of the spike are neuter (*cf.* cornflower) and larger, thus adding to the conspicuousness of the whole spike. This plant sets seed copiously and so spreads easily.

The well-known **crown imperial** (*Fritillaria imperialis*) and other species closely resembling the wild snake's-head are frequently grown in borders.

Many herbaceous borders possess at least one clump of **red-hot poker** (*Kniphofia* species) which hailed originally from South Africa. It stands out in any environment owing to the large, long, dense inflorescences which are highly coloured resembling torches. The tall spikes vary in colour—yellow, lemon, orange, scarlet and deep red. Each flower has a very close perianth-tube—so close, in fact, that bees are frequently seen to force their way in after the nectar and then finding themselves unable to return.

Gloriosa is a very attractive genus of climbers (rare in this family), sometimes cultivated in greenhouses. The most popular species is *G. superba*, which has pendulous flowers of a rich glowing red with a yellow base. The plant climbs by means of its leaf-tips which act like tendrils.

The **dog-toothed violets** are unfortunately named, for they are not members of the family VIOLACEAE but of the LILIACEAE. The species most commonly cultivated in this country is *Erythronium dens canis* with bright rose-pink flowers. Other species present shades of yellow, purple and white, and flowers of one colour with bases of a different colour.

Without doubt, the two most popular genera of the whole lily family in our flower gardens and greenhouses are *Tulipa* and *Lilium*.

To the genus *Tulipa* belong the **tulips**—those lovely spring and early summer flowers of infinite variety of colour and form—single and double, tall and dwarf, smooth and wavy (Fig. 143).

> Not one of Flora's brilliant race
> A form more perfect can display ;
> Art could not feign more simple grace
> Nor Nature take a line away.
> *On Planting a Tulip-Root* : J. MONTGOMERY

The whole tulip plant is typical of the lily family. There is a bulb from which grow the broad, lance-shaped foliage leaves. Then the flower appears, borne on a long stalk which also bears one or two foliage leaves. This comes from the terminal bud, that is, the most central bud of the bulb. Occasionally, a branch bud also sends up a flower-stalk. The flower itself is very typically liliaceous, having six free perianth segments to which are due the whole form and beauty of the flower ; six stamens borne one on each segment ; three carpels fused to form a long three-chambered ovary with three large stigmas on the top with no intervening style. The fruit is a capsule which remains erect.

Tulipa is a north-temperate genus and was at one time represented by native members in this country. Wild species abound in Central Asia, chiefly on the steppes. Though the flower is frequently insect-pollinated it is entirely scentless.

> Clean as a lady,
> cool as glass,
> fresh without fragrance
> the tulip was.
>
> *Tulip* : HUMBERT WOLFE

FIG. 143.—Tulips.

It would be impossible in any mere general review of flowers to do justice to that great genus *Lilium*. It calls for a book of its own, and indeed many works have been devoted exclusively to the lilies. So wide in form is the genus that many gardening enthusiasts have specialised in it as others do in roses. Only a pictorial artist could depict at all faithfully the beauty of the many species, for words, even the glowing vocabulary of the eloquent Dutch seedsmen, are scarcely adequate.

The genus is confined to north temperate regions, where it is widely distributed. Yet, strange to say, there are no wild members of *Lilium* in this country. What there were have disappeared—the price paid for their beauty and exacted by wanton, or at least heedless, gathering without any thought of replacement ; for the legal protection of flowers is a recent innovation. But the absence of wild species is somewhat counterbalanced by extensive garden and greenhouse cultivation. So many different species and varieties are there, that only a few of the most common will receive mention here.

All species and varieties of the genus *Lilium* conform to a general plan. They are herbs—some of them very large ones and tending to woodiness, with scaly bulbs and leafy stems. Unlike the genus *Tulipa*, the flowers are not often solitary but are borne in racemes. The flower itself conforms to a typical liliaceous plan, namely, six perianth segments with nectar secreted in long grooves at their bases ; six stamens, usually large and conspicuous ; three carpels joined to form a long, three-chambered ovary, with no style but with three large stigmas fixed on the top. In those species and varieties where the flowers are pendulous when open, the fruit-capsule becomes upright so that it has to be shaken in order to release the seeds. Many species are delicately perfumed.

Some lilies are of the purest white : in fact, so frequently is reference made in literature to the whiteness of the lily that one sometimes tends to forget that there are many beautifully coloured lilies also.

> Is not this lily pure ?
> What fuller can procure
> A white so perfect, spotless clear
> As in this flower doth appear ?
> *School of the Heart* : F. QUARLES

Of all white lilies, it is not easy to conceive of a more beautiful example than the **golden-rayed lily of Japan** (*Lilium auratum*) (Fig. 144). This is a tall, somewhat woody species with its large white trumpets borne in racemes at the ends of tall leafy stems.

Closely similar to this is the lovely old-fashioned **Madonna or white lily** (*L. candidum*), one of the most easily cultivated lilies because it is so hardy.

The **regal lily** (*L. regale*) has lately achieved great popularity, and increase in its popularity seems to vary directly with that of its size. Frequently only one flower is allowed to grow on each stem. The campanulate blooms are flushed internally with yellow shading to white towards the edges of the perianth segments, and the lower parts of the outside of the tubular portion are streaked with brown, whereas the outside of the perianth tips is flushed with pink. This species is usually grown outdoors in warm situations ; but the plant is sometimes grown in pots in greenhouses.

L. giganteum, as its name implies, is a giant among lilies, sometimes attaining a height of twelve feet, with long, trumpet-shaped flowers, white streaked inside with reddish-purple. This species will grow in shady places, even woods.

Of the **white trumpet lily** (*L. longiflorum*) there are several varieties which indicate their country of origin—chiefly South Africa, Bermuda, St. Helena and Formosa. In this country, this very large-flowered species is usually cultivated in greenhouses.

FIG. 144.—*Lilium auratum.*

FIG. 145.—*Lilium chalcedonicum.*

Among the coloured species of lily are the very popular orange lily, the tiger lily and the Turk's cap or martagon.

The **orange lily** (*L. bulbiferum*) is an outdoor species useful for borders. This plant can reproduce itself vegetatively by means of bulbils produced in the axils of the leaves.

The **tiger lily** (*L. tigrinum*) is a tall, free-flowering species comprising several varieties. Most of the species have flowers which are orange, scarlet with black spots and trumpet-shaped. Some varieties are double.

The **Turk's cap** or **martagon** (*L. chalcedonicum* and *L. martagon*) has, in all its varieties, pronounced recurved perianth segments (Fig. 145). The species *L. chalcedonicum* has vivid scarlet flowers, whereas those of *L. martagon* are usually purple ; but a white variety (*L. martagon* var. *album*) is also sometimes cultivated. These species emit their scent at night.

Among the many other coloured species of lily may be mentioned *L. canadense*, yellow and orange ; *L. carolinianum*, bright orange ; *L. grayi*, deep crimson outside, yellow blotched with purple inside ; *L. henryi*, orange-yellow ; *L. pomponium*, brilliant scarlet of Turk's cap form ; *L. wallacei*, rose and apricot yellow ; and there are many others.

Two other genera of the lily family must not pass unmentioned. They are *Funkia* and *Aspidistra*. To the genus *Funkia* belong the **plantain lilies** with lilac flowers. They hail from China and Japan.

The genus *Aspidistra*, which took a strange hold on the affections of our more recent forebears, hails from eastern Asia. It has large, radical, broad, lance-shaped leaves. Under cultivation, it blooms but rarely. The flower is, however, very insignificant and grows close to the ground. It is unusual because its floral parts are in whorls of four and not three. The style is flat and very large, forming a lid to the cavity made by the eight perianth segments.

ECONOMIC PLANTS

The family LILIACEAE seems to limit its service to man to the beauty which it has brought into the world, for it offers very little else.

Among the food plants, the only one familiar to us in this country is **asparagus** (*Asparagus officinalis*), and even that is not very familiar, for it requires careful cultivation and is consequently expensive to buy in the shops. There is a wild variety of this plant to be found in certain parts of the country, especially in the west. On the steppes of the U.S.S.R. it is so abundant that the cattle eat it. The plant spreads by means of thick creeping underground stems which send up erect shoots. It is these thick, young aerial shoots which are eaten. A special variety of asparagus, noted for its quality and size, is cultivated at Argenteuil, near Paris.

The so-called **asparagus fern** (*A. plumosus*) is a climber native to South America. Many varieties are grown in this country. But the fine feathery tufts are not leaves but branches called cladodes (see butcher's broom, p. 329) borne in the axils of insignificant scale leaves.

In all species of *Asparagus*, the flower is insignificant and white, and the fruit is a bright red berry.

Colchicine or colchicum is obtained from the **autumn crocus** (*Colchicum autumnale*). It is an irritant poison and also a narcotic. It is used as a drug in the treatment of gout.

Aloes is a purgative juice extracted from different species of the genus *Aloe* of South Africa, mainly the Karroo Desert. The Cape species yield the strongest drug; the Natal species the weakest. The leaves are borne in dense rosettes, and, since they live under arid conditions, are thick and fleshy. The leaves are cut and the juice which exudes is evaporated in order to obtain the drug.

There are three small families which are so closely related to the LILIACEAE that some botanists do not recognise them as separate families but include their members within the lily family. They are TRILLIACEAE, SMILACACEAE and RUSCACEAE. All three contain some exceptionally curious plants.

Y

HERB-PARIS

The family TRILLIACEAE is native to the temperate and mountainous regions of the northern hemisphere, and is represented in this country by the common though curious herb-Paris, a poisonous plant which grows in woods and displays its strange flowers during May and June.

Herb-Paris (*Paris quadrifolia*) spreads by means of an underground stem which sends up aerial shoots not annually but at irregular periods. The long stem bears a whorl of four large leaves (as indicated by the specific name of the plant). These leaves are very like those of the plantain, and unlike most monocotyledonous leaves, they are net-veined.

At the top of the stem is a solitary flower. There are usually four green sepals, each ending in a long point. The petals are generally four in number, though sometimes there are only three, and they are long, linear and yellow. The long stamens vary in number between six and twelve. The fruit is a black berry.

It can be seen that, both in vegetative and in floral form, herb-Paris deviates very much from the typical monocotyledonous plan. A few examples of the family, especially the **wood-lily** (*Trillium*), are sometimes cultivated.

SMILAX

The well-known genus *Smilax* belongs to the family SMILACACEAE which is not represented in the native flora of Britain. The family consists chiefly of climbing herbs, often with tendril-like leaf-stalks and prickly stems and branches. It is widely distributed in tropical and temperate regions.

The leaves are usually heart-shaped, though long and pointed, and even these often have prickly margins. Their stalks act as twining tendrils.

The flowers are unisexual and the two sexes are borne on different plants.

The cultivated greenhouse species of *Smilax* are very popular because the slender graceful stems and bright green foliage are un-equalled for use in bouquets and for festooning walls and decorating tables.

The dried roots of several species of *Smilax*, most of which are native to South America, produce sarsaparilla.

BUTCHER'S BROOM

The family RUSCACEAE is perhaps the most curious of these three small families. It is confined to western Europe, the Azores, Madeira and the Canaries. Some of its members bear hermaphrodite flowers, whereas others are unisexual.

There is one representative of the family native to Great Britain, namely, **butcher's broom** (*Ruscus aculeatus*), which is unisexual and usually bears the male flowers on one plant and the female on another, though sometimes the two sexes are borne on the same plant but on different branches.

The plant is shrubby and spreads by means of a thick root-stock (Plate 17). The shoot is woody and appears to be covered with small, broad, oval and very pointed thick leaves. But this is not so, for closer examination will show that towards the centre of the upper surface of these 'apparent' leaves a flower is frequently borne, and leaves never bear flowers in this way. The true leaves are small insignificant scales. But, like most leaves, they bear axillary buds, which, in this case, grow out to form these 'apparent' leaves, which are called phyllodes. It will be noticed that the phyllode is turned edgeways to the main rays of the sun (unlike most true leaves), and this reduces water-loss. The phyllode performs the main function of the true leaf, that is, food manufacture; but being really a flattened stem, it is able to bear other leaves and flowers. Half-way up the phyllode is a very much reduced scale-leaf, and in the axil of this a flower is borne.

Each female flower has six perianth segments (Plate 17). The ovary is three-chambered and the fruit a bright red berry (Plate 17). The male flowers have usually six stamens in two whorls of three each (Plate 17).

67

ARUMS
(*Araceae*)

The arum family (ARACEAE) exhibits unique peculiarities especially in floral arrangement. It is a family of herbs often containing a watery, bitter or milky juice, and is distributed throughout temperate and tropical regions, chiefly the latter.

WILD PLANTS

The arum family is represented in Great Britain by two genera, namely, *Arum*, which is very common, and *Acorus*, which is rather rare.

The **cuckoo-pint** (*Arum maculatum*), which in localised areas is called **wild arum, wake-robin, lords and ladies, cows and calves** or **Jack-in-the-pulpit,** is a common plant of our hedgerows distributed throughout most parts of Great Britain. The plant probably has so many popular names because it is very curious yet so handsome that for ages it has attracted the attention of all and sundry.

The cuckoo-pint spreads by means of a very thick root-stock (Plate 17). At intervals this sends up aerial flowering shoots and foliage leaves. The leaves are particularly attractive, having long stalks bearing large leaf-blades shaped like arrow-heads often spotted with purple or black and with wavy margins (Plate 17). They are net-veined.

The most curious part of this plant is the inflorescence which appears during March and April. The flowers are unisexual. Both are borne on the same inflorescence though segregated into male and female groups. These are inserted towards the swollen part of the top of a long green stalk. This swollen portion is then crowned with a long deep purple or red, succulent, club-shaped structure. The whole structure bearing the flowers and hence to the top, including the highly coloured club, is called a spadix. When young, this is surrounded by a very large bract which is inserted on the stem just below the spadix and continues upwards to about twice its length. This large pale-green bract is called the spathe. As the whole inflorescence becomes ripe the spathe opens at the top and finally exposes the coloured club-shaped part of the spadix (Plate 17).

> ... the old cuckoo pint—like an apoplectic saint in a niche of malachite.
>
> *Far from the Madding Crowd*: T. HARDY

The inflorescence can be examined only by dissecting the lower part of the spathe, for there it is thicker and completely surrounds the flower-bearing part of the spadix like an urn (Fig. 146).

At the base of the spadix is a collection of female flowers. Each flower is quite naked and is composed of one carpel only. Above this mass of female flowers is a zone of long, stiff, wavy hairs. Above this is a zone of male flowers. These are packed very closely together and each bears nothing but two to four stamens. Finally at the top is another zone of long stiff hairs which are really modified sterile male flowers. These actually fill up the mouth of the urn-shaped part of the spathe.

The foetid smell of the plant attracts flies, especially midges, which crawl past the downward-curling hairs and eventually reach the ripe carpels at the bottom where nectar is to be found. The insects are probably already covered with pollen from another cuckoo-pint, and thus the carpels are pollinated. Now the flies are kept prisoner by the rampart of downward-pointing hairs above the zone of female flowers until all the flowers have been fertilised. Then these hairs wither and the flies are free to crawl as far as the male flowers, where they collect the ripe pollen. After that, the upper zone of hairs withers and the flies can escape.

The fertilised carpels ripen into very conspicuous red berries, and while this is happening the rest of the inflorescence, including spathe and spadix, withers away, leaving the cluster of berries standing out prominently in their vivid redness against the greenness of the hedgerow (Plate 17). These berries are poisonous.

The tuberous roots of the cuckoo-pint contain much starch, but they are also poisonous. At one time, however, the poisonous substance was washed away and the tubers used as food under the name of Portland arrowroot.

The **sweet flag** (*Acorus calamus*) is rare; but it may sometimes be found growing in marshy districts and flowering during June and July. It has a thick root-stock. The leaves are like those of the true flag or iris (Chap. 70), and grow four to six feet in length. They are about an inch wide and form two layers like those of the iris. The flower-stalk is very like the leaf for most of its length, but towards the top it becomes a spadix

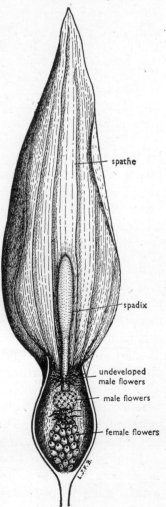

FIG. 146.
Section through Inflorescence of the Wild Arum.

spathe

spadix

undeveloped male flowers

male flowers

female flowers

bearing many very minute, yellowish-green flowers, male and female, each having a small membranous perianth of six segments. The whole inflorescence is surrounded by a spathe three to four inches long.

The interior of the inflorescence-stalk is sweet. The fleshy root-stock is bitter and yields the drug calamus. This used to be the basis of a sweetmeat, and the root is still collected for this purpose in certain parts of the United States. The root-stock is cut into slices and boiled. The slices are then boiled again in syrup and when dry produce a candied sweetmeat.

Some tropical genera of this extraordinary family produce organs of astounding dimensions. For example, *Amorphophallus titanum*, of tropical Asia, bears leaves ten feet high and a spadix three feet long which is dirty-red in colour and has an offensive smell.

CULTIVATED PLANTS

The only cultivated members of this family are the various arum-lilies and the water-arum.

The **arum-lily** (*Zantedeschia aethiopica*) is a native of South Africa. Its leaves are very like those of the cuckoo-pint. The inflorescence is borne on a very long stalk, and the spathe is pure white.

The **water-arum** (*Calla palustris*) is a north-temperate and sub-arctic plant, though it does not grow wild in this country. It grows in water, and also has a white spathe.

A family closely related to the ARACEAE is LEMNACEAE This family shows considerable reduction and modification of parts. It is usually considered to be reduced from the ARACEAE. All members of this family are water plants and most are free floating. It is represented in this country by several species of the genus *Lemna*, of which the most common is the **common duckweed** (*L. minor*).

This minute plant floats in thousands on still and stagnant water where it spreads to form a green layer on the surface. Each plant is very much reduced. There is no distinction between stem and leaves, but there are two or three flat green fronds, each about an eighth of an inch long, which float on the surface of the water and give off a small single root. At the centre of the fronds are two hermaphrodite flowers which make their appearance during July and August. The pair of flowers is enclosed in a minute spathe. Each flower is without a perianth, but has one or two stamens and a single-chambered ovary with a short style.

68

BURWEEDS AND REED-MACES
(*Sparganiaceae and Typhaceae*)

Some botanists place the burweeds and reed-maces in the same family (TYPHACEAE); but there seems to be sufficient distinction between the two to warrant two separate families, SPARGANIACEAE and TYPHACEAE, though these are closely related to each other.

BURWEEDS

The burweeds belong to the family SPARGANIACEAE which contains one genus only, namely, *Sparganium*, and this is distributed throughout temperate and sub-arctic regions of the northern hemisphere and also Australasia, but is absent in Africa and South America.

There are about fifteen species in the genus, two of which are common in this country, namely, **branched burweed** (*Sparganium ramosum*) and **unbranched burweed** (*S. simplex*) (Fig. 147).

The branched burweed grows in ditches, and flowers during June and July; whereas the unbranched burweed is more widely distributed in ditches, rivers and ponds, and flowers a little later (August and September). Another distinction between the two species is that of size; for the branched burweed grows to a height of two to four feet, whereas the unbranched seldom attains two feet. Except for being branched or unbranched the two species are similar in all respects, especially floral structure.

The burweed spreads by means of a thick creeping underground stem which gives off aerial stems projecting above the shallow water. These bear the leaves and flowers. The leaves are long, linear, rigid and pointed with pronounced veins. They are triangular at their bases, which, lower down still, form a sheath around the stem (Fig. 147). The blades of the leaves are somewhat concave.

The inflorescence is almost spherical (Fig. 147), and therein lies the main distinction between this family and the TYPHACEAE, for in the latter the inflorescences are long and cylindrical.

The flowers are unisexual, but both male and female are borne on the same inflorescence, the former a little above the latter. Both sexes have a perianth of three small segments in the form of scales. The male flower has three stamens, and the female flower usually one carpel with an awl-shaped stigma. The flower is wind-pollinated. The fruit is dry and single-chambered and contains one seed.

W H. Spreadbury

FIG. 147.—Unbranched Burweed.

REED-MACES

The TYPHACEAE also comprises aquatic herbs distributed throughout temperate and tropical regions and usually of gregarious habit. There is one genus only, namely, *Typha*, which is represented in this country by the **reed-mace** (*T. latifolia*) found growing in ponds and other damp places. This striking plant (Fig. 148) is sometimes called ' reed-mace bulrush ' or simply ' bulrush ', and this is confusing, for the term ' bulrush ' is also frequently and more correctly applied to a number of rushes belonging to a totally different family, CYPERACEAE (Chap. 74). The true common bulrush is *Scirpus lacustris* (CYPERACEAE), and the bulrush associated with Moses was *Cyperus papyrus* (CYPERACEAE). The reed-mace is locally called **black poker** and **cat's tail**.

The plant is very similar to that of the burweed, having leaves three to six feet long. The greatest distinction between the two families lies in the shape of the inflorescence, which here is very long and cylindrical and particularly conspicuous. The lower part of the inflorescence is thick and brown, being six to twelve inches long and made up of female flowers only. The upper part is thinner, curved and yellow and is composed solely of male flowers. The female flower has one carpel surrounded by dark brown silky hairs. The male flower has three to six stamens which are surrounded by a few silky hairs. The flowers are wind-pollinated and produce fruit in the form of achenes to which the dark brown hairs of the female flower remain attached and thus aid in wind distribution.

The inflorescences are sometimes used for household decoration, for they are very handsome. At one time the stalks of the inflorescences and the leaves were used in making a kind of coarse matting.

FIG. 148.—Reed-Mace.

Harold Bastin

69

DAFFODILS AND SNOWDROPS: GARLIC AND ONIONS

(Amaryllidaceae)

The family AMARYLLIDACEAE contains many showy and very beautiful flowers, a large variety of which are cultivated. In most cases the flowers are borne in umbels, though some of our most attractive wild species have solitary flowers. The family is distributed throughout temperate and sub-tropical regions; it is rarer in the tropics.

Many members of the family are bulbous.

In certain genera, for example, *Narcissus* (daffodil), there is an extra, very conspicuous, floral structure, usually trumpet-shaped, called the corona. This corona appears between the perianth segments and the stamens. Its origin is not fully understood: some authorities look upon it as the result of the fusion of outgrowths from the bases of the perianth segments; others consider it to be the fused stipules of the stamens.

WILD PLANTS

One of the most familiar early flowers of moist woodlands and copses is the **wild daffodil** (*Narcissus pseudo-narcissus*), and the throngs of golden blossoms during March and April are one of the most welcome signs of spring. In some localities it is known as the **Lent lily**. Unhappily it is not so common now as it used to be owing to wanton plucking and destruction in the past.

> The boys are up the woods with day,
> To fetch the daffodils away,
> And home at noonday from the hills
> They bring no dearth of daffodils.
> *The Shropshire Lad* : A. E. HOUSMAN

This lovely flower is the forebear of many a prouder garden variety, and its beauty has been the topic of writers and the inspira-

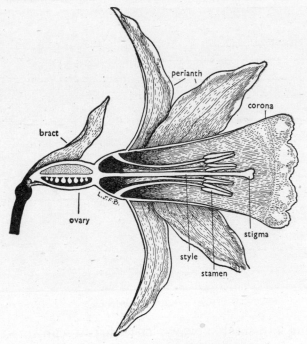

FIG. 149.—Section through a Daffodil Flower.

tion of poets so often that most people know at least one stanza
devoted to it.

> O Love-star of the unbelovéd March,
> When cold and shrill,
> Forth blows beneath a low, dim-lighted arch
> The wind that beats sharp crag and barren hill,
> And keeps unfilmed the lately torpid rill.
>
> *Ode to the Daffodil* : AUBREY DE VERE

The daffodil plant has a typical fleshy bulb which grows just below
the surface of the soil. From it the aerial leaves shoot up during
February. They are linear and nearly flat and are typically monocotyledonous (Plate 16).

The flower is borne singly at the top of a double-ridged flower-
stalk. It is subtended by a long, almost colourless, tissue-like bract
(Plate 16). Apart from its corona and the fact that the ovary is below
the other floral organs and not above them, the flower is fundamentally
similar to any typical lily (Fig. 149). There are six yellow petaloid
perianth segments joined at their bases and for part of the way up, and

Harold Bastin

FIG. 150.—Snowdrops.

then spreading into six thin, wavy, lance-shaped segments. The corona takes the form of a long yellow trumpet ending in a serrated wavy crown. Then there are six stamens inserted, not on the corona, but just below it on the joined part of the perianth segments. The three carpels are joined to form a three-chambered ovary with a long style which carries its three-lobed stigma well beyond the stamens. The fruit is fleshy.

The **snowdrop** (*Galanthus nivalis*) is one of the earliest flowers in the year, presenting its pendulous white blooms in February and March, and often distributed in masses over the floors of damp woods (Fig. 150). So beautiful in design is the whole plant, so perfect are the form and whiteness of the flower, and so welcome is it at the time of year when the weather is still wintry and we have been many months with scarcely any flowers, that one cannot wonder at its figuring so often in our poetry, and especially in the works of the greatest of all Nature poets—Wordsworth :

> Lone Flowers, hemmed in with snows and white as they
> But hardier far, once more I see thee bend
> Thy forehead, as if fearful to offend,
> Like an unbidden guest. Though day by day,
> Storms, sallying from the mountain tops waylay

The rising sun, and on the plain descend;
Yet art thou welcome, welcome as a friend
Whose zeal outruns his promise.

To a Snowdrop: WORDSWORTH

The plant is similar in many respects to the daffodil, though it is smaller in habit and the flower has no corona. From the bulb a single flower-stalk grows, and sheathed around it for some distance are two leaves which further up separate into two green blades (Plate 16).

The flower is subtended by a membranous bract and hangs downward.

There are two whorls of perianth segments. The outer three are long, white and boat-shaped. The inner three are shorter and are white, each with a double green spot on the inside surface a short distance from the tip. Tennyson alludes in *The Princess* to the " lines of green that streak the white of the first snowdrop's inner leaves." Those green spots secrete nectar to attract bees, but since these insects are so seldom about so early in the year, self-pollination is very frequent.

The genus *Allium* contains onion and garlic (in fact, *Allium* is Latin for ' garlic '). In most Floras, this genus is included in the LILIACEAE; but for various reasons which cannot be detailed here, it seems to have closer affinities with members of the AMARYLLIDACEAE and is therefore placed in that family. The genus contains herbs with

FIG. 151.—Broad-leaved Garlic.

bulbs and having linear or hollow centric foliage leaves and flowers borne in umbels.

Its commonest wild members are the **broad-leaved garlic** or **ramsons** (*A. ursinum*) and the **crow garlic** (*A. vineale*).

The broad-leaved garlic is very common in woods and damp hedgerows, where it shows up boldly with its large, broad, oval, lance-shaped leaves sheathing at their bases, and the flat-topped umbels of flowers (Fig. 151). Each umbel contains about fifteen pure white flowers surrounded by a two-leaved spathe.

The flower has a perianth of six lance-shaped segments. The rest of the flower is typical of the family. The whole plant has a foetid smell characteristic of garlic. The white umbels appear during April to June.

The crow garlic grows in habits rather drier than those of the broad-leaved garlic—usually waste places. There are about twelve flowers in each umbel and these are greenish or pink. Curiously enough, they frequently bear bulbs like the little-known so-called **tree onion**. The crow garlic also emits the characteristic smell.

Both these species of garlic are so pungent that their odour taints the butter made from the milk of cows which have merely walked among them even without eating them.

Several species of *Allium* are cultivated for food (p. 341). The **wild meadow garlic** (*A. canadensis*) of North America was formerly used as food by North American Indians.

ORNAMENTAL PLANTS

The wild members of this family are very attractive so it is no cause for surprise that they have all been taken over and cultivated by man for their floral beauty.

The **snowdrop** (*Galanthus nivalis*) is naturally a favourite, for it brightens our gardens when they have for months been at their barest. There are some double varieties, but they are no more beautiful than the ordinary single ones.

Daffodil (*Narcissus pseudo-narcissus*) needs no introduction. There are many single varieties and some double ones, though here again, the double varieties do not surpass the single in beauty.

Other species and varieties of *Narcissus* are also very popular, and most of them are early-flowering. Perhaps the most popular apart from daffodil itself is the **poet's narcissus, pheasant's eye narcissus**

or **primrose pearl** (*N. poeticus*) with lovely
white spreading perianth segments and a very
attenuated corona usually bright yellow or
red in colour (Fig. 152). Then there are
other species and varieties, some with yellow
perianths and short coronas, others with several
flowers borne in an umbel, such as **jonquil**
(*N. jonquilla*), and so forth, and the shades of
white, cream and yellow are legion. In fact,
there seems to be every combination of solitary and clustered flowers ; yellow and white
colours ; long and short coronas.

The genus *Allium* also gives us several
popular garden species which fortunately do
not emit the usual pungent odour. For example, *A. albo-violaceum* has large heads of
violet flowers, and there are several other
species with heads of purple or red flowers.

The genus *Agapanthus* is a native of South
Africa, but a few species are cultivated in
British greenhouses. The so-called **African**

FIG. 152.—Pheasant's Eye
Narcissus.

lily (*Agapanthus umbellatus*) will grow even outdoors in the warmer parts.
This attractive plant has large clear-blue flowers borne in big clusters.

ECONOMIC PLANTS

The genus *Allium* is the only member of this family which contributes anything of economic value, and it contains several important
food plants. The most important is the **onion** (*Allium cepa*), too
familiar to need detailed description. The bulb is white and fleshy
and surrounded by a few brown membranous scale-leaves. It is the
main source of food supply, though the young hollow centric leaves
are very much favoured in green salads. The plant bears its flowers
at the ends of long green stalks which are often swollen towards their
bases. The mass of flowers forms an almost spherical head (Fig. 153).
Many varieties of the onion have been cultivated for food from time
immemorial in most parts of the world. It is probably a native of
western Asia, though cultivation has spread it all over the earth. It
is even depicted on some Egyptian monuments, and one species in that
ancient country was awarded divine honours.

Harold Bastin

FIG. 153.—Onions in Bloom.

The **shallot** (*Allium ascalonicum*), sometimes called **eschallot,** forms a valuable bulb for pickling and is probably a modification of *Allium cepa*. It apparently dates from about the beginning of the Christian era.

Chives (*A. schoenoprasum*) is not so popular. It grows wild in certain parts of the north of England and in Cornwall. It is sometimes cultivated, for it is so often available when the onion is not. It bears leaves which are highly flavoured and so useful for salads and soups.

The popularity of the **leek** (*A. porrum*) is increasing. It differs from other species so far mentioned in that the bulb is very elongated and the leaves are wide and flat. Its origin is uncertain, but it is known that it was cultivated in Egypt at the time of the Pharaohs and was probably brought to this country by the Romans. It was popular in Italy at the time of Pliny, and Nero ate leeks on several days every month in order to clear his voice. No-one appears to know why it has been chosen as the national symbol of Wales. Sometimes this distinction is given to another member of the family—the daffodil.

The **edible garlic** (*A. sativum*) is more popular in certain Continental countries than here. It is indigenous to south-west Siberia and was probably brought to this country for cultivation in the middle of the sixteenth century. The bulbs are preserved by being hung up to dry. The plant is used chiefly for seasoning and flavouring, and is so pungent that for some dishes sufficient flavour is obtained by merely rubbing the utensil with parts of the bulb.

Leeks and garlic are believed to have medicinal properties.

Eat leeks in Lide[1] and ramsons[2] in May
Then all the year after physicians can play.

[1] March.   [2] Wild garlic.

70

THE IRIS FAMILY
(*Iridaceae*)

The family IRIDACEAE contains nearly sixty genera, but only one, namely *Iris*, is indigenous to this country to any great extent, though several exotic genera are cultivated for their handsome flowers. The family is distributed chiefly in sub-tropical regions and is centred around South Africa and sub-tropical America. It is composed mainly of herbs with thick underground stems, though some produce bulbs : most of them bear lovely flowers, often of exquisite colours.

WILD FLOWERS

The genus *Iris* is native to Britain and is represented by the **yellow flag** or **wild iris** (*Iris pseuda-corus*) which is often seen grow-ing in marshes and ditches and along river banks, displaying its bright golden flowers during May to August (Fig. 154).

FIG. 154.—Yellow Flag or Wild Iris.

Some, with many an anxious pain,
　Childish wishes to pursue,
From the pondhead gazed in vain
　On the flag-flower's yellow hue ;
Smiling in its safety there,
　Sleeping o'er its shadow'd bloom,
While the flood's triumphing care
　Crimpled round its guarded home.
Recollections after a Ramble :
J. CLARE

The stem is thick and grows along beneath the soil-level, sending up aerial leaves at in-tervals. These are sword-shaped, two to four feet long, and nearly an inch wide. They are folded

z

343

Harold Bastin

longitudinally and have parallel venation (Plate 16). Several flowers are borne in a terminal inflorescence, and each flower grows in an enfolding bract-like spathe. The lower flower opens first, and is usually well on the way to fruiting before the next flower opens. Therefore one rarely sees more than one or two flowers open in any one inflorescence at the same time (Plate 16).

The flower is exceptionally beautiful and often attains a diameter of three inches. There are six highly petalloid perianth segments. The three outer ones are yellow, very large and delicately waved. Towards the end each outer segment widens and bends downwards. The three inner segments, alternating with the outer ones, are yellow, lance-shaped and spreading. Opposite the three outer segments and almost resting on them are the three lobes of the style. These have become petalloid also—an unusual floral characteristic. Each lobe arches and covers a stamen, so there are only three stamens in this flower. The outermost part of the style-lobe then bends upwards into a flattened oval portion. The outer surface of the arching part of the style-lobe is stigmatic. The visiting bee therefore touches this stigmatic surface and deposits on it any pollen it may be carrying on its head from a flower previously visited. Then it forces its way down into the flower and in doing so brushes against the stamens. The ovary is composed of three fused carpels, and is three-chambered. The fruit is a thick fleshy capsule (Plate 16) which opens by three valves.

A rarer species of *Iris* is the **gladdon** or **roast beef plant** (*I. foetidissima*). This is smaller in general habit, having a stem one to two feet in length which bears many narrow leaves. The outer perianth segments are usually purple and the inner ones either purple or yellow.

There is some doubt whether the iris is the original of the *fleur-de-lys* of heraldry. Some authorities claim that this design was inspired by the yellow flag ; others that the original was some form of true lily.

ORNAMENTAL PLANTS

The IRIDACEAE has given us many fine garden plants, the majority of which belong to the genera *Iris*, *Crocus* and *Gladiolus*.

There are dozens of different irises, some of which are used for bedding, others for borders, and many beautiful varieties for decorating the edges of ornamental lakes and ponds.

The old-fashioned common **blue iris**, a hardy perennial border plant, is *Iris germanica*. This has very thick underground stems by means of which it spreads. Then there is the lemon-yellow variety.

For border and landscape effect, it is not easy to surpass the many different species and varieties of *Iris* that hybridists and horticulturists have produced (Fig. 155). Many varieties belong to the group of so-called **bearded irises,** because the upper surfaces of the outer perianth segments are covered with pronounced hairs. It will be noticed that in these flowers the inner perianth segments are not lance-shaped and spreading like those of the wild flag, but are upright, broader and more delicate and wavy. Among the bearded irises there is a great diversity of beautiful colours, too numerous to describe—some flat, others shaded, reticulate, veined or tinted in all manner of ways. Most varieties originated from *Iris germanica.*

The beardless irises have smaller flowers and more closely resemble the wild flag or the gladdon. There are also many different shades of these.

Of special interest is the **clematis-flowered iris of Japan** (*I. kaempferi*). The flowers of this plant are nine to twelve inches across and comprise many exquisite combinations of colour.

The **bulbous** or so-called **Spanish irises** are usually treated as annuals. Their flowers resemble those of the wild flag and their leaves are fine and grass-like. The most common bulbous irises cultivated in gardens are : *Iris reticulata,* with rich purple flowers having yellow beards ; *I. bucharica* with white and bright yellow flowers ; and *I. orchioides,* which is deep yellow.

The cultivated **crocus** belongs to the genus *Crocus* which is indigenous to the Old World and is sometimes, though very rarely, found growing wild in this country. It is a very welcome flower in the garden, for, like the snowdrop, it comes early in the year and presents a splash of colour when the garden still looks dreary in its winter drabness. The most commonly cultivated species are : *Crocus vernus, C. versicolor* and the Dutch crocus (*C. aureus*), which produce lovely flowers in shades and streaks of white, yellow, and blue.

The crocus corm is very familiar to gardeners. It is not the same as a bulb, for the latter is composed mainly of swollen fleshy leaves, whereas the former is a swollen stem surrounded by a few membranous brown scale-leaves. In the axils of the scale-leaves are axillary buds, some of which sometimes develop into aerial shoots, but the main aerial shoot grows from the terminal bud of the corm. After the flower has died away, the leaves become much larger and are then able to

FIG. 155.—Garden Iris.

manufacture more food than they immediately require. The excess food is passed down to the bottom of the shoot, that is, to the stem near the old corm, and there it is stored, the storage facilities gradually increasing as the lower part of the stem swells to form the next year's corm. The number of new corms formed corresponds to the number of aerial shoots which have developed, and thus does the plant vegetatively multiply, eventually forming large clumps if left undisturbed each year. This also explains why the large untidy leaves must be left for several weeks after the flowers have disappeared if strong healthy new corms are required.

Birds have an unfortunate habit of biting off the flowers of this plant, perhaps in an attempt to get at the deeply seated nectar when so little other food is available ; yet it is remarkable that they concentrate on the yellow varieties and ignore the blue and white.

The genus *Gladiolus* contains about a hundred and twenty species, most of which are natives of South Africa. Some of these are the forebears of the lovely gladioli seen growing in flower beds and borders. One species of *Gladiolus* is native to this country, namely, *G. illyricus*, but it is extremely rare and is confined to certain areas of the New Forest and the Isle of Wight.

Gladiolus, like the crocus, forms corms. In vegetative habit, the plant resembles the iris, having large sword-like leaves equal on both sides. The very large flowers are borne in long spikes, and open from below upwards (Fig. 156). Each flower is surrounded by a green spathe when in bud. The flower is somewhat irregular. There are some exquisite shades of colour—pure white, deep blue, purple, yellow, orange, pink and scarlet, and many intermediate shades and variegations.

A very old-fashioned relative of the genus *Gladiolus* is the genus *Tritonia* or *Montbretia* which contains some plants of very slender and graceful habit. The most common cultivated species grows in large perennial clumps which develop each year from veritable necklaces of corms. The leaves are fine and grass-like and the bronze flowers are borne in long slender spikes. The genus is native to tropical and South Africa.

The American genus *Sisyrinchium* comprises the so-called **satin flowers** of gardens. There are several species with grassy leaves and flowers which are white or of various shades of blue.

The South African genus *Ixia* has also given the gardener some exquisite flowers.

FIG. 156.—*Gladiolus.*

Tigridia is a Mexican and Central American genus. To it belong the so-called **tiger flower** (*T. pavonia*), sometimes cultivated in greenhouses and presenting various shades of white, yellow, orange and scarlet. The extraordinary feature of the flowers is that they seldom last more than half a day.

Another very handsome genus which hails from South Africa is *Freesia*, whose singular form and delicate perfume have made it a favourite for greenhouse cultivation and household decoration. The leaves are long and graceful and the campanulate flowers are borne in one-sided inflorescences at the end of very long thin stems (Fig. 157). There are many shades of colour—white, yellow, bronze, deep rose, mauve, etc.

R. A. Malby & Co.

FIG. 157.—Hybrids of *Freesia*.

ECONOMIC PLANTS

The family IRIDACEAE is not of any great economic importance though it does yield some perfumes and flavourings.

The dried thick underground stems of the *Iris* species *florentina*, *germanica* and *pallida* give the so-called orris root, which smells like violets and is therefore used in perfumery. Essence of violets is made from it.

Saffron is a product manufactured from the dried stigmas and part of the styles of the purple *Crocus sativus*. The history of this substance goes back beyond record, though it is known that it was cultivated in ancient Persia and was mentioned in the *materia medicas* of sixteenth-century China. The chief centre for the cultivation of the plant was Cilicia. It was also cultivated by the Arabs in Spain more than a thousand years ago. Though saffron is mentioned also in early

English leech-books it seems to have disappeared from Western cultivation for a time, and to have been brought back by the Crusaders.
Corms were introduced into England and were cultivated chiefly in
Cambridgeshire and at Saffron Walden in Essex (hence the town's
name). Here cultivation went on from the time of Edward III until
its extinction about 1770.

In early times saffron was used in medicine and as a flavouring in
cookery. As a perfume it was strewn by the Greeks in their halls and
theatres, and the Romans used it in their baths. Today the crocus is
cultivated for saffron production in France, Spain and Sicily. Though
the product was once used as an orange-yellow dye, it is now chiefly
employed in flavouring and colouring dishes, liqueurs, and so forth.
' Saffron killeth moths if it be sowed in paper bags verie thin, and laid
up in presses amongst tapistrie or apparell.' (Sixteenth century.)

71

SOME TUBEROUS CLIMBERS

(Dioscoreaceae)

Climbing plants are rare among the monocotyledons, but the DIOS-
COREACEAE comprise several genera of climbers which also bear
conspicuous stem-tubers. The family is distributed chiefly in the
tropical and warm temperate regions where it is represented by the
edible yams. There is only one genus, *Tamus*, indigenous to this
country, and to it belongs the only species, namely, black bryony.

The **black bryony** (*Tamus communis*), which must not be confused
with the white bryony (p. 111), is a very beautiful climbing plant
frequently seen growing in hedgerows. It climbs by means of a twining
stem (Plate 16) and has no tendrils. The leaves are arranged alternately.
Each leaf is large and deep green, and is shaped like a heart very pointed
at the tip.

The small flowers are unisexual, though both sexes are borne on
the same plant. They appear during May and June. They are grouped
in small racemes which are borne in the axils of the leaves. Each flower
is greenish and insignificant. The six perianth segments of the male
flower are somewhat larger than those of the female. The male flower
has six stamens, and the female three carpels which are joined to form

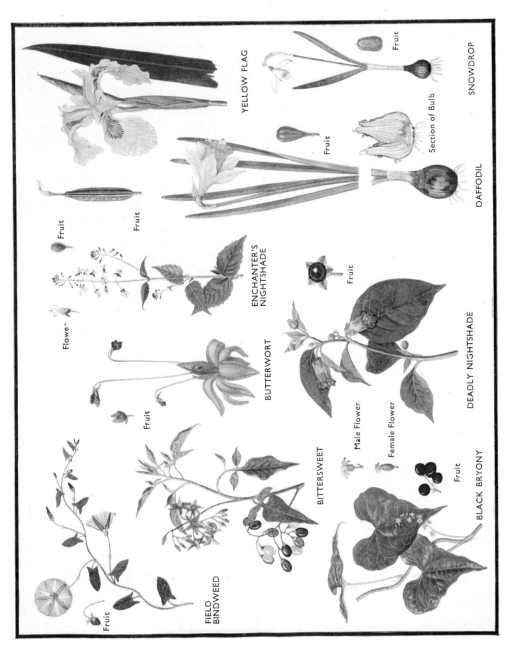

YELLOW FLAG

SNOWDROP

Fruit

Section of Bulb

DAFFODIL

Fruit

Fruit

Fruit

ENCHANTER'S NIGHTSHADE

Flower-

Fruit

BUTTERVORT

Fruit

DEADLY NIGHTSHADE

Male Flower

Female Flower

Fruit

BITTERSWEET

BLACK BRYONY

FIELD BINDWEED

Fruit

PLATE 16

a three-chambered ovary with three short styles (Plate 16). The fruit is a red berry (Plate 16), shining out brightly on the trailing festoons of bryony that decorate the hedges during autumn and winter.

The plant hibernates during the winter by means of stem-tubers. These are really swollen outgrowths of the lowest two internodes of the stem, which are below ground-level.

The family DIOSCOREACEAE is more fully represented in tropical and sub-tropical regions. There about half a dozen different genera are to be found, and perhaps the most familiar is the genus *Dioscorea* which comprises the edible **yams**. One species of yam (*Dioscorea pyrenaica*) grows in the Pyrenees, but this is the only European species.

The most widely distributed species of yam are *D. sativa* and *D. alata*. Tropical American species include *D. alata*, *D. cayennensis*, *D. trifida*, *D. sinuata*, *D. pentaphylla* and *D. villosa*. In some species the swollen underground portion is actually a stem-tuber like that of the potato, in others it is merely a swollen stem which is rather shapeless. All yams contain much starch and are useful articles of diet. One of the best from this point of view is *D. aculeata* of India, Cochin China and the South Seas. The Chinese yam (*D. batatus*) sometimes produces underground stem-tubers three feet long. This species has been shown to be capable of growth even in this country, but the swollen stems grow at such enormous depths that it is scarcely worth while cultivating.

The genus *Testudinaria* is represented in South Africa by the so-called **elephant's foot** or **Hottentot bread** (*T. elephantipes*). The name is derived from the enormous tuber, which is really the first internode of the stem and projects out from the soil. It becomes coated with a thick layer of cork and looks very like an elephant's foot.

72

PALMS AND THEIR RELATIVES
(*Agavaceae and Palmae*)

MONOCOTYLEDONS WITH SECONDARY THICKENING

Before considering the palms (PALMAE) we must not overlook those plants which, unlike most other monocotyledons, have an anomalous sort of secondary thickening in their stems. These plants belong to the family AGAVACEAE, which include some plants cultivated for

Harold Bastin

Fig. 158.—Adam's Needle (*Yucca*) in bloom.

ornamental purposes in the warmer parts of this country, though the whole family is indigenous to semi-desert regions.

The plant called **Adam's needle** (*Yucca filamentosa*) is sometimes seen growing in our parks and gardens, usually in the coastal regions of the south. The thickened stem is short and is crowned with a tuft of long, thick, sword-like leaves. The plant seldom blossoms here, but when it does it presents an impressive sight because the large, pendulous, creamy, bell-shaped flowers are borne massed in a panicle which sometimes rises up for five feet above the tuft of leaves (Fig. 158).

The genus *Yucca* contains about thirty species, all of which are native to Mexico, the southern United States and Central America. Though *Y. filamentosa* has a short stem, some species attain a height of thirty to forty feet.

The flower has a three-chambered ovary with a thick style bearing three stigmas. It is almost unique in that it has become adapted for pollination by one insect only, namely, the night yucca-moth (*Pronuba*), and between this moth and the flower there has developed a mutual dependence. The flower emits a sweet scent, chiefly at night, when the moth is at large. The female moth is attracted to the flower, and with her strong spiny tentacles collects the pollen which she moulds into a ball about three times the size of her own head. Then she flies to another flower carrying the ball of pollen with her. With her ovipositor she pierces the ovary-wall of the second flower and there deposits a few eggs. Then she climbs to the top of the ovary and deliberately presses the ball of pollen on the stigmas, thus pollinating the flower. Eventually the moth's eggs in the ovary of the flower hatch and the young larvae feed on the ovules which by now have become fertilised. But there are enough ovules for the larvae and to spare, so that some seeds are produced.

The fruit of *Yucca* are either three-valved capsules or succulent berries, according to the species. Some of the berries are edible.

The genus *Dracaena* is interesting, for to it belong some of those plants which yield the so-called dragon's blood. The genus comprises about forty Old World species. All of them have secondarily thickened stems and often attain the size of trees. The leaves are long and narrow, and the white flowers are borne in panicles. The fruits in all cases are berries. Perhaps the most famous example of this genus was the **dragon tree of Teneriffe** (Canary Islands) (*D. draco*) which was blown down in 1868. It was seventy feet high and forty-five feet in girth and was supposed to be six thousand years old.

Dragon's blood is a red resin. It is produced not only by species of *Dracaena* but also by other plants, for example, *Calamus draco* (p. 357). It is used for colouring varnishes and lacquers and, in China, for facing writing-paper with red. Sometimes it is used medicinally as an astringent.

The genus *Agave* is of considerable importance because several species belonging to it yield valuable fibres. It is native to tropical America, where it is often cultivated. The **century plant** or **American aloe** (*A. americana*) is supposed to blossom once in every hundred years and then die. This is not quite true, though often nearly a hundred years elapse before the plant produces any flowers.

The leaves of several species of *Agave* yield fibres, among which is the well-known **sisal hemp**. The fibres are used chiefly as cordage. Most of the species which produce cordage fibres are American.

In India, species of *Agave* are now cultivated to form hedges.

The species *A. americana* was introduced into Europe several centuries ago and is still cultivated for its handsome habit. There are several variegated forms.

The tropical genus *Cordyline* has a habit similar to that of *Dracaena*. It is very often cultivated in greenhouses in this country for its beauty of form, and the colour and variegation of its foliage. As a potted plant it is often used for household decoration. The species most popular for this purpose are *C. terminalis* and *C. indivisa*.

The genus *Phormium* furnishes the **New Zealand flax** (*P. tenax*). *Sansevieria* also contains some fibre-yielding species, for example, **bow-**

string hemp (*S. zeylanica*). There are some other fibre-yielding genera in this family.

PALMS

There must be many people in this country who have never seen a living palm, yet very few of us are unfamiliar with palms in some form or other, for they furnish so many of the necessities of life in the tropics where they flourish, and a large number of these products have found their way over here. Palms also dominate the tropical scene so much that they have figured considerably in literature and song, and for centuries they have been the symbol of victory.

Cuncti adsint, meritaeque expectent praemia palmae. (Let all be present and expect the palm, the prize of victory.)

Æneid, Bk. 5 : VERGIL

Lord Nelson's motto was :

Palmam qui meruit, ferat. (Let him who has deserved it bear the palm.)

The palm is believed by some to grow faster if weighed down— hence the symbol of victory, the triumph of resolution over odds. Some Orientals believe it sprang from the clay of which Adam was made.

There are about a hundred and thirty genera of palm. They form a characteristic feature of tropical regions, sometimes growing alone, but more often gregariously, dominating the scene along river banks, in dense forests and along seashores.

So many species are of economic importance that it is impossible to survey them exhaustively here. A more detailed consideration of the coco-nut palm, followed by a brief enumeration of a few others, must suffice.

The **coco-nut palm** (*Cocos nucifera*) grows throughout tropical regions and succeeds best near the seashore. It abounds in many parts of India, Ceylon, Africa, the East Indies, the West Indies, tropical America, and the Pacific Islands, especially the Hawaiian group. It is a graceful tree attaining a height of sixty to a hundred feet (Fig. 159). The long trunk is bare, but it terminates in a crown of most beautiful large leaves which are divided into many leaflets.

The fruit is very large and is formed by the fusion of three carpels though only one of the ovules usually develops to form a seed. It is roughly triangular in cross-section and fifteen to twenty inches in length. It is divided into three layers : an outer thin tough layer (epicarp) ; an inner, thicker, very woody layer (endocarp) ; and a very thick, fibrous layer (mesocarp) between. Inside these layers is the seed. It is composed of a very thin brown skin lined by a thick layer of white food-reserve (endosperm) which is the edible portion of the ' nut ', and at the base of the endosperm is the small seed. (The fruit is not a real nut, but is similar to a plum except that the fruit layers are not juicy.) The endosperm does not completely fill up the seed, but encloses a large cavity containing fluid usually called coco-nut milk. The whole coco-nut is not often seen in this country, for usually the two outer layers (epicarp and mesocarp) have been removed, and what is left is the seed surrounded by the woody endocarp, sometimes with a part of the meso-carp attached as a tuft.

Nearly the whole of the coco-nut palm is commercially useful. In some parts of the world, the local inhabitants depend upon it for almost everything. This is especially so in Ceylon, where it is estimated that more than twenty million of the trees are flourishing.

The white endosperm of the seed forms a good food, and the so-called milk makes a refreshing drink, especially if extracted from unripe fruit. The juice of the unexpanded flowers is sometimes distilled by local in-habitants to make an alcoholic toddy. Even the young leaf-bud at the top of the tree is sometimes cooked as a vege-table and is called palm cab-bage. The trunk of the palm is used in building and furniture-making, and the leaves are plaited and used for roofing huts or woven into mats. The wooden shell (endocarp) is used for making drinking and other utensils, and the fibrous mesocarp for making mats, ropes and string.

The fruit of the coco-nut

Fig. 159.—Coco-nut Palms.

Gilchrist

also supplies valuable products for export. The most important is the coco-nut oil extracted from the white fleshy endosperm. This is used in the manufacture of soap, candles, margarine, and certain types of brilliantine. The endosperm is removed from the fruit, cut into small pieces and then dried in the sun. This dried product is called copra.

The fibrous mesocarp is also exported and used in the manufacture of coco-nut mats, cheap matting for passages and lobbies, and brushes. The fresh nuts exported for food to this country come chiefly from the West Indies. As a food the endosperm is eaten either raw or shredded on cakes and biscuits.

Within the past few decades cultivation of the coco-nut palm has increased considerably so that now there are more than seven million acres under cultivation. More than half this acreage is within the British Empire. The increase in cultivation is due chiefly to the demand for copra in the soap and margarine industries.

The coco-nut palm can thus claim to be a veritable utility plant and has been well described from this point of view by Whittier.

> Of threads of palm was the carpet spun
> Whereon he kneels when the day is done,
> And the foreheads of Islam are bowed as one !
>
> To him the palm is a gift divine,
> Wherein all uses of man combine—
> House, and raiment, and food, and wine !
>
> And, in the hour of his great release,
> His need of the palm shall only cease
> With the shroud wherein he lieth in peace.
>
> ' Allah il Allah ! ' he sings his psalm,
> On the Indian sea, by the isles of balm ;
> ' Thanks to Allah, who gives the palm ! '
>
> *The Palm Tree* : WHITTIER

Another palm of considerable economic importance is the **date palm** (*Phoenix dactylifera*), a native of Africa and south-west Asia. The berries are familiar to us in the form of dates. These grow in large bunches. Each berry contains a very hard seed, but unlike a true nut, the hardness is not due to a wooden shell but to a dense food-reserve (endosperm) composed of cellulose. This palm supplies (besides its edible fruit) wine, sugar, hats, mats and thatch.

The **sago palms** (*Metroxylon rumphii* and *M. laeve*) flourish from Siam to New Guinea and they are specially cultivated in Malaya. The tree is cut down just as the inflorescence appears, and the starchy sago is extracted by crushing and washing the pith.

Oil is obtained not only from the coco-nut palm but also from other palms, especially the **oil palm** (*Elaeis guineensis*) of tropical Africa.

The **palmyra palm** (*Borassus flabellifer*), of India and Ceylon has many uses—an old Tamil song enumerates eight hundred and one.

Areca or betel nuts are the products of the **areca palm** (*Areca catechu*) of Indo-Malaya. The seed is cut into slices and rolled in a leaf of the betel pepper (*Piper betle*) with lime. In this form it is chewed by the inhabitants. It turns the saliva a bright red. It stimulates the digestive organs and is believed by those who chew it to prevent dysentery.

The genus *Phytelephas*, together with some other genera, comprises some short-stemmed palms. The food-reserve of the seed is composed of extremely hard cellulose which yields so-called vegetable ivory. So hard is this that it is used in the making of billiard balls.

The genus *Calamus* is an unusual one in that it comprises leafy climbers with reed-like stems. From these, malacca canes are produced. From some species, for example, *C. draco*, dragon's blood is obtained (p. 353).

Gardeners will be interested to know that raffia is produced from the palm genus *Raphia*.

One could go on enumerating the many uses to which members of the PALMAE are put, but those already cited must suffice.

A large number of beautiful examples of palms can be seen in the Palm House at the Royal Botanic Gardens, Kew, and in similar houses elsewhere in this country.

73

ORCHIDS
(Orchidaceae)

The word 'orchid' is apt to inspire ideas of beauty, rarity, fragility, expensive florists and luxurious settings. It is indeed true that the most attractive orchids in this country are either exotics grown in greenhouses or are very rare natives. Yet all this tends to mask the fact that the family ORCHIDACEAE is very well represented in the wild flora of Great Britain. There are about a dozen indigenous genera, though several are very restricted in their distribution.

The ORCHIDACEAE contains about 500 genera comprising about 17,000 species in Nature, though the hybrids and varieties produced in cultivation are legion. The family is cosmopolitan, though representatives are rarely found in arctic regions. Tropical countries are its favourite habitat.

All orchids are perennial herbs, though they differ widely in vegetative habit. Some are normal terrestrial plants, and most British genera are of this type. A few are saprophytic, that is, they have no green parts and therefore cannot make their own food from raw materials (the function of the normal green leaf) but obtain it from dead or decaying organic matter. The British genus *Neottia* (p. 362) is saprophytic.

Most of the beautiful orchids that form such an unforgettable feature of a tropical jungle are epiphytic. An epiphyte is a plant which, instead of leading a terrestrial life, grows above the soil, on the branches and in the axils of trees, on old gates and palings, and so forth. Lacking normal roots, the tropical epiphytes, in which orchids are predominant, cleave to the branches of trees by means of so-called clinging roots which twine round them. The epiphyte absorbs no nutrition or water from the tree itself (for then it would be a parasite), but from the humus (chiefly dead leaves) which collects around it. Such absorption is carried out by the so-called absorbing roots. Then there are the aerial roots, which are long and hang suspended in the humid jungle atmosphere (Fig. 160). The exterior layers of these roots are of a spongy texture. This

FIG. 160.—Scene in a Tropical Forest.
Note the epiphytes with their aerial roots.
From Kerner's ' Natural History of Plants ' (Blackie)

spongy tissue is called the velamen and it offers a very large surface on which moisture from the surrounding air condenses, and provides the epiphyte with its water supply.

GENERAL PLAN OF THE ORCHIS FLOWER

Most orchids conform to a general floral plan which is monocotyledonous though unique. The flower differs from most monocotyledons in being highly irregular. This is evidenced in the perianth itself, in the stamen—there is only one, since the other five have become suppressed (in the genus *Cypripedium* two have survived), and in the union of the stamen with the style. All this leads to special adaptation for insect pollination.

The perianth is composed of two whorls of three segments each. All the segments are petaloid. The three outer segments are usually equal in size and are comparatively small. The three inner segments are very unequal both in size and form, and in some of the exotic flowers they are very large and highly coloured. The lower front segment called the labellum is the largest and is extended forwards to form a platform with drooping wings and backwards to form a spur. The other two inner segments form an upright hood over the fused stamen and style. The single stamen together with the fused style form what is called the column. The apical ends of the two anther-lobes of the stamen are directed downwards and are covered with a globular structure called the rostellum. This blocks the entrance to the spur of the labellum which contains nectar. After alighting on the platform of the labellum, the insect, in trying to force its proboscis down the spur, pushes the rostellum aside and thus two adhesive disks are exposed which stick to the insect's head. In withdrawing, the insect thus pulls the coherent contents of the anther-lobes (which are called pollinia) with it. The two pollinia are really masses of pollen which stand erect like two Indian clubs on the insect's head. After a few seconds, the pollinia gradually curve forwards and downwards. In this position they are carried by the insect to the next flower and immediately strike its stigma. Thus cross-pollination is ensured.

This process can be reproduced artificially by gently inserting the point of a pencil into the spur of an orchis flower. If it has not already been visited by an insect, the two pollinia will be found to be standing erect on the side of the tip of the pencil when withdrawn.

2 A

WILD PLANTS

One of the most common orchids native to Britain is the **early purple orchis** (*Orchis mascula*) of pastures (Plate 17). It is frequently seen growing among bluebells in more open pastures.

> Dark bluebells drench'd with dews of summer eves,
> And purple orchids with spotted leaves.
> *The Scholar Gipsy* : MATTHEW ARNOLD

This plant has pronounced root-tubers (Plate 17). The long green leaves are blotched with brown. The purple flowers are borne in a lax spike which appears during April to June. The three outer segments of the perianth are reflexed upwards. The labellum is three-lobed and has a long spur (Plate 17).

The root tubers of the early purple orchis gave it the ugly name of ' dead men's fingers ' in early times.

> long purples,
> That liberal shepherds give a grosser name,
> But our cold maids do dead men's fingers call them.
> *Hamlet*, Act 4, Sc. 7 : SHAKESPEARE

Almost as common in pastures is the **pyramidal orchis** (*O. pyramidalis*) ; but it blooms later than the early purple (July to September). The rose-coloured flowers are borne in a dense pyramidal spike and have an unpleasant smell.

The **spotted orchis** (*O. maculata*) grows in moist places and blooms during June and July. It has root-tubers lobed in palmate form. The leaves are spotted. The flowers are pale purple and are borne in dense oblong and pointed spikes.

There are several other species of the genus *Orchis* which are indigenous to this country, but they are rarer than those described.

The **lady's slipper orchis** (*Cypripedium calceolus*) is often cultivated here, and produces large greenish-yellow flowers. The lip of the labellum is inflated but there is no spur. This is the only genus in the family which has two stamens. The lady's slipper was at one time to be found growing wild in certain limy districts of Great Britain ; but as an indigenous plant it has now probably become extinct.

To the genus *Habenaria* belong two very attractive wild orchids, though they are restricted to certain localities only. The **butterfly orchis** (*H. bifolia*) is a lovely plant with a seductive perfume. It grows in a few wet meadows and heaths and sometimes in copses, producing its whitish flowers in open spikes during June to August. The three outer segments of the perianth are long and spreading. The labellum has an entire lip and a very long spur. The **frog orchis** (*H. viridis*) is even rarer than the butterfly orchis, being confined to a few areas among dry hilly pastures. The flowers appear during June to August and are green. The three outer segments arch over the rest of the flower. The lip of the labellum is two-lobed and its spur is very short.

The **fragrant orchis** (*Gymnadenia conopsea*) is found, but rarely, in dry pastures, presenting its rose-coloured flowers in narrow spikes during June to August. The three outer perianth segments are long. The lip of the labellum is three-lobed and its spur is small and slender.

To the genus *Epipactis* belong two of the helleborines, which again are far from common. The flowers of these plants are borne in dropping racemes. The **broad-leaved helleborine** (*E. latifolia*) grows in woods, and blooms during July and August. Each flower is subtended by a long bract. The flower is green and is marked with purple and yellowish-white. Its leaves are oval and ribbed. The **marsh helleborine** (*E. palustris*) grows in marshy places and blooms at the same time as its near relative. The leaves are lance-shaped. The subtending floral bracts are short. There are only a few flowers in each raceme. They are greenish and are marked with red and purple.

The other helleborines belong to the genus *Cephalanthera*. They are the **white helleborine** (*C. grandiflora*), with, as its specific name implies, large white flowers, and the **narrow-leaved helleborine** (*C. ensifolia*), also with pure white flowers. Both these species are very rare.

The **twayblade** (*Listera ovata*) is not very rare. It grows in moist pastures and woods and produces its small flowers during May to July. This plant is easily identified because its stem, which grows one to two feet high, bears, half-way up, two large, oval, strongly ribbed leaves. The flowers are greenish-yellow. The labellum is two-lobed. The rostellum, when touched by an insect visitor, ruptures violently and ejects a glutinous fluid which helps to fix the pollinia on the insect's head. The **heart-leaved twayblade** (*L. cordata*) is not so common and is confined to mountain and moorland. Its leaves are heart-shaped, and its greenish-brown flowers minute.

To the genus *Ophrys* belong three rare but very attractive orchids—the bee orchis, the fly orchis and the spider orchis. All three of these orchids are confined to very restricted areas. The **bee orchis** (*O. apifera*) presents bee-like flowers. The inner surfaces of the outer perianth seg-

R. A. Malby & Co.

FIG. 161.—Hybrid of *Cymbidium*.

ments are pink. The labellum is three-lobed and brownish-purple in colour. The **fly orchis** (*O. muscifera*) has yellowish-green outer perianth segments and reddish-brown inner ones with a blue patch on the labellum. The **spider orchis** (*O. aranifera*) has yellowish-green outer perianth segments with a dull brown, variously marked labellum.

Lady's tresses (*Spiranthes autumnalis*) is somewhat more common than most orchids, and may be found flowering late in the year (August to September) in dry pastures. There is a spreading tuft of three or four leaves. The flowers are borne in a spirally twisted spike. They are small and white and they smell like almonds. The perianth segments are usually extended at their tips.

The **musk orchis** (*Herminium monorchis*) is another rare specimen. It bears its small green flowers, smelling of musk, in long slender spikes. There is no spur.

A saprophytic orchis indigenous to Great Britain is the **bird's nest orchis** (*Neottia nidus-avis*), found growing on the floors of very dark woods. It is therefore most likely to be found in beech woods, for these cast the densest shade. The very low light-intensity makes no difference to this plant, for it has no green leaves and therefore cannot make its own food—a process for which light would be required. The underground stem gives off roots which form a nest-like mass in the decaying leaf-mould of the soil. Surrounding this root-mass are myriads of threads of a fungus which aid absorption of foodstuffs from the humus. The stem of the plant grows about a foot high and bears leaves which are reduced to brown scales. At the top of the stem are the unattractive brown flowers crowded together in a dense spike.

ORNAMENTAL PLANTS

Many different tropical orchids are cultivated in the greenhouses of almost every temperate country. It is estimated that throughout the world nearly three thousand species are so cultivated ; many of these are epiphytes. Innumerable hybrids have been produced from them by crossing. New plants are produced either from seeds or from cuttings.

In Great Britain, the **lady's slipper orchis** (*Cypripedium calceolus*) is easily cultivated in greenhouses and sometimes outdoors. This species is terrestrial, with large, not very attractive, greenish-yellow flowers borne singly (p. 360). The flowers are sold more for personal adornment than for household decoration.

FIG. 162.—*Orchis ericetorum.*

The many other exotic orchids, usually of epiphytic forms, which are now cultivated defy description so far as their variety, form and colour are concerned The most commonly cultivated genera are: *Cymbidium* (Fig. 161), *Orchis* (Fig. 162), *Cypripedium*, *Dendrobium*, *Cattleya*, *Epidendrum*, *Laelia*, *Odontoglossum*, *Phalaenopsis*, and so on.

Successful cultivation of orchids requires a specialist. Many books are devoted to the

R. A. Malby & Co.

subject, and they must be consulted to do justice to this very popular family of greenhouse plants.

ECONOMIC PLANTS

The family ORCHIDACEAE does not offer much of economic importance. The only product of any substantial value is vanilla, the flavouring substance used in the manufacture of chocolate, confectionery, and many culinary dishes, perfumery, etc. The essence is obtained from certain species of *Vanilla*, which are tropical climbing orchids with aerial roots, by fermenting and drying the pods. The species *V. planifolia* is cultivated for the purpose in Mexico, the Seychelles, Tahiti, Java, etc. This climber bears its greenish flowers in spikes. The fruit-pods are six to ten inches long. The peculiar fragrance of vanilla is due to a chemical substance called vanillin which is now produced synthetically in some countries.

Salep, a drug used in certain Oriental countries as a restorative and to produce fatness, but rarely used in European medicine, is extracted from the dried tubers of certain species of *Orchis* and *Eulophia*.

74

RUSHES AND SEDGES

(*Juncaceae and Cyperaceae*)

The JUNCACEAE contains the common rushes, and though some of these abound in Britain, the family is a small one. On the other hand, the CYPERACEAE is a very large family containing, among others, the many sedges and the true bulrushes.

RUSHES

JUNCACEAE comprises several genera, two of which are represented in this country, and is distributed throughout the cool and damp parts of the temperate and frigid zones and in the mountainous parts of tropical regions.

The larger of the two British genera is *Juncus*; this comprises about eight British species, the most widely distributed being the

common rush (*Juncus communis*). The plant is seen in almost any marshy place growing gregariously or in clumps. The creeping underground stem sends up leafy shoots which are composed of the familiar long, green, shiny, smooth cylindrical stems, one to three feet high, which end in a yellowish point. The stem contains a continuous pith. The leaves are reduced to sheaths at the base of the aerial stem.

The flowers are borne during July and August in spreading clusters—usually one cluster a little more than half-way up each stem.

Each flower is regular. The perianth is sepalloid and divided into six segments. There are only three stamens, though other species of *Juncus* have six. The three carpels are joined to form a three-chambered ovary with a common style bearing three brush-like stigmas. The flower is wind-pollinated. The fruit is a capsule.

Some species of *Juncus* are cultivated in water-gardening. There is one particularly attractive golden-striped variety.

The other British genus is *Luzula*, and this contains the wood-rushes. There are three common species, all inhabitants of woods. The **great hairy wood-rush** (*L. sylvatica*) is a typical example. It spreads by means of a thick underground stem; but its aerial leaves, unlike the cylindrical ones of *Juncus*, are flat. Most of them grow from ground-level and attain a height of six to twelve inches, are about half an inch wide and are scantily covered with long white hairs.

The flowers are borne in long inflorescences on a stem about two feet high. The flower is similar in fundamental structure to that of *Juncus*.

The other British wood-rushes are the **broad-leaved hairy wood-rush** (*L. pilosa*) and the **field wood-rush** (*L. campestris*).

SEDGES AND BULRUSHES

The CYPERACEAE is a large cosmopolitan family comprising about sixty-five genera, most of which are marsh plants dominant in temperate and cold regions, though some are very prolific in warmer regions.

The family shows close relationships with the grass family (GRAMINEAE), especially in floral structure.

Most members of the family spread by means of creeping underground stems. The aerial shoot is usually grass-like, though the stem is often solid and bears three ranks of leaves. Each leaf has a long sheath at its base which, however, is not split as in grasses.

The flowers are inconspicuous. They are usually hermaphrodite, but in some genera and species they are unisexual, though in such cases both male and female flowers are, more often than not, borne on the same plant. Each flower tends closely towards the specialised structure of grass flowers. It is borne in the axil of a single scale called a glume, and a number of glumes are arranged overlapping like the tiles of a roof in a group called a spikelet. The spikelet may be borne singly, though very often there are several or many spikelets together forming a spike, so that the complete inflorescence is a spike of spikelets.

The perianth may be absent, or it may take the form of three to six small scales or a tuft of hairs. There are three stamens. The two or three carpels are fused to form a single-chambered ovary with a single style bearing two or three feathery stigmas. In the genus *Carex* (sedges) the female flower is borne in the axil of a second smaller glume called a utricle, and this completely surrounds the flower.

The family CYPERACEAE is well represented in this country, but only a few examples can be considered here.

The largest British genus is *Carex*, which comprises the many sedges. Most of these grow in very damp situations, though a few are of mountainous habit and some even grow on sand-dunes.

The **common sedge** (*Carex vulgaris*) is an inhabitant of marshes and river banks, and flowers during June to August. This plant is typical of the family. In this case, the flowers are unisexual. The spikelets are short and without stalks, three to five of them making up a spike. The terminal spikelet contains all male flowers and the rest contain nothing but female flowers. Each female flower has the extra glume or utricle and bears two stigmas. All glumes are purplish brown.

There are about sixty different sedges in this country, and quite half of them are common, so a Flora must be consulted for a more detailed description of the genus.

The genus *Cyperus* is distributed chiefly through tropical and warmer temperate regions, though there are two rare species in Great Britain. The **paper-reed** (*Cyperus papyrus*) is particularly interesting. It grows in many tropical areas, especially along river banks, and attains a height of three to twelve feet. It is very abundant along the banks of the Nile, and it was among the shoots of this plant that Moses is said to have been hidden. The leaves and stems were also used for making papyrus, the ancient writing-paper. They were split and the strips were then pressed together while still wet. The thick underground stems are edible. The stems and leaves of this and other species are often used in making mats and baskets.

The genus *Scirpus* is a cosmopolitan one and contains about two hundred species, about a dozen of which are native to this country, though only three are common. This genus contains the true bulrushes.

The **common bulrush** (*Scirpus lacustris*) grows in marshes. The stem is erect and spongy, attaining a height of one to seven feet. The base forms a short thick underground stem. Some species have stem-tubers like those of the potato. The leaves are reduced to sheaths on the stem.

The flowers are hermaphrodite and are arranged in many-flowered spikelets. Each spikelet is borne on a long stalk and a large number of spikelets are clustered into panicles at the ends of tall erect stems. There are six perianth bristles.

The common bulrush is sometimes cultivated in water-gardening. It is also used for making mats and chair-seats.

The two other common British species are the **wood club-rush** (*S. sylvaticus*) of moist woods, and the **sea club-rush** (*S. maritimus*) of salt marshes.

The cotton-grasses belong to the genus *Eriophorum*, of which there are four species common to the wet moors and bogs of Britain. The two most likely to be found are the **hare's tail cotton-grass** (*E. vaginatum*) and the **common cotton-grass** (*E. polystachyon*). The flowers are borne in a solitary spikelet in the former species and in many lateral

Flatters & Garnett, Ltd.

FIG. 163.—Cotton-grass in Fruit in a Bog.

spikelets in the latter. The perianth is composed of bristles which, after fertilisation has taken place, grow out into long white hairs which aid in the wind-dispersal of the fruit (Fig. 163). The hairs are sometimes used for stuffing cushions.

Several other genera of the family CYPERACEAE are native here, but those already described are the most common. Those interested in this very extensive family should consult a Flora for further details.

75
GRASSES AND CEREALS
(Gramineae)

The grasses (GRAMINEAE) comprise one of the largest and most valuable of all flowering plant families. In fact, it probably exceeds all other families in economic importance, for it provides, among other things, staple foods for man and fodder for his domestic animals. It is quite impossible in one chapter adequately to survey the botanical significance and the economic importance of this family, so we must be content here to examine a few examples which might act as a useful guide and a stimulus to those who wish to pursue their studies of GRAMINEAE further. For such a purpose, other more specialised books on botany and agriculture must be consulted.

There are more than five hundred genera of grasses and cereals and these are distributed throughout the world; in fact, everywhere that it is possible for flowering plants to exist.

> Here I come creeping, creeping everywhere;
> My humble song of praise,
> Most joyfully I raise
> To Him at whose command
> I beautify the land
> Creeping, silently creeping everywhere.
> *The Voice of the Grass* : SARAH ROBERTS BOYLE

A TYPICAL GRASS

Most grasses are herbaceous with fibrous root systems (Fig. 164), though some tropical forms such as bamboos attain a height of more than a hundred feet. Many grasses are perennials and reproduce

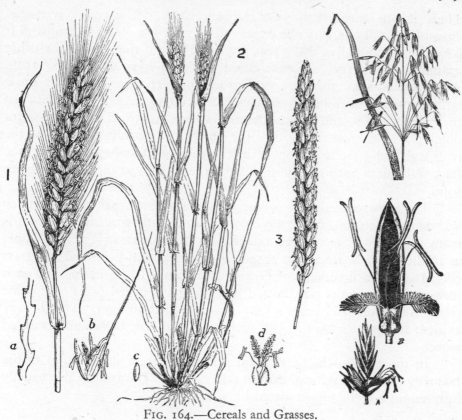

FIG. 164.—Cereals and Grasses.

Left, 1, ear, and 2, whole plant of bearded wheat; 3, ear of beardless wheat; a, axis of ear; b, spikelet; c, fruit; d, flower. Top right, inflorescence of oat. Bottom right, meadow fescue; A, spikelet with two open flowers; B, flower, from which the outer pale has been removed.

themselves vegetatively by means of underground stems (for example, couch grass) or runners (for example, common bent). In most cases the internodes of the stem are hollow, though in maize they are solid. The leaves are characteristically linear and are arranged on the stem alternatively in two ranks. Few grasses have stalked leaves, but each leaf has a sheathing base which surrounds the stem. On the upper surface where the leaf-sheath joins the leaf-blade there is a small membranous growth called a ligule.

The flowers are usually hermaphrodite and are borne in groups called spikelets (Fig. 164) which are enclosed in bracts called glumes. There is no perianth to the flower. The stamens are very conspicuous, and there are usually three. Each anther is borne on a long thin stalk.

There is one carpel with two feathery styles. The ovary is single-chambered and contains one ovule. The fruit is called a caryopsis. It is well exemplified in the wheat grain. Though this grain, like other graminaceous grains, is often called the seed it is actually the fruit. After fertilisation, the fruit undergoes little change except to grow larger, and in this respect resembles the buttercup achene. But between the wheat grain and the buttercup achene there is one important difference : whereas the seed of the buttercup remains enclosed in the fruit wall but separated from it, in the case of the wheat caryopsis the fruit wall fuses with the outer coat of the seed. So the grain is quite solid.

The appearance of the inflorescence of grasses varies according to whether the stalks of the spikelets are long and spreading outwards from the stem, as in oat and quaking or quake grass (Fig. 164), short as in the meadow fescue, or absent as in wheat and perennial rye grass (Fig. 164). Each spikelet of flowers is subtended by a glume and each flower in the spikelet is protected by two bracts called palea. In some cases, the outer pale bears a long bristle called an awn. This is very evident in some grasses and in such cereals as oat, barley and bearded wheat.

In most cases the grasses are pollinated by wind, though in the majority of cereals self-pollination takes place. The fruit is also usually light enough to be disseminated by wind.

WILD PLANTS

Nearly all British members of the GRAMINEAE are grasses which grow in all sorts of places. A few examples must suffice here, for there are nearly sixty genera comprising many more species.

The **sweet vernal grass** (*Anthoxanthum odoratum*) is common in meadows, and displays its panicles of flower spikelets during June and July (Plate 17). In this case, the spikelet and the flower are unusual. Each spikelet contains two neuter flowers with awns and one perfect hermaphrodite flower without awns, and this has two stamens—not three. The sweet vernal grass is so called because its stems contain large quantities of an odorous substance which smells of new-mown hay.

The **mat grass** (*Nardus stricta*) is very common on our drier grass moors. The spikelets are arranged in a markedly one-sided spike.

To the genus *Hordeum* belongs the wild barleys, the two most common of which are the **meadow barley** (*H. pratense*) and the **wall** barley (*H. murinum*). In these barleys, as in the cultivated barley, the spikelets are arranged in groups of three on a long axis forming a dense spike. Usually in each group of three spikelets two of the spikelets are sterile and the third has one flower only. The exterior palea end in the characteristically erect awns. The meadow barley grows in moist pastures and blooms during June and July; the wall barley grows on old walls and in other dry places, and it blooms at the same time.

The genus *Lolium* contains the familiar **perennial rye grass** (*L. perenne*) and several other species. The rye grass is very common in meadows and fields and usually flowers during June and July. The spikelets are arranged alternately in a two-ranked spike.

The fox-tail grasses, especially the **common fox-tail** (*Alopecurus pratensis*) is often cultivated for pasture. The spikes are compressed into thick cylindrical panicles which are very conspicuous.

Other valuable pasture grasses are the bent grasses, especially the **white bent** or **fiorin** (*Agrostis alba*).

On seashores, and especially on sand-dunes, may be seen the **marram grass** or **sea reed** (*Ammophila arundinacea*) growing in tufts. It has long ridged leaves covered with a pale green bloom. This grass is often deliberately planted on sand-dunes and elsewhere in order to bind the sand.

The **couch grass** (*Agropyron repens*) is an abominable weed in gardens and on farmlands because it spreads by means of very persistent underground stems which are difficult to eradicate, for they grow so long and are very tenacious. A small portion of such a stem if left in the ground will send up aerial shoots and thus re-establish the weed.

To the genus *Festuca* belong several species of fescue grass, some of which are very common. The **meadow fescue** (*Festuca pratensis*) grows one to two feet high, and bears its five- to ten-flowered spikelets in close nodding panicles eight to ten inches long. It makes good pasture (Fig. 164). The **tall fescue** (*F. elatior*) grows along river banks and in wet places. It attains a height of three feet; but the panicles of spikelets are only three to six inches long. Some species of *Festuca*, especially when growing on mountains, display a curious method of reproduction. Instead of the usual floral spikelets there are small leafy shoots. These develop adventitious roots at their bases and eventually fall off and take root in the soil.

The genus *Avena* comprises several species of wild and cultivated oats. The **wild oat** (*Avena fatua*) is probably the forerunner of the **cultivated oat** (*A. sativa*). The wild oat grows in cornfields and attains a height of one to three feet. The spikelets are green and drooping and are borne in loose panicles. Each spikelet usually contains three flowers. The awns are rather long. Several other species of wild oat may be found growing in dry pastures.

A very attractive grass is the **quaking** or **quake grass** (*Briza media*), found growing in dry pastures, especially among taller grasses, and flowering during June and July. The many-flowered spikelets droop at the ends of long thin stalks. There are no awns (Plate 17).

Another handsome grass is the very tall **common** or **great reed** (*Phragmites communis*). It grows in marshes, rivers and ponds and attains a height of anything from five to ten feet. Its leaves are broad and flat and the inflorescence is very conspicuous. This takes the form of a loose, nodding panicle, ten to eighteen inches long, of a dull purple colour (Plate 17). Each spikelet contains three to five flowers. The lower flowers bear stamens only ; but the upper ones are hermaphrodite and are enclosed in silky hairs. This plant spreads rapidly by means of creeping stems. At the mouth of the Danube it forms floating fens.

A valuable pasture grass is the **cock's-foot** (*Dactylis glomerata*), which bears its flowers in panicles which are distinctly branched. The spikelets form dense tufts.

Molinia caerulea is characteristic of wet moors. The genus *Glyceria* is also characteristic of wet places. The **reed meadow grass** (*Glyceria aquatica*) is very common in watery places, whereas the **sea meadow grass** (*G. maritima*) is very common in salt marshes.

Perhaps the most useful pasture grasses are contained in the genus *Poa*. There are several common species. The **common meadow grass** (*Poa annua*) can be found growing almost everywhere. Its spreading panicles of flowers must be a familiar sight to everybody. The **wood meadow grass** (*P. nemoralis*) is taller and grows in woods. There are several species of *Poa* to be found growing in meadows and on dry banks and old walls.

ORNAMENTAL PLANTS

It is doubtful if the beauty of grasses is appreciated so much as it ought to be. It might surprise many what a beautiful show can be made of a vase containing a mixture of nothing but tall grasses.

No doubt lawns are the outstanding example of the collective beauty of grasses. But in making lawns, only certain species can be used if the desired effect is to be obtained. For example, it is unwise to

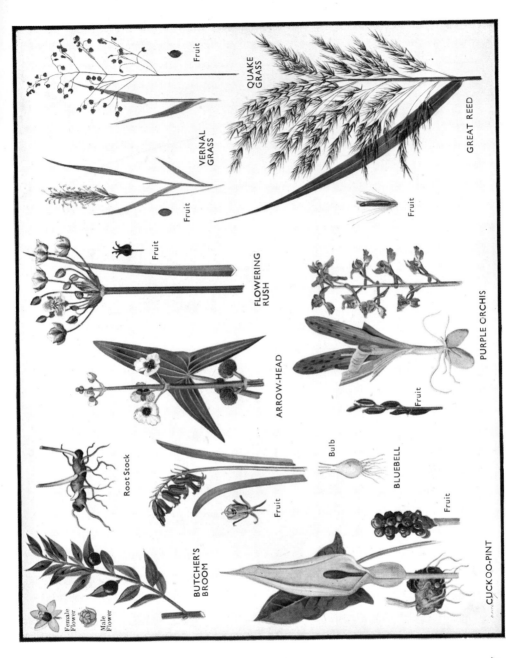

QUAKE GRASS

Fruit

VERNAL GRASS

Fruit

GREAT REED

Fruit

FLOWERING RUSH

Fruit

PURPLE ORCHIS

Fruit

ARROW-HEAD

Fruit

Root Stock

Bulb

BLUEBELL

Fruit

Fruit

BUTCHER'S BROOM

Female Flower

Male Flower

CUCKOO-PINT

PLATE 17

use the perennial rye grass as anyone who has mown a lawn on which it is growing can testify.

Some grasses are, however, cultivated for their own intrinsic beauty. There are, for example, the large species of **quaking grass** (*Briza maxima*) ; several species of **bent grass,** for example, *Agrostis nebulosa* ; the **sterile oat** (*Avena sterilis*) ; the **feather grass** (*Stipa pennata*), a native of steppe-lands ; the **ribbon grass** (a variety of *Phalaris arundinacea*), having leaves with stripes of white ; and so forth. The **pampas grass** (*Gynerium argenteum*), which is frequently grown in our larger gardens and parks, is a native of Argentina and Brazil. Its long dark arching leaves and its enormous white plumes borne at the ends of long straight stalks add dignity to any landscape (Fig. 165).

ECONOMIC PLANTS

It is doubtful if the family GRAMINEAE is rivalled by any other plant family in economic importance, though the LEGUMINOSAE and the PALMAE run very closely to it.

The GRAMINEAE supplies the wheat, our 'staff of life', and rice, its counterpart in the East, together with many other cereals of prime importance. Together with these are many hundreds of others whose utility varies within wide limits. Books could be, and in many cases have been, written on each single graminaceous plant which yields something of value to man, so it would be absurd to give here even the shortest résumé which could do justice to the family. A short categorical list of the most important of all can be given as a guide to those who wish to know more about these plants.

FIG. 165.—Pampas Grass.

Harold Bastin

Harold Bastin

FIG. 166.—Wheat.

Fodder. Many different grasses are used as fodder for feeding domestic animals. A few were mentioned in the section on wild grasses. The production of good fodder, both from the point of view of the animal and for storage, is a matter of prime importance and much research is now being carried out on the subject. Some grasses are so good that they are actually cultivated for this purpose; on the other hand, some grasses are worse than useless.

Cereals. Cereals form the staple article of diet for man everywhere except in arctic regions.

Wheat (*Triticum*), of which there are several species and many hybrids is cultivated in most parts of the world, and is also one of the oldest of cereals (Fig. 166). Research and hybridisation have succeeded in producing many sub-species and varieties which thrive under certain known conditions. The work on this problem which has gone on in the U.S.S.R. during the past twenty years, for example, has shown what science can do to help man with his crops. The Russians have succeeded in producing winter wheats and wheats which will thrive in very northerly regions to an extent undreamt of twenty-five years ago. There is still some doubt about the identity of the parent species of wheat. The species commonly cultivated in this country is *Triticum vulgare* and its many varieties. *T. monococcum* is the **small spelt,** and *T. dicoccum* is the **emmer,** a wheat many centuries old. The small **Polish wheat** is *T. polonicum.* The **hard wheat** (*T. durum*) yields flour from which macaroni is made.

Barley is more hardy than wheat and will therefore grow in regions much further north. The cultivated species is *Hordeum vulgare.* The most common variety of this is *H. vulgare* var. *distichum*, or two-rowed barley; there are also four-rowed and six-rowed barleys.

Oat (*Avena sativa*) forms a staple food for many people. It is also used for feeding horses and cattle. There are several forms.

Rye (*Secale cereale*) is a feature of north European agriculture, though its cultivation is now being encouraged not only in Scotland but also in certain parts of the north of England. It is used as food for man and his animals.

Maize or **Indian corn** (*Zea mays*) is now cultivated throughout tropical and sub-tropical regions, though it is also grown in certain temperate areas. It is a native of Mexico. It is indeed a useful plant for the grain is converted into flour by grinding, it is also eaten without grinding, and in this form when dry fed to poultry; the green cob is a very favourite vegetable; the leaves are used as fodder; the spathes surrounding the unopened spikes are used in paper-making; and the dry cobs are used for firing.

Rice (*Oryza sativa*) is one of the most important food crops in the world, often forming the staple diet of millions of people, especially in the East. It was probably originally derived from the wild forms of India and Malaya. It needs a unique cultivation, for the seedlings are planted under water and continue to grow in water-covered fields almost until the plant is ripe. Then the water is drained off, after which the plant ripens. The grain still in its husk is called ' paddy '.

Millet is the product of several different genera of plants. Those cultivated in India and other parts of Asia and also in southern Europe are various species of the genus *Panicum*. The Mediterranean millet or **guinea corn** is *Sorghum vulgare*.

There are several other cereals cultivated for food but they are restricted in distribution, chiefly in the tropics.

Phalaris canariensis is a grass of which the grain is used for the feeding of cage birds. It has now become naturalised to this country.

Sugar. Sugar is present in almost every green plant, and it is no cause for wonder, therefore, that more than one of these should contain the substance in sufficiently high concentration to warrant commercial extraction. The three most important plants from which sugar is extracted are the **sugar beet** (p. 90), the **maple** (p. 181) and the **sugar cane** (*Saccharum officinarum*) which is a member of the GRAMINEAE. The cane is usually grown from cuttings. In the American and West Indian plantations, the cuttings are planted out in October, and after about twenty months the first crop is taken; two years afterwards a second crop is ready. After the canes are cut, the juice is extracted by passing them through rollers. This is then purified and refined. The residue left after most of the sugar has crystallised out is called treacle or molasses which is used also as an article of diet or in the making of rum, cattle food and boot blacking. The pressed canes are used for fuel. About ten years ago it was discovered that if about six per cent of cane sugar be added to ordinary lime-sand mortar the tensile strength of the mortar is increased by sixty per cent. The sugar is added dissolved in water after the lime has been slaked.

The most important cane sugar producing countries are Cuba, India and Java.

Building and Construction. First and foremost among those grasses used for building and construction are the **bamboos,** which are the product of several genera. The most important genus is the tropical *Bambusa.* Bamboos grow in large clumps which spread by means of underground stems. The growth of the aerial stems is very rapid— sometimes as much as sixteen inches a day. The aerial stems gradually become wooded below as they get older. Some bamboos flower annually, others at longer intervals, and others (like *Agave,* p. 353) once only and then die.

The economic uses of bamboos, especially in Asia, are many. They frequently form the basis of building. Bridges are made from them. Since the stems are hollow they can be used for making water-pipes and various utensils ; also, since they split easily, other utensils, gutters, household furniture and so forth can be constructed from them. Some bamboos are used in paper-making, and others are even valuable as medicines. Though *Bambusa* is the most important genus, there are altogether more than forty genera of bamboos.

Many grasses, owing to their persistent and tenacious underground stem systems, are used for sand- and soil-binding, even in this country. Some, on the other hand, are used for land reclamation. One of the most outstanding examples of this is the salt-marsh grass called **rice grass** (*Spartina townsendii*). This plant grows so prolifically in salt-water areas that it has been known to choke harbours. Now it is being used for reclaiming land from the sea. In Holland, for example, it was introduced for this purpose during 1924, and since then it has grown so prolifically that acres of land which were previously salt marshes or actually under the sea are now used for various agricultural purposes. The rice grass is doubly useful in this respect for it is also a good fodder plant.

Paper and Cordage. Perhaps the most valuable grasses used in paper-making and for cordage are the **esparto grasses.** There are several genera of these. *Lygeum spartum* is native to Mediterranean regions. *Stipa tenacissima* of North Africa is one of the most important esparto grasses and is extensively used in the production of paper.

THE GOOD EARTH

And another angel came out of the temple, crying with a loud voice to him that sat on the cloud, Thrust in thy sickle, and reap; for the time is come for thee to reap; for the harvest of the earth is ripe.

Revelation, 14, 15

He findeth God who finds the earth He made.

The Wise Years : JOHN BUCHAN

Earth cares for her own ruins, naught for ours.
Nothing is certain, only the certain spring.

The Burning of the Leaves : LAURENCE BINYON

There is nothing grateful but the earth; you cannot do too much for it; it will continue to repay tenfold the labour and the pains bestowed upon it.

Bewick, Life : LORD RAVENSWORTH

Earth's crammed with heaven,
And every common bush afire with God;
And only he who sees takes off his shoes;
The rest sit round it and pluck blackberries.

Aurora Leigh : E. B. BROWNING

FIG. 167.—Gathering in the Harvest.
A Youth Service Volunteer from the Technical Institute, Neath.

SPRING

At length the finish'd garden to the view
Its vistas opens, and its alleys green. . . .
Along these blushing borders, bright with dew,
And in yon mingled wilderness of flowers,
Fair-handed Spring unbosoms every grace;
Throws out the snow-drop and the crocus first;
The daisy, primrose, violet, darkly blue,
And polyanthus of unnumber'd dyes;
The yellow wall-flower, stain'd with iron-brown;
And lavish stock that scents the garden round:
From the soft wing of vernal breezes shed,
Anemones; auriculas, enrich'd
With shining meal o'er all their velvet leaves;
And full ranunculas of glowing red.
Then comes the tulip-race, where beauty lays
Her idle freaks; from family diffus'd
To family, as flies the father-dust,
The varied colours run; and while they break
On the charmed eye the exulting florist marks,
With secret pride the wonders of his hand.
No gradual bloom is wanting; from the bud,
First-born of Spring, to Summer's musky tribes:
Nor hyacinths, of purest virgin white,
Low bent, and blushing inward; nor jonquils
Of potent fragrance; nor narcissus fair,
As o'er the fabled fountain hanging still;
Nor broad carnations, nor gay-spotted pinks;
Nor, shower'd from every bush, the damask-rose.
Infinite numbers, delicacies, smells,
With hues on hues expression cannot paint,
The breath of Nature and her endless bloom.

The Seasons: JAMES THOMSON

Abelia, 207
Abronia umbellata, 110
Abutilon, 122
Acacia, 153, 159; A. dealbata, 159
Acaena, 144
Acanthaceae, 293
Acanthus lusitanicus, 294; A. spinosus, 294
Acer campestris, 181, 182; A. pseudoplatanus, 181; A. saccharum, 181
Aceraceae, 181
Achillea millefolium, 216
Achimenes, 293
Achyrachaena, 227
Acroclinium, 227
Aconitum, 34; A. napellus, 34, 42, 45
Acorus calamus, 331
Adansonia digitata, 118
Adonis, 34; A. autumnalis, 35, 42
Adoxa moschatellina, 206
Aesculus hippocastanum, 181
Aethusa cynapium, 185
Agapanthus umbellatus, 341
Agavaceae, 351
Agave americana, 353
Ageratum, 225; A. conyzoides, 225
Agrimonia, 140; A. eupatoria, 140
Agropyron cristatum, 11; A. repens, 371
Agrostis alba, 371; A. nebulosa, 373
Ajuga chaemopitys, 298; A. reptans, 298
Alchemilla, 141; A. arvensis, 141; A. vulgaris, 141
Alisma plantago, 309
Alismataceae, 309
Allium, 339; A. albo-violaceum, 341; A. ascallonium, 342; A. canadensis, 340; A. cepa, 341; A. porrum, 342; A. sativum, 342; A. schoenoprasum, 342; A. ursinum, 340; A. vineale, 340
Alnus glutinosa, 163
Aloe, 327
Alopecuris pratensis, 371
Alsodeia, 66
Althaea, 119, 120; A. officinalis, 120; A. rosea, 121
Alyssum, 64

Amarantaceae, 91
Amaranthus, 91; A. caudatus, 91; A. hypochodriacus, 91
Amaryllidaceae, 336
Amelanchier, 144
Ammobium alatum, 227
Ammophila arundinacea, 371
Amorphophallus titanum, 332
Ampelidaceae, 177
Anagallis, 241, 244; A. arvensis, 241; A. tenella, 241
Ananas sativus, 312
Anchusa, 258; A. officinalis, 258
Androsace, 244
Anemone, 34, 40, 44; A. nemorosa, 35, 40
Angelica officinalis, 217; A. sylvestris, 186
Anthemis arvensis, 217; A. cotula, 217
Anthoxanthum odoratum, 370
Anthriscus, 185; A. cerefolium, 188; A. sylvestris, 185, 188; A. vulgaris, 185
Anthyllis vulneraria, 150
Antirrhinum, 280; A. majus, 280; A. speciosum, 280
Apium graveolens, 187, 188
Apocynaceae, 196
Aquifoliaceae, 172
Aquilegia, 34, 44; A. vulgaris, 35, 42
Arabis, 61, 64; A. hirsuta, 61
Araceae, 329
Arachis hypogaea, 161
Araliaceae, 182
Arbutus, 192
Arctium lappa, 221
Areca catechu, 357
Arenaria, 80, 83; A. peploides, 80
Aristolochia gigas, 52; A. sipho, 52
Aristolochiaceae, 52
Armeria maritima, 244
Artemisia absinthium, 218
Artocarpus, 165; A. incisa, 165
Arum maculatum, 330, 331
Asparagus officinalis, 327; A. plumosus, 327
Asperula odorata, 202
Aspidistra, 314, 326
Aster, 226; A. subcoeruleus, 226
Astilbe, 77
Astragalus glycyphyllos, 150;

A. gummifer, 161; A. hypoglottis, 150
Atriplex, 89, 90; A. patula, 89
Atropa, 260, 261; A. belladonna, 261
Aubretia, 64
Aucuba, 142, 183; A. japonica, 183
Avena fatua, 371; A. sativa, 371; A. sterilis, 373
Azalea, 191

Ballota nigra, 302
Balsaminaceae, 96, 99
Balsamodendron, 181
Bambusa, 376
Bartsia odontites, 276
Begonia, 114, 115
Begoniaceae, 114
Bellis perennis, 214, 225
Berberidaceae, 35, 51
Berberis, 51; B. vulgaris, 35, 51
Beta, 89; B. maritima, 90; B. maritima *var.* rapa, 91
Betula alba, 163; B. pendula, 164; B. pubescens, 164
Betulaceae, 163
Bidens tripartita, 216
Bignonia, 293
Bignoniaceae, 293
Boehmeria, 168
Bombacaceae, 118
Bombax malabaricum, 119
Boraginaceae, 254
Borago officinalis, 257
Borassus flabellifer, 357
Boswellia carteri, 181
Brassica, 62, 64; B. campestris, 65; B. napus, 65, B. oleracea, 64; B. oleracea bullata, 65
Briza maxima 373; B. media, 372
Bromeliaceae, 312
Bryonia dioica, III
Buddleia, 197; B. alternifolia, 197, 198
Bunium flexuosum, 187
Bupleurum rotundifolium, 187
Burseraceae, 181
Butomaceae, 307
Butomus umbellatus, 307
Buxaceae, 162
Buxus sempervirens, 162

Caesalpinia, 154; C. japonica, 158; C. pulcherrima, 158

Caesalpiniaceae, 158
Calamintha acinos, 302; C. clinopodium, 302; C. officinalis, 302
Calamus, 357; C. draco, 353, 357
Calandrinia, 86; C. umbellata, 86
Calathea allouia, 315
Calceolaria, 282
Calendula officinalis, 230
Calla palustris, 332
Callistephus, 226; C. hortensis, 226
Callitrichaceae, 109
Callitriche verna, 109
Calluna, 189; C. vulgaris, 189
Caltha, 34; C. palustris, 35, 41
Calystegia sepium, 269; C. soldanella, 270
Camellia japonica, 116; C. thea, 116
Campanula, 249, 251; C. calycanthema, 251; C. latifolia, 250; C. medium, 251; C. persicifolia, 251; C. rotundifolia, 249, 317; C. trachelium, 249
Campanulaceae, 248
Canna indica, 314
Cannabinaceae, 168
Cannabis, 171; C. sativa, 171
Cannaceae, 314
Capparidaceae, 99
Capparis spinosa, 99
Caprifoliaceae, 204
Capsella bursa-pastoris, 60
Capsicum annuum, 52, 265; C. frutescens, 265
Cardamine amara, 61; C. hirsuta, 61; C. pratensis, 60, 64
Carduus lanceolatus, 220
Carlina vulgaris, 220
Carex vulgaris, 366
Carpenteria, 128
Carpinus betula, 164
Carum bulbocastanum, 187; C. carvi, 188
Caryophyllaceae, 78
Cassia acutifolia, 161; **C.** obovata, 161
Castanea vulgaris, 165
Catalpa, 293; C. bignonioides, 293
Cattleya, 363
Ceiba pentandra, 119
Celastraceae, 174
Celastrus, 174
Celosia cristata, 91; C. plumosa, 91
Centaurea, 221, 223; C. nigra, 221; C. scabiosa, 222; C. cyanus, 222

Centranthus, 208; C. ruber, 208
Centunculus minimus, 241
Cephalanthera ensifolia, 361; C. grandiflora, 361
Cerastium, 81; C. glomeratum, 81; C. triviale, 81
Ceratostigma, 246; C. plumbaginoides, 246
Ceratophyllaceae, 35
Ceratophyllum submersum, 35
Chaerophyllum temulum, 187
Cheiranthus, 59, 63; C. allionii, 63; C. cheiri, 59; C. kewensis, 63
Chelidonium majus, 54, 55
Chenopodiaceae, 89
Chenopodium, 89, 90; C. album, 90; C. bonus henricus, 90; C. rubrum, 90
Chlora perfoliata, 236
Choisya, 181; C. ternata, 181
Chrysanthemum, 30, 217, 230; C. indicum, 231; C. leucanthemum, 217, 231; C. segetum, 217; C. sinense, 231
Chrysosplenium, 75; C. alternifolium, 75, C. oppositifolium, 75
Cichorium endivia, 233; C. intybus, 225, 233
Cinchona, 4, 203
Cineraria, 231
Cinnomomum camphora, 47; C. cassia, 47; C. zeylanicum, 47
Circaea, 102, 104; C. alpina, 105; C. lutetiana, 104
Cistaceae, 110
Citrullus vulgaris, 113
Citrus, 181; C. aurantium, 181; C. aurantium var. amara, 181; C. aurantium var. bergamia, 181; C. decumana, 181; C. medica, 181; C. medica var. limetta, 181; C. medica var. limonum, 181; C. nobilis, 181
Clarkia, 35, 102, 106
Clematis, 34, 39, 44, 98; **C.** vitalba, 35, 40
Cobaea scandens, 254
Cochlearia armoracia, 66
Cocos nucifera, 354
Coffea arabica, 202
Cola vera, 118
Colchicum autumnale, 319, 327
Coleus, 303
Collomia coccinea, 253
Commelina benghalensis, 311; C. coelestris, 311
Commelinaceae, 311
Compositae, 208, 211
Conium maculatum, 185

Convallaria majalis, 318
Convolvulaceae, 268
Convolvulus althaeoides, 271; C. arvensis, 270, 271; C. scammonia, 272; C. sepium, 269; C. soldanella, 270
Corchorus capsularis, 118; C; clitorius, 118
Cordyline indivisa, 353; C. terminalis, 353
Coreopsis, 227, 229
Coriandrum sativum, 187, 188
Cornaceae, 183
Cornus sanguinea, 184
Corydalis, 57; C. cheilanthifolia, 58; C. claviculata, 57; C. lutea, 58; C. solida, 58
Corylaceae, 164
Corylopsis, 162
Corylus avellana, 164
Cosmos, 227, 229
Cotoneaster, 144
Cotyledon, 73, 74; C. umbilicus, 73
Crassulaceae, 72
Crataegus, 134; C. oxyacantha, 134, 135; C. oxyacantha var. praecox, 136
Crithmum maritimum, 188
Crocus aureus, 345; C. sativus, 349; C. vernus, 345; C. versicolor, 345
Cruciferae, 58, 99
Cucumis, 113; C. anguria, 113; C. melo, 113; C. sativus, 113
Cucurbita maxima, 113; C. pepo, 112
Cuphea, 101; C. miniata, 102; C. platycentra, 102
Curcuma angustifolia, 314; C. longa, 314; C. zedoaria, 314
Cuscuta epithymum, 270; C. europaea, 270
Cyclamen, 243; C. europaeum, 243; C. persicum, 244
Cymbidium, 362, 363
Cynara scolymus, 233
Cynoglossum, 258, 259; C. montanum, 258; C. officinale, 258
Cyperaceae, 365
Cyperus, 366; C. papyrus, 335
Cypripedium, 359, 360, 363; C. calceolus, 360, 366
Cytisus, 147, 157; C. adami, 158; C. purpureus, 158; C. scoparius, 147

Dactylis glomerata, 372
Dahlia, 35, 225, 227, 228; D. variabilis, 228
Daphne laureola, 109; D. mezereum, 109

Datura stramonium, 267
Daucus carota, 186, 188
Delphinium, 34, 43 ; D. ajacia, 35, 43
Dendrobium, 363
Desfontania spinosa, 197
Deutzia, 128
Dianthus, 79 ; D. barbatus, 81 ; D. caryophyllus, 79, 82
Dicentra spectabilis, 58
Dielytra spectabilis, 58
Diervillea, 207
Digitalis purpurea, 278, 280
Dimorphotheca aurantiaca, 232
Dionaea muscipula, 288
Dioscorea aculeata, 351 ; D. alata, 351 ; D. batatus, 351 ; D. cayennensis, 351 ; D. pentaphylla, 351 ; D. pyrenaica, 351 ; D. sativa, 351 ; D. sinuata, 351 ; D. trifida, 351 ; D. villosa, 351
Dioscoreaceae, 350
Dipsacaceae, 208, 213
Dipsacus fullonum, 210 ; D. sylvestris, 209
Distylium racemosum, 162
Draba verna, 60
Dracaena draco, 353
Drosera longifolia, 288 ; D. rotundifolia, 288
Droseraceae, 77, 285

Ecballium elaterium, 113
Echinops, 233
Echium, 258, 259 ; E. vulgare, 258
Elaeis guineensis, 357
Elodea canadensis, 308
Epidendrum, 363
Epilobium, 102, 108 ; E. augustifolium, 103 ; E. hirsutum, 104 ; E. montanum, 104 ; E. palustre, 104 ; E. parviflorum, 104 ; E. tetragonum, 104
Epipactis latifolia, 361 ; E. palustris, 361
Erica, 189, 192 ; E. arborea, 191 ; E. cinerea, 191 ; E. tetralix, 190
Ericaceae, 189, 194
Erigeron acris, 214
Eriophorum polystachyon, 367 ; E. vaginatum, 367
Erodium, 92 ; E. cicutarium, 93 ; E. moschatum, 94
Eryngium maritimum, 188
Erysimum, 62, 63 ; A. alliaria, 62
Erythraea centaurium, 236 ; E. massonii, 236
Erythronium dens canis, 322
Erythroxylaceae, 123

Erythroxylon coca, 123
Eschscholtzia, 55
Eucryphiaceae, 118
Eugenia caryophyllata, 99
Eulophia, 364
Euonymus europaeus, 174
Eupatorium cannabium, 213, 225
Euphorbia, 123, 124 ; E. amygdaloides, 124 ; E. helioscopia, 124 ; E. exigua, 124 ; E. peplus, 124
Euphorbiaceae, 123, 162
Euphrasia officinalis, 276
Eurya, 116
Exacum affina, 237

Fagaceae, 164
Fagopyrum, 89 ; F. esculentum, 89
Fagus sylvatica, 165
Festuca elatior, 371 ; F. pratensis, 371
Ficoidaceae, 84
Ficus elastica, 165
Foeniculum capillaceum, 188
Forsythia, 200
Fothergilla major, 162
Fragaria, 138, 144 ; F. vesca, 138, 145
Fraxinus excelsior, 198
Freesia, 349
Fritillaria imperialis, 321, 322 ; F. meleagris, 320
Fuchsia, 102, 106
Fumaria, 57 ; F. capreolata, 57 ; F. officinalis, 57
Fumariaceae, 57
Funkia, 326

Gagea lutea, 320
Gaillardia, 230
Galanthus nivalis, 338, 340
Galeopsis ladanum, 302 ; G. tetrahit, 302 ; G. versicolor, 302
Galium, 200, 284 ; G. aparine, 200 ; G. mollugo, 201 ; G. palustre, 201 ; G. verum 201, 202
Garrya, 163
Garryaceae, 163
Gazania, 232
Genista, 149, 157 ; G. anglica, 149 ; G. tinctoria, 149
Gentiana, 234, 235 ; G. acaulis, 236 ; G. amarella, 235 ; G. campestris, 235 ; G. pneumomanthe, 235
Gentianaceae, 234
Geraniaceae, 92, 97
Geranium, 30, 92 ; G. molle, 93 ; G. pratense, 92 ; G. robertianum, 93 ; G. sanguineum, 93

Gesneria, 293
Gesneriaceae, 292
Geum, 140, 144 ; G. rivale, 141 ; G. urbanum, 140
Gilia, 253
Gladiolus, 315, 347, 348 ; G. illyricus, 347
Glaucium flavum, 54
Glaux maritima, 242
Gleditschia, 158 ; G. trianthos, 158
Gloriosa superba, 322
Gloxinia, 292
Glyceria aquatica, 372 ; G. maritima, 372
Glycine hispida, 160 ; G. max, 160
Godetia, 102, 106
Gossypium, 122 ; G. arboreum, 122 ; G. barbadense, 122 ; G. herbaceum, 122
Gramineae, 306, 365, 368
Grevillea, 110
Grossulariaceae, 74, 125
Gunnera, 109
Guttiferae, 118
Gymnadenia conopsea, 361
Gynerium argentium, 373
Gypsophila, 83

Habenaria bifolia, 360 ; H. viridis, 361
Halorrhaginaceae, 107
Hamamelidaceae, 162
Hamamelis virginiana, 162
Hedera helix, 182
Helianthemum, 110 ; H. vulgare, 110
Helianthus annuus, 227, 233 ; H. tuberosus, 233
Helichrysum, 227
Heliotropium, 258 ; H. peruvianum, 258
Helipterum, 227
Helleborus, 34 ; H. foetidus, 35 ; H. niger, 35 ; H. viridis, 35
Helminthia echioides, 224
Helosciadium inundatum, 187 ; H. nodiflorum, 187
Heracleum giganteum, 186 ; H. sphondylium, 186
Herminium monorchis, 362
Heucheria, 77
Hevea, 5, 125 ; H. brasiliensis, 125
Hibiscus, 121, 122 ; H. rosa sinensis, 121 ; H. trionum, 121
Hippuris vulgaris, 108
Hordeum, 370, 374 ; H. murinum, 371 ; H. pratense, 370 ; H. vulgare, 374 ; H. vulgare var. distichium, 374

Hottonia palustris, 242, 244
Humulus, 168; americanus, 168; H. lupulus, 168
Hyacinthus nonscriptus, 316; H. orientalis, 321
Hydrangeaceae, 74, 127
Hydrangea, 74, 127
Hydrocharis morsus-ranae, 308
Hydrocharitaceae, 307
Hydrocotyle vulgaris, 188
Hydrophyllaceae, 254
Hyocyamus niger, 259
Hypericaceae, 99, 116
Hypericum, 116; H. androsaemum, 117; H. calycinum, 118; H. dubium, 117; H. hirsutum, 117; H. humifusum, 117; H. moserianum, 118; H. perforatum, 117; H. polyphyllum, 118; H. prolificum, 118; H. pulchrum, 117; H. quadrangulum, 117; H. reptans, 118
Hypochaeris radicata, 224

Iberis amara, 63
Ilex aquifolium, 172; I. paraguensis, 174
Impatiens, 96, 99; I. nolitangere, 99
Indigofera tinctoria, 161
Inula conyza, 215; I. dysenterica, 215
Ipomoea, 271, 272; I. batatas, 272; I. purga, 272; I. purpurea, 271
Iridaceae, 343
Iris, 343; I. bucharica, 345; I. florentina, 349; I. foetidissima, 344; I. germanica, 344, 349; I. kaempferi, 345; I. orchioides, 345; I. pallida, 349; I. pseudacorus, 343; I. reticulata, 345
Isatis tinctoria, 63, 150
Ixia, 347

Jamesia, 128
Jasione montana, 250
Jasminum fruticans, 200; J. nudiflorum, 200; J. officinale, 200
Juncaceae, 364
Juncaginaceae, 309
Juncus, 365; J. communis, 365

Kniphofia, 322
Kochia, 90
Koelreuteria, 182

Labiatae, 272, 295
Laburnum anagyroides, 158
Lactuca muralis, 224, 233; L. sativa, 233

Laelia, 363
Lagenaria vulgaris, 113
Lagerstroemia, 102
Lamium, 296; L. album, 296, 297; L. amplexicaule, 298; L. galeobdolon, 297; L. purpureum, 297
Lantana, 294
Lapsana communis, 224
Lathraea clandestina, 284; L. squamaria, 284
Lathyrus, 150, 153, 159; L. latifolius, 156; L. macrorhizus, 154; L. nissolia, 154; L. odoratus, 154, 155; L. pratensis, 154
Lauraceae, 46
Laurus benzoin, 46; L. nobilis, 46
Lavandula, 302; L. spica, 304; L. stoechas, 304; L. vera, 304
Lavatera, 121; L. arborea, 121; L. rosea, 121, 122
Lawsonia alba, 102
Leguminosae, 146, 373
Lemna minor, 332
Lemnaceae, 332
Lens esculenta, 161
Lentibulariaceae, 285
Lepidium, 60, 65; L. sativum, 65
Lewisia, 86; L. rediviva, 86
Liguliflorae, 213, 222
Ligustrum ovalifolium, 199; L. vulgare, 198
Liliaceae, 315, 339
Lilium, 315, 323; L. auratum, 324, 325; L. bulbiferum 326; L. canadense, 326; L. candidum, 324; L. carolinianum, 326; L. chalcedonicum, 326; L. giganteum, 324; L. grayi, 326; L henryi, 326; L. longiflorum, 324; L. martagon, 326; L. martagon var. album, 326; L. pomponium, 326; L. regale, 324; L. tigrinum, 326; L. wallacei, 326
Limnanthemum nymphaeoides, 236
Linaceae, 95
Linaria, 276, 282; L. cymbalaria, 276; L. vulgaris, 277
Linum, 95; L. catharticum, 95; L. grandiflorum, 96; L. usitatissimum, 95
Liquidambar, 162; L. styraciflua, 162
Liriodendron tulipifera, 46
Listera cordata, 361; L. ovata, 361

Lithospermum, 256; L. arvense, 256; L. officinale, 256
Littorella, 247, 248; L. lacustris, 248
Lobelia, 252; L. dortmanna, 252
Loganaceae, 197
Lolium perenne, 371
Lonicera periclymenum, 205
Loranthaceae, 174
Lotus corniculatus, 152; L. major, 153
Luffa cylindrica, 114
Lunaria biennis, 63
Lupinus, 156; L. arboreus 157; L. polyphyllus, 156
Luzula campestris, 365; L. pilosa, 365; L. sylvatica, 365
Lychnis, 78, 83; L. diurna, 78; L. flos-cuculi, 79; L. githago, 79; L. vespertina, 79
Lycopsis arvensis, 257
Lygeum spartum, 376
Lysimachia nummularia, 241, 244; L. nemorum, 241, 244; L. vulgaris, 240
Lythraceae, 100
Lythrum, 100, 101; L. salicaria, 100

Magnolia, 46; M. grandiflora, 46
Magnoliaceae, 46
Malus pumila, 34, 136, 144, 145
Malva, 119, 120; M. moschata, 119, 120; M. rotundifolia, 119; M. sylvestris, 119
Malvaceae, 119
Mandragora officinarum, 261
Manihot aipi, 125; M. glaziovii, 125; M. utilissima, 125
Maoutia puya, 168
Maranta arundinacea, 315
Marantaceae, 315
Marrubium vulgare, 302
Matthiola, 63; M. incana, 63
Meconopsis, 55; M. baileyi, 55; M. cambrica, 55; M. sativa, 160
Medicago, 150; M. lupulina, 150, 160; M. sativa, 160
Melampyrum pratense, 275
Meliaceae, 181
Melilotus alba, 151; M. officinalis, 151
Mentha, 301, 304; M. aquatica, 301; M. arvensis, 301; M. piperita, 301, 304; M. pulegium, 304; M. rotundifolia, 301; M. sativa, 301; M. sylvestris, 301; M. viridis, 301
Menyanthes trifoliata, 235

Mercurialis, 123 ; M. perennis, 124
Mesembryanthemum, 84 ; M. crystallinum, 85 ; M. edule, 85
Metroxylon laeve, 356 ; M. rumphii, 356
Mimosa, 154, 159 ; M. pudica, 159
Mimosaceae, 159
Mimulus lutea, 282 ; M. moschatus, 282
Molinia caerulea, 372
Monotropa hypopitys, 194
Monotropaceae, 193
Montbretia, 347
Moraceae, 165
Morus, 165 ; M. alba, 165 ; M. nigra, 165
Musa cavendishii, 314 ; M. paradisica, 314 ; M. paradisica var. sapientum, 314 ; M. textilis, 314
Musaceae, 313
Muscari racemosum, 321
Myosotis, 255 ; M. arvensis, 256 ; M. caespitosa, 256 ; M. palustris, 255 ; M. repens, 256 ; M. versicolor, 256
Myosurus, 34 ; M. minimus, 35
Myriophyllum spicatum, 108
Myrrhis odorata, 187
Myristica fragrans, 47
Myristicaceae, 46
Myrtaceae, 99

Naegelia, 293
Najadaceae, 311
Najas, 311
Narcissus jonquilla, 341 ; N. poeticus, 341 ; N. pseudonarcissus, 336, 337, 340
Nardostachys jatamansi, 208
Nardus stricta, 370
Narthecium ossifragum, 318
Nasturtium, 61, 98 ; N. officinale, 61, 65 ; N. palustre, 61 ; N. sylvestre, 61
Nelumbium, 50 ; N. speciosum, 50
Nemophila, 254
Neottia nidus-avis, 362
Nepenthaceae, 289
Nepenthes, 289
Nepeta, 299, 303 ; N. cataria, 299 ; N. glechoma, 298 ; Nerium oleander, 197
Nicotiana, 259, 265, 266 ; N. affinis, 266 ; N. tabacum, 265
Nigella, 34, 44
Nolana grandiflora, 271
Nothofagus cunninghami, 165
Nuphar luteum, 35, 49

Nyctaginaceae, 110
Nymphaeae alba, 35, 48
Nymphaeaceae, 35, 47

Odontoglossum, 363
Oenanthe, 187 ; O. crocata, 187 ; O. fistulosa, 187 ; O. lachenalii, 187 ; O. phellandrium, 187
Oenothera, 102, 105 ; O. biennis, 105
Olea europaea, 199
Oleaceae, 128, 198
Onagraceae, 102, 160
Onobrychis sativa, 160
Ononis, 150 ; O. arvensis, 150 ; O. spinosa, 150
Ophrys apifera, 361 ; O. aranifera, 362 ; O. muscifera, 362
Orchidaceae, 357
Orchis, 360, 364 ; O. ericetorum, 363 ; O. maculata, 360 ; O. mascula, 360 ; O. pyramidalis, 360
Origanum majorana, 304 ; O. onites, 304 ; O. vulgare, 301, 304
Ornithogalum umbellatum, 320
Orobanchaceae, 283
Orobanche, 283 ; O. caryophyllacea, 284 ; O. elatior, 284 ; O. major, 284 ; O. minor, 284 ; O. rubra, 284
Oryza sativa, 375
Oxalidaceae, 96, 97
Oxalis, 97 ; O. acetosella, 97

Paeonia, 34 ; sinensis, 35, 44
Palmae, 351, 354, 373
Panicum, 375
Papaver, 53 ; P. argemone, 54 ; P. nudicaule, 55 ; P. orientale, 55 ; P. rhoeas, 53, 55 ; P. somniferum, 56
Papaveraceae, 52
Papilionaceae, 146, 154
Parietaria officinalis, 167
Paris quadrifolia, 327
Parnassia palustris, 75
Parrotia persica, 162
Parthenocissus, 180 ; P. quinquefolia, 180 ; P. tricuspidata, 180
Passiflora, 111 ; P. edulis, 111 ; P. laurifolia, 180 ; P. maliformis, 111 ; P. quadrangularia, 111
Passifloraceae, 111
Paulownia, 283 ; P. imperialis, 283
Pedicularis palustris, 275 ; P. sylvatica, 275
Pelargonium, 30, 94, 95 ; P. odoratissimum, 95

Penicillium notatum, 5 ; P. patulum, 5
Pentstemon, 281 ; P. cobaea, 281 ; P. hartwegii, 281
Peplis portula, 101
Persea gratissima, 47
Petasites vulgaris, 219
Petroselinum crispum, 188
Petunia, 259, 267, 268
Peucedanum sativum, 186, 188
Phacelia campanularia, 254 ; P. tanacetifolia, 254 ; P. viscida, 254
Phalaenopsis, 363
Phalaris arundinacea, 373 ; P. canariensis, 375
Phaseolus, 160 ; P. multiflorus, 160 ; P. mungo, 161 ; P. mungo var. radiatus, 161 ; P. vulgaris, 160
Philadelphus, 128
Phlox, 253 ; P. drummondii, 253 ; P. paniculata, 253
Phoenix dactylifera, 356
Phormium tenax, 353
Phragmites communis, 372
Physalis, 267 ; P. alkenzi, 267 ; P. peruviana, 267
Physocalymma, 102
Phyteuma orbiculare, 250
Phytelephas, 357
Pimpinella anisum, 188 ; P. saxifraga, 187
Pinguicula lusitanica, 286 ; P. vulgaris, 286
Piper betle, 357 ; P. nigrum, 52
Piperaceae, 52
Pisum, 159 ; P. sativum, 159
Plantaginaceae, 247
Plantago, 247 ; P. coronopus, 248 ; P. lanceolata, 248 ; P. major, 247 ; P. maritima, 248 ; P. media, 248
Platanaceae, 162
Platanus acerifolia, 162 ; P. occidentalis, 163 ; P. orientalis, 163
Plumbaginaceae, 245
Poa annua, 372 ; P. nemoralis, 372
Podophyllum peltatum, 262
Poinsettia, 125
Polemoniaceae, 253
Polemonium caerulum, 243
Polygala, 71 ; P. senega, 71 ; P. vulgaris, 71
Polygalaceae, 71
Polygonaceae, 86, 88
Polygonatum multiflorum, 318
Polygonum, 88 ; P. amphibium, 88 ; P. bistorta, 88 ; P. hydropiper, 88 ; P. lapathifolium, 88 ; P. persicaria, 88

Populus, 163; alba, 163; P. italica, 163; P. nigra, 163; P. tremula, 163
Portulaca, 85; P. oleracea, 86
Portulacaceae, 85
Potamogetonaceae, 310
Potamogeton crispus, 311; P. lucens, 311; P. heterophyllus, 310; P. natans, 310; P. pusillus, 311
Potentilla, 139, 144; P. anserina, 139; P. fragariastrum, 139; P. reptans, 139; P. tormentilla, 140
Poterium obtusum, 140, 144; P. sanguisorba, 140
Pouzolzia tuberosa, 168
Primulaceae, 237
Primula, 237, 242, 293; **P.** auricula, 243; P. bulleyana, 242; P. elatior, 240, 243; P. japonica, 242; P. malacoides, 242; P. obconica, 242; P. sinensis, 242; P. stellata, 242; P. veris, 238; P. vulgaris, 238
Proteaceae, 110
Prunella vulgaris, 298
Prunus, 142, 144; P. amygdalus, 142, 145; P. armeniaca, 145; P. cerasus, 134, 145; P. communis, 133; P. domestica, 145; P. inistitia, 145; P. laurocerasus, 142; P. padus, 134; P. persica, 145; P. serrulata, 142; P. spinosa, 145
Psychotria ipecacuanha, 203
Pyrethrum, 230, 234
Pyrola minor, 191; P. rotundifolia, 191; P. uniflora, 191
Pyrus communis, 145

Quercus ilex, 164; Q. robur, 164; Q. petraea, 164

Radiola, 95; R. millegrana, 95
Rafflesia arnoldii, 195
Ramondia, 293
Ranunculaceae, 34, 35, 37
Ranunculus, 33; R. acris, 35, 37; R. aquatilis, 34, 35, 39; R. bulbosus, 34, 35, 37; R. ficaria, 34, 35, 38; R. repens, 34, 35, 37; R. scleratus, 34, 35, 38
Raphanus raphanistrum, 63; R. sativus, 66
Raphia, 357
Rehmannia, 282, 283
Reseda, 70; R. lutea, 70; R. luteola, 70; R. odorata, 71
Resedaceae, 70

Rheum, 89; R. officinale, 89; R. rhaponticum, 89
Rhinanthus crista-galli, 275
Rhodanthe, 227
Rhododendron, 191, 192
Ribes, 126; R. alpinum, 126; R. americanum, 126; R. aureum, 126; R. grossularia, 127; R. nigrum, 127; R. rubrum, 127; R. sanguineum, 126; R. speciosum, 126
Ricinus communis, 125
Robinia, 158; R. pseudacacia, 158
Rogersia, 77
Romneya, 56
Rosa, 131; R. arvensis, 132; R. canina, 130, 131, 132, 142; R. centifolia, 34, 142; R. damascena, 142; R. rubiginosa, 132; R. spinosissima, 132
Rosaceae, 129
Rosmarinus officinalis, 302
Rubiaceae, 200
Rubia tinctorum, 202
Rubus, 132, 142, 144, 145; R. caesius, 133, 145; R. fruticosus, 132, 145; R. idaeus, 133, 145
Rumex, 86, 88; R. acetosa, 87; R. acetosella, 87; R. conglomeratus, 87; R. crispus, 87; R. hydrolapathum, 87; R. obtusifolius, 87; R. sanguineus, 87
Ruscaceae, 329
Ruscus aculeatus, 329
Rutaceae, 180

Saccharum officinarum, 375
Sagina, 80
Sagittaria sagittifolia, 309
Salicaceae, 163
Salicornia, 89; S. herbacea, 90
Salix, 163; S. alba, 163; S. babylonica, 163; S. caprea, 163; S. coerulea, 163; S. fragilis, 163; S. viminalis, 163
Salpiglossis, 259, 267
Salvia, 300, 303; S. officinalis, 305; S. verbenaca, 300, 303
Sambucus ebulus, 204; S. nigra, 204
Sanicula europaea, 188
Sanguisorba minor, 140; S. officinalis, 140
Sansevieria zeylanica, 354
Sapindaceae, 181
Saponaria, 83; S. officinalis, 83
Sarracenia, 291
Sarraceniaceae, 77, 291

Satureia hortensis, 305; S. montana, 305
Saxifraga, 75, 76; S. granulata, 75; S. tridactylites, 75; S. umbrosa, 77
Saxifragaceae, 74, 126, 285, 287
Scabiosa arvensis, 205; S. columbaria, 208; S. succisa, 208
Scandix pecten-veneris, 186
Schizanthus, 259, 267, 268
Scilla nutans, 316, 321
Scirpus lacustris, 335, 367; S. maritimus, 367; S. sylvaticus, 367
Scrophularia aquatica, 278; S. nodosa, 277
Scrophulariaceae, 272
Scutellaria galericulata, 299; S. minor, 299
Secale cereale, 374
Sechium edule, 114
Sedum, 72, 74; S. acre, 72, 74; S. album, 73; S. telephium, 72
Sempervivum, 73, 74; S. arachnoides, 73; S. tectorum, 73, 74
Senecio, 219, 231; S. elegans, 231; S. jacobaea, 230; S. multibracteatus, 231; S. vulgaris, 219
Sherardia arvensis, 202
Sidalcea, 122
Silene, 79, 83; S. inflata, 79; S. maritima, 79
Sinapis, 62, 65; S. alba, 63, 65; S. arvensis, 62, 65; S. nigra, 63, 65
Sinningia, 292; S. speciosa, 292
Sisymbrium officinale, 62
Sisyrinchium, 347
Sium angustifolium, 187
Smilacaceae, 328
Smilax, 328
Smyrnium olusatrum, 187
Solanaceae, 259
Solanum, 260, 262; S. dulcamara, 260; S. lycopersicum, 264; S. melongena, 265; S. nigrum, 260; S. tuberosum, 34, 262, 263
Soldanella alpina, 243
Solidago virgaurea, 216, 226
Sonchus arvensis, 224
Sorbus aria, 144; S. aucuparia, 137, 144
Sorghum vulgare, 375
Sparganiaceae, 333
Sparganium ramosum, 333; S. simplex, 333
Spartina towsendii, 376

Spergularia marina, 80
Spinacia oleracea, 91
Spiraea, 77, 141 ; S. filipendula, 141 ; S. ulmaria, 141
Spiranthes autumnalis, 362
Stachys, 299, 303 ; S. arvensis, 299 ; S. betonica, 299 ; S. palustris, 300 ; S. sylvatica, 299
Statice, 246 ; S. limonium, 246 ; S. suworowi, 246
Stellaria, 80 ; S. aquatica, 81 ; S. glauca, 81 ; S. graminea, 80 ; S. holostea, 80 ; S. media, 81 ; S. nemorum, 81 ; S. uliginosa, 87
Sterculiaceae, 118
Stewartia, 116
Stipa pennata, 373 ; S. tenacissima, 376
Stratiotes aloides, 308
Streptocarpus, 293
Strychnos, 4, 198 ; S. nuxvomica, 198 ; S. toxifera, 198
Stuartia, 116
Swietenia mahogani, 181
Sycopsis sinensis, 162
Symphoricarpus albus, 216
Symphytum officinale, 256 ; S. tuberosum, 257
Syringa, 128, 199 ; S. vulgaris, 199

Tacsonia, 111
Tagetes, 230
Tamus communis, 350
Tanacetum vulgare, 217
Taraxacum officinale, 222
Teucrium scorodonia, 302
Testudinaria elephantipes, 351
Thallictrum, 34 ; T. flavum, 35 ; T. minus, 35
Theaceae, 114, 116
Theobroma cacao, 118
Thunbergia, 294
Thymeliaceae, 109
Thymus serpyllum, 301, 302 ; T. vulgaris, 301, 305
Tigridia pavonia, 349
Tilia americana, 118 ; T. vulgaris, 118
Tiliaceae, 118

Torenia, 283
Torilis anthriscus, 185 ; T. nodosa, 185
Trachelium, 252
Tradescantia virginiana, 312
Tragopodon pratensis, 223
Trapa, 107
Trifolium, 151, 157, 160 ; T. arvense, 152 ; T. filiforme, 152 ; T. fragiferum, 152 ; T. minus, 152 ; T. pratense, 151 ; T. procumbens ; T. repens, 151 ; T. striatum, 152
Triglochin maritimum, 309 ; T. palustre, 309
Trilliaceae, 327, 328
Trillium, 328
Triticum durum, 374 ; T. dicoccum, 374 ; T. monococcum, 374 ; T. polonicum, 374 ; T. vulgare, 374
Tritonia, 347
Trollius, 34 ; T. europaeus, 35, 44
Tropaeolaceae, 96, 98
Tropaeolum, 61, 98 ; T. perigrinum, 98
Tubuliferae, 213
Tulipa, 322
Tunica, 83 ; T. saxifraga, 84
Tussilago farfara, 218
Typha latifolia, 335
Typhaceae, 333, 335

Ulex, 148 ; U. europaeus, 148
Ulmus glabra, 165 ; U. procera, 165
Umbelliferae, 184
Ursinia, 232
Urtica dioica, 166 ; U. pilulifera, 166 ; U. urens, 166
Urticaceae, 165, 168
Utricularia minor, 287 ; U. vulgaris, 286, 287

Vacciniaceae, 189, 192, 194
Vaccinium myrtillus, 193 ; V. oxycoccus, 193 ; V. pennsylvanicum, 193 ; V. vitisidaea, 193
Valeriana, 208 ; V. dioica, 207 ; V. officinalis, 207

Valerianaceae, 207
Valerianella olitoria, 207
Vanilla planifolia, 364
Verbascum, 274, 275, 287 ; V. phoenicium, 281 ; V. thapsus, 274
Verbena, 294 ; V. officinalis, 294
Verbenaceae, 294
Veronica, 273, 275, 283 ; V. agrestis, 274 ; V. anagallis, 274 ; V. arvensis, 274 ; V. beccabunga, 274 ; V. buxbaumii, 274 ; V. chamaedrys, 273 ; V. officinalis, 274 ; V. scutellata, 274
Viburnum lantana, 205 ; V. opulus, 205 ; V. sterile, 206
Vicia, 150, 153, 159, 160 ; V. cracca, 153 ; V. hirsuta, 153 ; V. faba, 160 ; V. sativa, 153 ; V. sepium, 153 ; V. sylvatica, 153
Victoria regia, 50
Vinca major, 196 ; V. minor, 197
Viola, 66, 69 ; V. canina, 66 ; V. hirta, 67 ; V. lutea, 67 ; V. odorata, 66, 69 ; V. palustris, 67 ; V. tricolor, 67, 69
Violaceae, 66, 322
Viscum album, 176
Vitaceae, 177
Vitis, 178 ; V. vinifera, 178

Wahlenbergia hederacea, 250
Wistaria, 35, 158
Woodfordia floribunda, 102

Xeranthemum, 227

Yucca filamentosa, 352

Zantedeschia aethiopica, 332
Zea mays, 375
Zingiber officinale, 314
Zingiberaceae, 314, 315
Zinnia, 227, 229
Zostera marina, 310, 311
Zosteraceae, 310

GENERAL INDEX

Abaca, 314
Absinthe, 218
Acacia, 159 ; False, 158
Achene, 32, 40, 132, 139, 140, 170, 209, 214, 217, 310, 311
Achilles, 216
Adam's needle, 352
Agrimony, Common, 140 ; Hemp, 212, 213, 225
Alchemist's plant, 141
Ale, 170
Alder, 163
Alexanders, 187
Alfalfa, 160
Alizarin, 202
Alleluia, 97
All-heal, 208
Allseed, 95
Almond, 134, 142 ; Bitter, 145 ; Sweet, 145
Aloe, American, 353
Aloes, 327
Anchusa, 238
Anemone, Garden, 44 ; Wood, 34, 35, 40
Angelica, 188 ; Wild, 186
Aniseed, 188
Anther, 20, 21
Antirrhinum, 280
Apple, Crab, 136, 137 ; Cultivated, 34, 144, 145, 175 ; May, 262 ; Thorn, 267
Apricot, 145
Archangel, 297
Areca nut, 357
Aril, 42, 47, 49
Arimathea, Joseph of, 136
Arnold, Matthew, 177, 320, 360
Arrow-head, 309 ; grass, 309 ; root, E. Indian, 314 ; root, Portland, 331 ; root, W. Indian, 314
Artichoke, 233 ; Jerusalem, 233
Arum-lily, 47, 315 ; Water-, 322 ; -Wild, 330, 331
Ash, 16, 17, 198
Asparagus, 327 ; fern, 327
Aspen, 163
Asphodel, Bog, 318
Aspidistra, 316
Aster, Annual, 226 ; China, 226 ; Perrenial, 226
Atabrine, 203
Atropine, 261
Attar of roses, 95, 142
Auricula, 243

Avens, Water, 141 ; Wood, 140
Avocado pear, 47
Awn, 140, 370
Azalea, 191

Bacchus, 182
Bacon, 303
Bacteria, 147
Balder, 176
Balsam, 162
Bamboo, 368, 376
Banana, 313
Banks, Sir Joseph, 264
Banyan, 165
Baobab, 118
Barbados pride, 158
Barberry, 35, 51 ; Common, 51
Bark, 15
Barley, 2, 170, 370, 371, 374 ; Cultivated, 374 ; Meadow, 370 ; Wall, 370
Bartsia, Red, 276
Basil thyme, 302 ; Wild, 302
Basswood, 118
Bay, Sweet, 45
Bayly, T. H. 174
Bean, Broad, 153, 160 ; Dwarf, 160 ; French, 160 ; Haricot, 160 ; Indian, 293 ; Kidney, 160 ; Scarlet runner, 160 ; Soy, 160
Beaumont and Fletcher, 239, 240, 294
Bedstraw, Great hedge, 201 ; Lady's, 201, 202 ; Water, 201 ; Yellow, 201, 202
Beech, 15, 164
Beer, 3, 168, 170
Beet, Cultivated, 90 ; Sugar, 10, 89, 90, 91 ; Wild, 89, 90
Begonia, 114
Belladonna, 261
Bell-flower, 248 ; Ivy-leaved, 250 ; Nettle-leaved, 249
Benson, A. C., 100, 221
Berry, 49, 52, 110, 112, 115, 126, 138, 144, 175, 178, 181, 183, 193, 198, 204, 205, 206, 260, 261, 262, 264, 267, 313, 318, 329, 331, 353, 356
Betel nut, 357 ; pepper, 357
Betony, Wood, 299
Beverages, 2 ; Alcoholic, 2
Bhang, 171
Bilberry, 192, 193
Bilimbi, 97
Billiard Ball, 357

Bindweed, Great, 269 ; Small, 270 ; Seaside, 270
Binyon, Laurence, 377
Birch, 163
Birdlime, 138
Bird's eye, 273 ; nest, Yellow, 194
Bistort, Amphibious, 88 ; snake-root, 88
Bitter-cress, Hairy, 61 ; Large-flowered, 61
Bittersweet, 260
Blackberry, 132, 145
Black poker, 335
Blackthorn, 133
Bladderwort, Common, 286, 287 ; Lesser, 287
Bluebell, 17, 23, 316, 321 ; Giant, 250 ; Nettle-leaved, 249 ; of Scotland, 249, 317
Blue-bottle, Corn, 222
Bogbean, 235
Borage, 257
Borecole, 65
Botta, Anne, 27
Boyle, Sarah, R., 368
Box, 134, 162
Bramble, 132, 182
Brandy, 3, 301 ; -bottle, 49
Bread-fruit, 165
Briar pipe, 191 ; Sweet, 132
Bridges, R., 39, 54
Broccoli, 65
Brooklime, 274
Broom, Common, 147, 148, 284 ; Garden, 157
Broomrape, Clove-scented, 284 ; Greater, 284 ; Least, 284 ; Red, 284 ; Tall, 284
Brown, T. E., 281
Browning, E. B., 81, 149
Brussels sprout, 65
Bryant, W. C., 234
Bryony, Black, 112, 350 ; White, 112, 113, 350
Buchan, John, 377
Buckbean, 235
Buckwheat, 89
Bud, 11 ; Axillary, 12 ; Lateral, 12 ; Terminal, 12
Budding, 129, 130, 142
Buddleia, 197, 198
Bugle, 298 ; Yellow, 298
Bugloss, Small, 257 ; Viper's, 258
Bulb, 30, 317, 322, 337, 339, 340
Bulbil, 38, 75, 320
Bulrush, 335 ; Common, 367

Bur, 221
Burdock, 212, 221
Bur-marigold, 216
Burnet, Great, 140 ; Salad, 140;
    -saxifrage, 187
Burns, R., 59
Burweed, Branched, 333, 334 ;
    Unbranched, 333, 334
Butcher's broom, 329
Butler, Dr. W., 146
Butterbur, 219
Buttercup, 8, 9, 18, 19, 22, 23,
    24 ; Bulbous, 33, 34, 37 ;
    Celery-leaved, 34, 38 ; Com-
    mon, 35, 37 ; Creeping, 33,
    34, 37 ; Water, 33, 34, 39
Butterfly flower, 268
Butter-flower, 38
Butterwort, 286
Byron, 5

Cabbage, 17, 64 ; Garden, 64 ;
    Savoy, 64
Cacao, 118
Calabash, Cucumber, 113;
    Sweet, 111
Calamint, 302
Calamus, 332
Calceolaria, 282
Calf's snout, 280
Calyx, 19, 22
Camden, W., 166
Camellia, 116
Campanula, 251
Camphora, 47
Campion, Bladder, 79, 83 ;
    Garden, 83 ; Red, 78 ; Rose,
    78 ; Sea, 79 ; White, 79
Canadian water weed, 29, 308
Canary creeper, 98
Candytuft, 63
Canna, 314
Canterbury bell, 249, 251 ; Cup-
    and-saucer, 251, 252
Caper, 41, 98, 99
Capitulum, 212
Capsicum, 265
Capsule, 44, 53, 68, 79, 80, 84,
    96, 97, 100, 103, 115, 117,
    190, 195, 238, 240, 241, 249,
    250, 260, 267, 273, 278, 284,
    318, 320, 321, 323, 344, 353,
    365
Carambola, 97
Caraway seed, 188
Carnation, Garden, 82 ; Wild,
    79
Carotene, 188
Carpel, 20
Carrot, Cultivated, 188 ; Wild,
    186
Caryopsis, 370
Cassava, Bitter, 125 ; Sweet,
    125

Cassia, 47
Castor-oil, 125
Catalpa, 293
Cat-mint, 299, 303
Cat's ear, 224 ; tail, 335
Cauliflower, 65
Celandine, Greater, 39, 54 ;
    Lesser, 22, 34, 38
Celery, Cultivated, 188 ; Wild,
    187
Centaury, Common, 236 ; Yel-
    low, 236
Century plant, 353
Cereals, 2, 374
Chalk plant, 83
Chamomile, Corn, 217
Champagne, 180
Charas, 171
Charlock, 62, 65
Chatterbox, 280
Chaucer, 214
Cherry, 134, 137, 145 ; Bird,
    134 ; Japanese, 142 ; laurel,
    142 ; pie, 258 ; Wild, 134 ;
    Winter, 267
Chervil, 188 ; Rough, 187
Chestnut, Horse-, 16, 17, 181 ;
    Spanish, 165
Chickweed, 81 ; Mouse-ear,
    81 ; Narrow-leaved mouse-
    ear, 81
Chicory, 225, 233
Chilli, 52, 265
Chinchon, Countess of, 203
Chiron, 216
Chives, 342
Chlorophyll, 194
Choco, 114
Chocolate, 118 ; root, 141
Christ's Thorn, 173
Chrysanthemum, 30, 230, 231
Cider, 145
Cineraria, 231
Cinnamon, 47, 301
Cinquefoil, Creeping, 139
Citron, 181
Clare, John, 104, 112, 120, 136,
    237, 239, 343
Clarkia, 35, 106
Clary, 300 ; water, 301
Classification, 31
Cleavers, 200
Clematis, Garden, 45 ; Wild,
    22, 34, 35, 39
Clove, 99
Clover, 147, 151, 284 ; Dutch,
    15, 160 ; Knotted, 152 ; Red,
    151, 160 ; Strawberry, 152 ;
    White, 151, 160
Club-rush, Sea, 367 ; Wood,
    367
Coca, 4, 123
Cocaine, 2, 123
Cock robin, 68

Cock's-comb, 91
Cocoa, 118, 141 ; -butter, 118
Coco-nut, 354, 355
Coffee, 2, 202, 225
Colchicine, 320, 327
Colchicum, 320, 327
Colour of flowers, 27
Coltsfoot, 19, 218
Columbine, 34, 35, 42
Column, 359
Colza-oil, 65
Comfrey, 256 ; Tuberous, 257
Condiments, 3, 65, 66
Convolvulus, 269, 271
Copra, 356
Coreopsis, 229
Coriander, 187, 188
Corm, 29, 243, 319, 345, 347
Corn blue-bottle, 222 ; cockle,
    79 ; marigold, 217 ; mint,
    301 ; sow-thistle, 224
Corn, Guinea, 375 ; Indian,
    375
Cornflower, Garden, 233 ;
    Wild, 222
Corolla, 19, 22
Corona, 336, 337
Corydalis, White climbing, 57 ;
    Yellow, 58
Cosmos, 229
Cotton, 5, 122 ; -grass, Com-
    mon, 367 ; -grass, Hare's
    tail, 367 ; tree, 119
Cotyledon, 33
Cowberry, 192, 193
Cowley, A., 280
Cowper, 71
Cows and Calves, 330
Cowslip, 31, 239
Cow-wheat, 275
Crab-apple, 136, 137 ; Flower-
    ing, 144
Crabbe, G., 48, 221
Cranberry, 192, 193
Crane's-bill, Bloody, 93 ;
    Dove's-foot, 92 ; Meadow,
    93 ; Stinking, 93
Creeping Jenny, 241, 244
Cress, Garden, 60, 65 ; Water-,
    61, 65, 98
Crocus, 23, 39, 319, 345 ;
    Autumn, 319, 327
Cross-breeding, 34
Crowfoot, Water, 33, 34, 39
Crown imperial, 321, 322
Cuckoo-flower, 60, 64
Cuckoo-pint, 19, 330, 331
Cucumber, 113 ; Calabash,
    113 ; Squirting, 113
Curare, 198
Currant, 74, 125 ; American,
    126 ; Black, 127 ; Buffalo,
    126 ; Dry, 180 ; Flowering,
    126 ; Red, 127 ; White, 127

Cyclamen, 243
Cypress, Summer, 90

Daffodil, Garden, 340 ; Wild, 336, 337
Dahlia, 35, 225, 228, 229
Daisy, 17, 31, 32, 213, 225 ; Dog, 217, 218 ; Garden, 225 ; Michaelmas, 226 ; Moon, 217, 218 ; Ox-eye, 217, 218
Damson, 145
Dandelion, 17, 23, 32, 33, 125, 212, 222
Darley, George, 317
Darwin, Charles, 288
Date, 356
Dead men's fingers, 360
Deadnettle, 24, 296 ; Henbit, 298 ; Red, 297 ; White, 296, 297 ; Yellow, 297
Delphinium, 34, 35, 43
De Vere, Aubrey, 337
de Vries, Hugo, 105
Dewberry, 133, 145
Dickens, 132, 260
Dicotyledon, 33, 35, 36
Digitalis, 278
Disraeli, 239
Dock, 86, 167 ; Broad-leaved, 87 ; Curled, 87 ; Red-veined, 87 ; Sharp, 87 ; Water, 87, 89
Dodder, Greater, 270 ; Lesser, 270
Dog's mercury, 124
Dog-wood tree, 184
Dore, Julia, 37
Douglas, A. E., 14
Dragon tree of Teneriffe, 353
Dragon's blood, 353, 357
Drake, 263
Drinkwater, 36
Dropwort, 141, 187 ; Fine-leaved, 187 ; Hemlock, 187 ; Parsley, 187 ; Water, 187
Druids, 176
Drupe, 133, 134, 173, 199
Duckweed, Common, 332
Dutchman's pipe, 52
Dyer's weed, 70 ; green weed, 149

Earth-nut, 161, 187
Eel-grass, 310
Egg, 18, 24, 28
Egg-fruit, 265
Eglantine, 132
Elaterium, 114
Elder, Common, 204, 206 ; Dwarf, 204
Elephant's ear, 114 ; foot, 351
Elm, 8, 15, 16, 17, 165 ; Common, 165 ; Wych, 165

Emerson, 36
Emmer, 374
Endive, 225, 233
Endocarp, 355
Epicalyx, 119, 139, 140
Epicarp, 355
Epictetus, 29
Epiphyte, 358
Esparto, 376
Eschallot, 342
Eucalyptus, 99
Euphrasy, 276, 294
Everlasting flowers, 220, 226, 227, 246
Evolution, 31
Eyebright, 276, 294

Fat, 194
Fennel, 188
Fernandez, Francisco, 265
Fertilisation, 28
Fescue, Meadow, 369; Tall, 371
Fig, Hottentot, 85 ; Sea, 85
Figwort, Knotted, 277 ; Water, 278
Filbert, 164
Fingers and thumbs, 152
Fireweed, 104
Flag, Sweet, 331 ; Yellow, 343
Flax, Common, 95 ; New Zealand, 353 ; Purging, 95
Fleabane, Blue, 214 ; Common, 215
Fleur-de-lys, 344
Flower, Structure of, 18 ; Diversity in structure of, 21
Flower of an hour, 121
Fodder grasses, 368, 374; plants, 89, 150, 151, 153, 160, 233
Follicle, 42, 43, 46, 72, 141, 196, 207
Food plants, 2
Forestry, 5, 6, 14
Forget-me-not, 255, 258
Forsythia, 200
Foxglove, 278, 279, 280
Frankincense, 181
Frazer, Sir James, 176
Freesia, 349
Frigg, 176
Fritillary, 326
Frog-bit, 308
Fruit, 28
Fuchsia, 106
Fumitory, Common, 57 ; Rampant, 57
Furze, 148

Gametes, 18
Ganja, 171
Garlic, Broad-leaved, 339, 340 ; Crow, 340 ; Edible, 342 ; Wild meadow, 340

Gentian, 234 ; Field, 235 ; Marsh, 235 ; Small-flowered, 235
Generic name, 33
Genista, 157
Genus, 33
Geranium, 30, 92, 94, 95
Germander, 302
Gherkin, 113
Gilliflower, 59, 63 ; Sea, 246 ; Water, 246
Gin, 3
Ginger, 314
Gladdon, 344
Gladiolus, 30, 315, 347, 348
Glasswort, 90
Glastonbury Thorn, 136
Globe flower, 34, 35, 44
Gloxinia, 292
Glucose, 170, 194
Glume, 365, 369
Goat's beard, 223, 224
Godetia, 106
Golden Bough, 174 ; rod, 216, 226
Goldsmith, 61
Good King Henry, 90
Gooseberry, 74, 125 ; Cape, 267 ; Cultivated, 127
Goose-foot, Red, 90 ; White, 90
Goose-grass, 200
Gorse, 147, 148, 270
Gourd, 113
Grafting, 30, 129, 130
Gram, 161
Granadilla, 111
Granny's bonnet. (See columbine.)
Grape, 3, 177, 178 ; fruit, 181 ; hyacinth, 321
Grass, 17, 33, 368 ; Bent, 368, 373 ; Cock's-foot, 372 ; Common fox-tail, 371 ; Common meadow, 372 ; Couch, 368, 371 ; Eel-, 310 ; Esparto, 376 ; Feather, 373 ; Fescue, Meadow, 369, 370, 371 ; Fescue, Tall, 371 ; Fiorin, 371 ; Mat, 370 ; of Parnassus, 76 ; Pampas, 373 ; Perennial rye, 370, 371 ; Quake, 370, 372, 373 ; Quaking, 370, 372, 373 ; Reed meadow, 372 ; Ribbon, 373 ; Rice, 376 ; Sea meadow, 372 ; Sweet vernal, 370 ; White bent, 371 ; Wood meadow, 372
Grass-wrack, 310
Grevillea, 110
Gromwell, Common, 256 ; Corn, 256
Ground-ivy, 298 ; -nut, 161
Groundsel, 219

Guelder rose, 205
Gum, Australian, 99; Sweet, 162; -tragacanth, 161
Gunga, 171
Gypsophila, 83

Hard-head, 213, 221
Hardy, T., 330
Harebell, 249
Hare's ear, 187
Hashish, 171
Haw, 136
Hawkins, 263
Hawthorn, 134, 135, 144, 175
Hazel, 19, 26, 164; 'Witch', 162
Heartsease, 67, 69
Heath, 189; Cross-leaved, 190; Fine-leaved, 190
Heather, 189
Heber, R., 249
Hedge-bell, 270; mustard, 62; -taper, 275
Heliotrope, 258
Hellebore, Green, 34; Stinking, 35
Helleborine, Broad-leaved, 361; Marsh, 361; Narrow-leaved, 361; White, 361
Hemlock, Common, 185
Hemp, 5, 171; Bow-string, 353; Manila, 314; Sisal, 353
Hempnettle, Common, 302; Large-flowered, 302; Red, 302
Henbane, 259
Henna, 102
Herb Bennet, 140; Paris, 328; -Robert, 93
Herbe aux Charpentiers, 216
Hermaphrodite flowers, 18, 32
Herrick, 67
Hill, Aaron, 167
Hip, 136
Holly, 172; Sea, 187
Hollyhock, 121
Holmes, O. Wendell, 5
Holy Tree, 172
Homer, 152, 179
Honesty, 63
Honeysuckle, 205
Hood, T., 67, 142
Hop, 19, 168; American, 168; European, 168
Horehound, Black, 302; Foetid, 302; White, 302
Hornbeam, 164
Hornwort, 35
Horse-chestnut, 16, 17, 181
Horse-mint, 301
Horse-radish, 66
Horsetail, 108

Hother, 177
Hottentot bread, 351; fig, 85
Hound's tongue, 258, 259; Green, 258
Houseleek, 73, 74
Housman, A. E., 62, 134, 166, 171, 336
Howitt, W., 149
Huckleberry, Blue, 193
Hutchinson, J., 32
Hyacinth, 321; Grape, 321
Hybridisation, 34
Hydrangea, 75, 127
Hyoscyamine, 260

Ice plant, 85
Impatiens, 96, 99
India-rubber, 165
Indian bean, 293; corn, 375; shot, 314
Indigo, 63, 150, 161
Inflorescence, 19, 32
Ingelow, Jean, 151
Insectivorous plants, 77, 284
Involucre, 209, 210
Ipecacuanha, 203
Iris, 17, 343; Bearded, 345; Blue, 344; Bulbous, 345; Clematis-flowered, of Japan, 345; Spanish, 345; Wild, 343
Ivory, Vegetable, 357
Ivy, 182, 284; Ground-, 298

Jack-by-the-hedge, 62, 330
Jack-go-to-bed-at-noon, 223
Jack-in-the-pulpit, 330
Jacobea, 231
Jacob's ladder, 253
Jalap, 272
Japonica, 144
Jasmine, 199
Jessamine, 199
Johnson, C. P., 81
Jonquil, 341
Jute, 5, 118

Kale, 65
Keats, 53, 155
Kif, 171
Kingcup. (See marsh marigold.)
Knapweed, Black, 213, 221, 284; Great, 222, 284
Kohl-rabi, 65
Kola nut, 118

Labellum, 359
Laburnum, 157
Lady's bedstraw, 201; mantle, 141; smock, 60, 64; tresses, 362
Lamina, 15
Landon, Letitia E., 136

Landor, W. S., 31
Lang, Andrew, 76
Larch, 14
Larkspur, 34, 35, 43
Latex, 222
Laurel, Cherry, 142; Japanese, 142, 183; Spurge, 109; True, 47
Lavender, 302, 304; Sea, 245; water, 304
Lawrence, D. H., 243
Leaf, 15, 16; Compound, 15, 17; Simple, 15, 17; -blade, 15; -stalk, 15
Leek, 342
Legume, 147
Leland, C. G., 200
Lemon, 180, 181; Water, 111
Lentil, 161
Lettuce, Cultivated, 224, 233; Lamb's, 207; Wall, 224, 233
Ligule, 369
Lilac, 199
Lily, 315; African, 341; Arum-, 315, 332; Golden-rayed, of Japan, 324, 325; Lent, 336; Madonna, 324; Martagon, 326; of the valley, 318; Orange, 326; Plantain, 326; Regal, 324; Tiger, 326; Turk's cap, 326; Water, 22, 35, 48; White, 325; White trumpet, 324; Wood-, 328
Lime, 118; Sweet, 181
Linen, 5, 96
Ling, Common, 189, 270
Linnaeus, 32, 149
Linné, Carl von, 32, 149
Linseed, 96
Lint, Medicinal, 96
Lion's mouth, 280
Liquorice, Spanish, 161
Lobelia, 252
Locust, 158; Honey, 158
Loganberry, 145
Loki, 177
London pride, 77
Loofah, 114
Loosestrife, Purple, 25, 100; Yellow, 240
Lords and ladies, 330
Lotus, 50, 152; eaters, 152
Lousewort, Field, 275; Marsh, 275
Love-in-a-mist, 25, 34, 35, 44
Love-lies-bleeding, 91
Lucerne, 160
Lupin, 156; Annual, 157; Perennial tree, 157
Lyre flower, 58

Macdonald, G., 41
Madder, 202; Field, 202

Madeley, 222
Madwort, 64
Magnolia, 45
Mahogany, 181
Maize, 2, 369, 375
Malacca cane, 357
Malaria, 203
Mallow, Common, 119; Dwarf, 120; Marsh, 120; Musk, 120; Tree, 121
Malt, 170
Mandrake, 261
Man-eating tree, 285
Mangel-wurzel, 91
Mangold, 91
Maple, 181; Sugar, 181
Mare's tail, 107, 108
Marguerite, 230
Marigold, African, 230; Bur-, 216; Corn, 217; English, 230; French, 230; Marsh, 22, 34, 35, 41
Marijuana, 171
Marjoram, 301; Pot, 304; Sweet, 304; Wild, 301
Markham, Lucia 316
Marmalade, 138, 181
Marriott-Watson, R., 40
Marrow, Vegetable, 112
Marshwort, Lesser, 187; Procumbent, 187
Martagon, 326
Marvell, A., 7
Maté, Yerba, 174
Materia medica, 5, 345
Matthew, St., 304
May, 134, 135, 144; apple, 262
Mayweed, Scentless, 217
Meadow rue, Common, 34, 35; Lesser, 34, 35
Meadow-sweet, 141
Medicine, Plants and, 3
Medick, 150, 156, 160
Medlar, 145
Melilot, Tall, 151
Melon, 113; Cantaloupe, 113; Water, 113
Menthene, 304
Menthol, 304
Meredith, George, 249
Mericarp, 185
Mesocarp, 355
Meteorology, 14
Mezereon, 109
Mignonette, Garden, 71; Wild, 70
Milfoil, 216; Water, 107, 108
Milkwort, 71; Sea, 242
Millet, 2, 375
Milton, 11, 239, 276
Mimosa, 154, 159
Mint, 301; Cat-, 299, 303; Corn, 301; Horse-, 301;

Marsh whorled, 301; Pepper, 301, 304; Round-leaved, 301; Spear, 301, 304; Water-, 301
Mistletoe, 172, 174
Money-wort, 241, 244
Monkey flower, 282
Monkey-nut, 161
Monkshood, 34, 35, 42, 44
Monocotyledon, 33, 35
Montbretia, 347
Montgomery, J., 322
Moore, Thomas, 97
Morning glory, 271
Morphine, 56
Moschatel, 206
Moses, 366
Mother of thousands, 276
Mountain ash, 137, 138, 144
Mouse-ear, 255; -tail, 34, 35
Mulberry, Black, 165; White, 165
Mullein, Great, 274, 281
Muscatel, 179
Musk, 282
Mustard, Black, 63, 65; Garlick, 62; Hedge, 62; White, 63, 65
Myrrh, 181
Myrtle, 165

Narcissus, 340; Pheasant's eye, 340; Poet's, 340
Nasturtium, 61, 96, 98, 99
Nectar, 20, 27
Nectary, 30
Nelson, Lord, 354
Nettle, Common, 166, 270; Roman, 166; Small, 166
Nietsche, 28
Night blindness, 188
Nightshade, Black, 260; Deadly, 261; Enchanter's 104; Woody, 260
Nipplewort, 224
Nitrate, 147, 284
Nodule, 147
Nonsuch, 150
Nut, 87, 89, 245, 255, 256, 257, 258, 297, 309
Nutmeg, 47

Oak, 13, 16, 17, 19, 164, 175, 176; British, 164; Cork, 164; Holm, 164
Oat, 2, 369, 370, 374; Cultivated, 371, 374; Sterile, 373; Wild, 371
Off-set, 73
Oil-cake, 96, 122
Old man's beard, 22, 34, 35, 40
Oleander, 197
Olive, 199
Onion, 30, 339, 341; Tree, 340

Opium, 4, 56
Orache, 89
Orange, 180, 181; Bitter, 181; Bergamot, 181; Mandarin, 181; Seville, 181; Tangerine, 181
Orange blossom, 75, 128; Mexican, 181
Orchis, 357; Bee, 361; Bird's nest, 362; Butterfly, 360; Early purple, 360; Fly, 362; Fragrant, 361; Frog, 361; Lady's slipper, 360, 363; Musk, 362; Pyramidal, 360; Spider, 362; Spotted, 360
Orpine live-long, 72
Orris root, 349
Ovary, 20, 21, 28
Ovule, 20, 21, 28
Ovum, 18, 28
Oxalic acid, 96
Oxslip, 240
Ox-tongue, Bristly, 224

Paddy, 375
Paeony, 34, 43; Chinese, 35, 43
Palea, 370
Palm, 163, 354; Areca, 357; Coco-nut, 354, 355; Date, 356; Oil, 357; Palmyra, 357; Sago, 356
Pan, Pipes of, 186
Pansy, Garden, 69; Tufted, 69; Wild, 67
Paper-reed, 366
Pappus, 209, 212, 213, 216, 217, 219, 223, 225
Papyrus, 366
Parasite, 175, 193, 270, 283; Semi-, 175, 273, 274, 275, 276
Parnassus, Grass of, 76
Parsley, Cultivated, 188; Common beaked, 185; Fool's, 185; Hedge, 185; piert, 141; Wild beaked, 185
Parsnip, Cultivated, 186, 188; Cow-, 186; Water, 187; Wild, 185
Passion flower, 111; fruit, 111
Pea, 16, 18, 20, 23, 28, 146; Everlasting, 156; Garden, 18, 153, 159; Sweet, 153, 154, 155
Peach, 145
Peacock flower, 158
Pea-nut, 161
Pear, 24, 145; Avocado, 47
Pearlwort, 80
Pelargonium, 30, 94, 95
Pelican flower, 30, 94, 95
Pellitory of the wall, 167
Pennyroyal, 304

Pennywort, Garden, 74; Marsh, 187; Wall, 73
Pentstemon, 281
Pepo, 112
Pepper, 52; Betel, 357; Poor man's, 72; Red, 265; Wall, 72
Peppermint, 301, 304
Pepperwort, 60
Perfumes, 3
Perianth, 23, 306
Periwinkle, Garden, 197; Great, 196; Lesser, 196
Perry, 145
Persicaria, Biting, 88; Pink, 88; Spotted, 88
Petal, 19
Peter the Great, 172
Petiole, 15
Petunia, 268
Pheasant's eye, 34, 35, 42
Phlox, 253
Phloem, 15
Phyllode, 329
Picotee, 83
Pignut, 187
Pimpernel, Bastard, 241; Bog, 241; Scarlet, 241, 244; Yellow, 241, 244
Pineapple, 312
Pink, Garden, 83; Maiden, 22, 79; Sea, 245
Pitcher plants, 289
Plane, London, 15, 162; Oriental, 162; Western, 162
Plantain, 25, 247, 314; Buck's horn, 248; Greater, 247; Hoary, 248; Lamb's tongue, 247; Rib-wort, 248; Seaside, 248; Water-, 309
Plants and man, 1
Plasmochine, 203
Pliny, 130, 235, 269
Ploughman's spikenard, 215
Plum, 134, 145
Pod, 54, 57, 147, 148, 149, 150
Pollen, 20, 21, 24; tube, 28
Pollination, 20, 21, 24; Cross-, 25; Insect, 26; Self-, 25; Wind, 25
Pollinia, 359
Polyanthus, 243
Pome, 137
Pond-weed, Broad-leaved, 310; Curly, 311; Shining, 310; small, 311; Various-leaved, 310
Poor man's weather glass, 241
Pope, 179
Poplar, 19, 163, 175; Black, 163; Lombardy, 163; White, 163
Poppy, 22, 23, 53; Californian, 55; Californian tree, 56;

Common red, 53, 55; Opium, 56; Oriental, 55; Tibetan blue, 55; Welsh yellow, 55; Yellow horned, 54; Yellow Iceland, 55
Porter, K. W., 223
Potato, 29, 34, 262; Sweet, 264, 272
Prickle, 131
Primrose, Cape, 293; Common, 20, 22, 31, 238; Evening, 102, 105, 107; pearl, 341
Primula, 237; Chinese, 242; Japanese, 242
Prince's feathers, 91
Privet, 198; Californian, 198
Procter, B. W., 179
Protein, 194
Prune, 145
Pulses, 161
Pumpkin, 113; Giant, 113
Purslane, 86; Rock, 86; Sea, 80; Water, 100, 101
Pyrethrum, 230, 234

Quarles, F., 324
Queen of the meadow, 141
Quinine, 4, 203

Radish, Cultivated, 66; Horse-, 66; Wild, 63
Raffia, 357
Ragged robin, 79
Ragwort, 220
Raisin, 180
Raleigh, Sir Walter, 5, 264, 265
Rampion, 250
Ramsons, 340, 342
Rape, 65; -oil, 65
Rayon, 5
Raspberry, 133; Cultivated, 145
Rattle, Yellow, 275
Red-hot poker, 322
Reed, Common, 372; Great, 372; -mace, 335; Paper-, 366; Sea, 371
Reproduction, Sexual, 18; Vegetative, 29
Rest harrow, Common, 150; Spiny, 150
Revelation, 377
Rhododendron, 191
Rhubarb, 86, 88; Medicinal, 88
Rice, 2, 373, 375
Righteous Branch, 173
Rings, Annual, 14
Roast beef plant, 344
Rock-cress, Hairy, 61
Rock rose, 110, 111
Root, 8, 31; Absorbing, 358;

Adventitious, 11, 114, 127, 138, 165, 182; Aerial, 358; Clinging, 358; Fibrous, 10, Tap, 10
Rose, 17, 30, 31, 33, 130; Burnet, 132; Christmas, 32, 34, 35; Damask, 142; Dog-, 26, 27, 130; Garden, 34, 142, 143; Rock, 110, 111; Trailing, 132; water, 142; White cabbage, 142
Rosemary, 303
Rosetti, Christina, 255
Rostellum, 359
Rowan, 137, 138, 144
Rubber, 5, 125, 196, 222; Ceara, 125; India-, 165
Rum, 3
Runner, 30, 129, 138, 248, 298
Rush, Common, 215, 365; Flowering, 307
Rye, 374

Sachs, Julius von, 285
Sage, 295, 300; Cultivated, 305; Wood, 302
Sago, 356
Saffron, 349; Meadow, 319
Sainfoin, 160
St. John's wort, Hairy, 117; Imperforate, 117; Perforated, 117; Small, 117; Square-stalked, 117; Trailing, 117
St. Patrick, 151
Salep, 364
Sallow, 163
Salpiglossis, 267
Salvia, 303
Samphire, 188
Sandwort, 80, 83
Sanicle, Wood, 187
Sap, 13
Saprophyte, 193, 235, 358, 362
Sarsaparilla, 328
Satin flower, 347; wood, 162
Savory, Summer, 305; Winter, 305
Saxifrage, Garden, 76; Golden, 75; Golden, Alternate-leaved, 75; Meadow, 75; Mossy-leaved, 77; Rue-leaved, 75
Scabious, Devil's bit, 209; Field, 208; Garden, 211; Sheep's bit, 250; Small, 209
Scammony, 272
Scent of flowers, 27
Schizanthus, 267
Schizocarp, 93, 99, 185
Scorpion grass, 255; Creeping, 256; Field, 256; Tufted, 256; Yellow-and-blue, 256
Scott, Sir Walter, 154
Scots pine, 16

Sea fig, 85 ; holly, 187 ; lavender, 245 ; pink, 245 ; purslane, 80
Sedge, Common, 366
Seed, 28 ; -leaf, 33
Self-heal, 298
Senega snake-root, 71
Senna, Alexandrian, 161 ; Italian, 161
Sensitive plant, 159
Sepal, 19
Service tree, 144
Sex in plants, 18
Shakespeare, 3, 8, 60, 129, 137, 179, 239, 261, 295, 304, 360
Shallot, 342
Shamrock, 96, 97, 151
Sheep's-bit, 250 ; scabious, 250
Shelley, 129, 318
Shên-nung, Emperor, 2
Shepherd's needle, 186 ; purse, 60
Shoe flower, 121
Shoot, 8, 11
Shore-weed, 248
Silicula, 60
Siliqua, 59
Silk, Artificial, 5
Silk-cotton tree, 119
Silver wattle, 159
Silver-weed, 139
Singhara flour, 107
Sisal, 353
Skull-cap, 299 ; Lesser, 299
Slipperwort, 282
Sloe, 133, 145
Smilax, 328
Smith, Horace, 18, 315
Snake's food, 185 ; -head, 320
Snapdragon, 280
Snowball tree, 206
Snowberry, 206
Snowdrop, 338, 340
Snuff, 5
Soapwort, 83
Socrates, 186
Soldier's button. (See marsh marigold.)
Solomon's seal, 318
Sorrel, Common, 86, 87 ; Sheep's, 87 ; Wood, 96, 97, 151
Sow-bread, 243 ; -thistle, Corn, 224
Spadix, 330, 331
Spathe, 330, 332, 375
Spearmint, 301, 304
Species, 33
Specific name, 34
Speedwell, 256, 283 ; Common, 274 ; Field, 274 ; Germander, 273 ; Marsh, 273 ; Small, 274 ; Wall, 274 ; Water, 274

Spelt, Small, 374
Sperm, 18, 21, 26
Spices, 3
Spider-wort, 312
Spike, 366, 369
Spikelet, 366, 369
Spikenard, 208 ; Ploughman's, 215
Spinach, 91, 167
Spine, 149, 150, 158, 172, 188, 210, 220
Spiraea, 77, 140
Spurge, Dwarf, 124 ; laurel, 109 ; Petty, 124 ; Sun, 124 ; Wood, 124
Spurrey, Seaside sandwort, 80
Squash, 113
Stamen, 20, 23
Star of Bethlehem, 320 ; Yellow, 320
Star of the veldt, 232
Star-wort, Water, 109
Statice, 246
Stem, 11
Stigma, 20, 21
Stipule, 16, 17, 87
Stitchwort, Bog, 81 ; Greater, 80 ; Lesser, 80 ; Marsh, 81 ; Water, 81 ; wood, 81
Stock, 63
Stolon, 127, 129, 132
Stonecrop, Biting, 72 ; Yellow, 72, 74 ; White, 73
Stork's-bill, Hemlock, 93 ; Musky, 94
Strawberry, Barren, 139 ; Cultivated, 138, 145 ; tree, 191 ; wild, 138
Strychnine, 4, 198
Style, 20, 21
Subspecies, 34
Sucker, 129
Sugar, 90, 194, 375 ; Beet, 10, 89, 90, 91, 375 ; cane, 375 ; maple, 181, 375
Sultana, 180
Sundew, Long-leaved, 288 ; Round-leaved, 288
Sunflower, 227, 228, 233
Sweet briar, 132 ; Cicely, 187 ; flag, 331 ; pea, 153, 154, 155; violet, 66, 69 ; William, 81
Swede, 65
Swinburne, 68
Sycamore, 19, 181
'Syringa', 127

Tansy, 217
Tare, Hairy, 153
Tea, 2, 116 ; Paraguay, 174
Teasel, Fuller's, 210 ; Wild, 209
Tendril, 16, 57, 153, 154, 178, 180, 254

Tennyson, 36, 62, 104, 136, 205, 339
Thickening, Secondary, 13
Thistle, Blue globe, 233 ; Carline, 220 ; Corn sow-, 224 ; Spear, 220
Thompson, Francis, 214
Thomson, James, 378
Thoreau, H. D., 1
Thorn, 131, 134, 158
Thrift, 245
Thyme, Basil, 302 ; Cultivated, 302, 304 ; Wild, 270, 284, 301
Tiger flower, 349
Timber, 5
Toadflax, 27, 276, 282 ; Ivy-leaved, 276 ; Yellow, 277
Tobacco, 5, 171, 265 ; Flowering, 266
Toddy, 355
Tom thumb, 152
Tomato, 264
Toothwort, Great, 284
Torch, 275
Tormentil, 140
Touch-me-not, 99
Traveller's joy, 22, 34, 35, 39
Trefoil, Bird's-foot, 23, 147, 152 ; Hare's-foot, 152 ; Hop, 152 ; Lesser yellow, 152 ; Narrow-leaved, bird's foot, 153 ; Slender yellow, 152
Trinity, The, 151
Trunk, 13
Tuber, Root, 38, 98, 114, 125, 187, 272, 277, 331, 360 ; Stem, 29, 97, 233, 257, 263, 314, 351
Tubercle, 147
Tulip, 17, 18, 20, 23, 24, 30, 33, 322, 323
Tulip tree, 46 ; wood, 102
Turk's-cap, 326
Turnip, 65
Tutsan, 117
Twayblade, 361 ; Heart-leaved, 31

Umbel, 94, 184, 237, 307, 340
Unisexual flowers, 18
Utricle, 366

Valerian, Great, 207 ; Marsh, 207 ; Red spur-, 207
Vanilla, 364
Vanillin, 364
Variety, 34
Velamen, 359
Venation, Net, 17 ; Parallel, 17
Venus's comb, 186 ; fly-trap, 288
Verbena, 294
Vergil, 354

Veronica, 274, 283 ; St., 274
Vervain, 294
Vetch, 147, 150, 153, 160, 270 ;
    Bush, 153 ; Common, 153 ;
    Grass, 154 ; Kidney, 150 ;
    Meadow, 154 ; Milk, 150;
    Tuberous bitter, 154 ; Tuf-
    ted, 153 ; Wood, 153
Victoria, Queen, 177
Vikings, 177
Vine, Grape, 3, 177, 178
Vinegar, 3
Viola, 69
Violet, 18, 25, 66 ; Calathian
    235 ; Dog, 66 ; Dog-
    toothed, 322 ; Essence of,
    349 ; Hairy, 67 ; Marsh, 67 ;
    Marsh, 67 ; Sweet, 66, 69 ;
    Water, 242, 244
Vitamin, 6, 91, 127, 132, 181,
    188, 264
Virginian creeper, 180

Wake-robin, 330
Wallflower, 8, 12, 18, 22, 23,
    59, 63 ; Alpine, 63 ; Siber-
    ian, 63
Water-arum, 332
Water-cress, 61, 65, 98
Water-lily, 22, 35, 48, 315 ;
    Victoria, 50 ; White, 22, 35,
    48 ; Yellow, 22, 35, 49
Water-mint, 301
Water-plantain, 309
Water-soldier, 308

Water-weed, Canadian, 29, 308
Wattle, Silver, 159
Wayfaring tree, 205
Weeds, 1, 7
Weld, 70
Wheat, 2, 369, 373 ; Bearded,
    364, 370 ; Beardless, 369 ;
    Hard, 374 ; Polish, 374
Whin, 148 ; Needle, 149
Whisky, 3
White beam, 144
Whitlow grass, 60
Whitman, 199
Whittier, 190, 356
Whorl, 19
Whortleberry, 192, 193
Wilde, Oscar, 5
Williams, Roger, 145
Willow, 19, 163, 284 ; Crack,
    163 ; Cricket-bat, 163 ; Goat,
    163 ; Osier, 163 ; Weeping,
    163 ; White, 163
Willow-herb, Broad smooth-
    leaved, 104 ; Great hairy,
    104 ; Narrow-leaved, 104 ;
    Rose-bay, 103, 107 ; Small-
    flowered, 104 ; Square-
    stalked, 104
Willow pattern, 181
Wine, 3, 179; Port, 179 ;
    Red, 179 ; Sparkling, 179 ;
    White, 179
Windflower, 41
Wintergreen, 191 ; Lesser, 191
Wistaria, 35, 157, 158

Witches' brooms, 164
Withwind, 270
Withy, 163
Woad, 63, 150
Wolfe, Humbert, 123
Wood, 13 ; Heart-, 13 ; Sap-,
    13
Woodbine, 205, 270
Woodruff, 202
Wood - rush, Broad - leaved
    hairy, 365 ; Great hairy, 365;
    Field, 365
Wood sage, 302
Wood sorrel, 96, 97, 151
Wordsworth, 39, 196, 214, 270,
    278, 338
Wormwood, 218
Wort, 170
Woundwort, Corn, 299;
    Hedge, 299 ; Marsh, 300
Wynne, John, 202

Yam, 351
Yarrow, 216
Yeast, 170, 179
Yellow bird's nest, 194
Yellow-cress, Creeping, 61 ;
    Marsh, 61
Yellow rattle, 275 ; toadflax, 277
Yellow-wort, 236
Yerba maté, 174
Yucca, 352

Zedoary, 314
Zinnia, 229

PRINTED IN GREAT BRITAIN
BY ROBERT MACLEHOSE AND CO. LTD.
THE UNIVERSITY PRESS, GLASGOW